D1206843

Ground Level Climatology

Ground Level Climatology

A symposium presented at the
Berkeley meeting of the
American Association for the
Advancement of Science - December, 1965

Edited by **ROBERT H. SHAW**

Publication No. 86

AMERICAN ASSOCIATION
FOR THE ADVANCEMENT OF SCIENCE
WASHINGTON, D. C. 1967

Second printing, 1970

Library of Congress Catalog Number 67-29427
Printed in the United States of America
The Horn-Shafer Company
Baltimore, Maryland

Preface

GROUND LEVEL CLIMATOLOGY may be very generally defined as the climate close to the ground, although individual contributors to this volume will differ as to exact definitions. Using this broad definition we have selected topics on the general theme of weather and agriculture (including forestry), and, more specifically, on the climate in the immediate vicinity of plants and animals.

This volume includes some of the papers presented at the Section on Agriculture (O), Symposium on Ground Level Climatology, at the 132nd Annual Meeting of the American Association for the Advancement of Science at Berkeley, California, December, 1965. Many of the papers have been revised and updated to include relevant works published since the Berkeley meeting.

Investigators from a variety of scientific fields are concerned with various aspects of ground level climatological problems and a wide range of disciplines meets in this volume. The goal of the researcher in ground level climatology is to determine the nature of the interrelationships between organisms and their environments. To attain this goal, he must find climatic indicators and study the relationship of climate to the distribution and abundance of plants and animals. He must, to take only one of many examples, project what effects weather modification might have on the physical processes within the microclimate, and weather modification must be considered both on the continental and microclimatic scale. Other aspects of ground level climatology which must be considered include, for example, moisture, temperature, energy balance, vapor pressure, and irrigation.

Some of the papers in this volume describe the effect of climate on particular plants or animals; one contribution is concerned with the effect of ground level climate on forest fires; several pertain, primarily, to climate and animal husbandry; others describe the reaction of plants and animals to various environments.

I have mentioned only a few of the topics discussed in *Ground Level Climatology,* but all have a far-reaching, sometimes discouraging sometimes encouraging, effect on plants and animals and, ultimately, on man. The reader, no doubt, can suggest topics which have not been included in this volume and which might have been added to the symposium program. The aim is to present a volume containing a catholicity of thought in a broad area without attempting to reconcile differing viewpoints or to fill obvious gaps. Each of the four parts of the book includes papers particularly pertinent to that part, but any one paper is not necessarily limited to the part in which it appears.

I wish to thank the American Association for the Advancement of Science for including this symposium in the Berkeley meeting and for making publication of this volume possible. My appreciation is also extended to the American Meteorological Society, the Ecological Society of America, and the Society of American Foresters for their valuable cooperation. I am especially grateful to Edward C. Stone for organizing the joint meetings with the Society of American Foresters and to Donald W. Lynch, Edward C. Stone, Harold F. Heady, Frederick A. Brooks, C. F. Kelly, and C. M. Winget for presiding over the various symposium meetings.

My gratitude is expressed to Horace D. Porter, who served as managing, copy, and production editor of this publication. His diligent and critical editing of the papers has contributed greatly to the readability of this volume.

ROBERT H. SHAW, *Editor*

Iowa State University of Science and Technology
Ames, Iowa
October, 1967

Contributors

T. E. Bond, Agricultural Engineering Research Division, Agricultural Research Service, U. S. Department of Agriculture, Davis, California

G. A. Cahoon, Ohio Agricultural Research and Development Center, Wooster, Ohio

W. C. Cooper, Crops Research Division, Agricultural Research Service, U. S. Department of Agriculture, Orlando, Florida

Joseph M. Caprio, Plant and Soil Science Department, Agricultural Experiment Station, Montana State University, Bozeman, Montana

Leo J. Fritschen, College of Forest Resources, University of Washington, Seattle, Washington

Harold C. Fritts, Laboratory of Tree-Ring Research, The University of Arizona, Tucson, Arizona

Donald M. Fuquay, Northern Forest Fire Laboratory, Intermountain Forest and Range Experiment Station, Forest Service, U. S. Department of Agriculture, Missoula, Montana

Dewayne E. Gilbert, Agricultural Extension Service, University of California, Davis, California

H. D. Johnson, Department of Dairy Husbandry, University of Missouri, Columbia, Missouri

Marston H. Kimball, Agricultural Extension Service, University of California, Los Angeles, California

William P. Lowry, School of Science, Department of Statistics, Oregon State University, Corvallis, Oregon

Jack Major, Botany Department, University of California, Davis, California

William E. Marlatt, Department of Atmospheric Science, Colorado State University, Fort Collins, Colorado

R. E. McDowell, Department of Animal Science, Cornell University, Ithaca, New York

J. E. Newman, Department of Agronomy, Purdue University, Lafayette, Indiana

Paul R. Nixon, Soil and Water Conservation Research Division Field Station, U. S. Department of Agriculture, Lompoc, California

A. Peynado, Crops Research Division, Agricultural Research Service, U. S. Department of Agriculture, Weslaco, Texas

W. Reuther, Department of Horticultural Science, University of California, Riverside, California

Norman J. Rosenberg, Department of Horticulture and Forestry, University of Nebraska, Lincoln, Nebraska

L. C. Ulberg, Animal Science Department, North Carolina Agricultural Experiment Station, Raleigh, North Carolina

Jack R. Wallin, Crops Protection Research Branch, Agricultural Research Service, U. S. Department of Agriculture, Iowa State University, Ames, Iowa

Warren C. Whitman, Botany Department, North Dakota State University, Fargo, North Dakota

R. H. Whittaker, Department of Population and Environmental Biology, University of California, Irvine, California

G. C. Whittow, Department of Animal Sciences, Rutgers, The State University, New Brunswick, New Jersey

C. M. Williams, Department of Animal Science, University of Saskatchewan, Saskatoon, Saskatchewan, Canada

Wilbor O. Wilson, Poultry Husbandry Department, University of California, Davis, California

Gale Wolters, Botany Department, North Dakota State University, Fargo, North Dakota

Contents

Preface v

Contributors vii

I. THE PROBLEM OF BIOMETEOROLOGICAL INFERENCE

Biometeorological Inference and Plant-Environment Interrelations, by WILLIAM P. LOWRY 3

Production of cones in Douglas fir. Analysis of cone production and weather data. Meteorological requirements for abundant cone production. (Figures and Table)

II. GROUND LEVEL CLIMATE AND PLANTS

Phenological Patterns and Their Use as Climatic Indicators, by JOSEPH M. CAPRIO 17

Effect of elevation on lilac development. Combined effect of latitude, longitude, and elevation. Lilac bloom dates and temperatures. Use of phenological maps. (Figures and Tables)

Growth Rings of Trees: A Physiological Basis for Their Correlation with Climate, by HAROLD C. FRITTS 45

Characteristics of tree-ring series. Climatic relationships. Physiological evidence. (Figures)

Plantclimate Mapping: The Key to Conservation of Resources, by MARSTON H. KIMBALL and DEWAYNE E. GILBERT 67

Plants as indicators of temperature. County-by-county mapping. Major and regional plantclimates. Plantclimate zones and subzones. Characterization with physical data. Uses and applications of plantclimate mapping. (Figures)

Potential Evapotranspiration and Plant Distribution in Western States with Emphasis on California, by JACK MAJOR 93

Potential Evapotranspiration. Kinds of California vegetation. Correlations between climates and vegetation. Coastal vegetation. Central Valley vegetation. Sierran vegetation. Northern Great Basin vegetation. Southern Desert vegetation. (Figures and Tables)

Orange Fruit Maturity and Net Heat Accumulations, by J. E. NEWMAN, W. C. COOPER, W. REUTHER, G. A. CAHOON, and A. PEYNADO 127

The maturity problem of citrus fruits. Analysis of phenological data for the Valencia orange. Use of radiant temperature to predict orange fruit growth. Implications in future work. (Figures and Tables)

Ground Level Climate in Relation to Forecasting Plant Diseases, by JACK R. WALLIN 149

Ground level climate and plant disease epiphytotics. Forecasting plant diseases. Apple scab. Downy mildew of grape. Downy mildew of lima bean. Potato late blight. Future possibilities. (Table)

Microclimatic Gradients in Mixed Grass Prairie, by WARREN C. WHITMAN and GALE WOLTERS 165

The general climate of the mixed grass prairie. Soil moisture. Temperature relations. Wind. Evaporation. Relative humidity. Implications of studies. (Figures and Tables)

III. GROUND LEVEL CLIMATE AND ANIMALS

Climatic Effects on Physiology and Productivity of Cattle, by H. D. JOHNSON 189

Environment. Microclimatic influence on physiology and performance. Heat balance. Hormonal effects on heat balance. Calorigenesis. Lactation. Energy utilization as related to environment and performance. Heat production. Estimates of heat loss requirements for lactation at high environmental temperature. (Figures)

Microclimate and Livestock Performance in Hot Climates, by T. E. BOND 207

Influence of air temperature. Effect of air movement. Importance of radiation. Data on humidity influences. (Figures and Tables)

Livestock Production in Cold Climates, by C. M. WILLIAMS 221

The general problem of a cold environment. Effect on the newborn animal. Effect on swine. Effect on beef cattle. Effect on sheep. Effect on milk production of dairy cattle.

Climatic Effects on Physiological Functions, by G. C. WHITTOW 233

Regulation of heat loss. Physiological consequences of an increased heat loss. Cardiovascular changes. Thermal polypnea. Adreno-medullary activity. Role of the hypothalamus. (Figures and Tables)

Environmental Temperature and Feed-Regulating Mechanisms, by WILBOR O. WILSON 247

Feed consumption. Experimental animals. Feed intake of chickens at different temperatures. Seasonal changes in feed consumption. Metabolic rate of domestic animals at different temperatures. Caloric intake of chickens. Force-feeding at high temperature. Regulatory mechanisms. Future research. (Figures and Tables)

Effects of Macro- and Microenvironment on the Biology of Mammalian Reproduction, by L. C. ULBERG 265

Climatic factors and mammalian reproduction. High ambient temperature and reproductive rate. Delayed embryonic death. Resistance of unfertilized ova. Response of sperm to stress. Direct effect of temperature on gametes. (Figures)

Factors in Reducing the Adverse Effects of Climate on Animal Performance, by R. E. MCDOWELL 277

Elements of environment. Characterizing animal response. Importance of breeds. Feed supply in adverse environments. Other considerations. (Figures and Tables)

IV. GROUND LEVEL CLIMATE AND WEATHER MODIFICATION

The Effect of Weather Modification on Physical Processes in the Microclimate, by WILLIAM E. MARLATT 295

Direct weather modification. Precipitation modification. Hurricane modification. Energy balance modification. Indirect weather modification. (Figures and Tables)

Weather Modification and Forest Fires, by DONALD M. FUQUAY 309

Forest fire conditions. Research on lightning. Characteristics of mountain thunderstorms. Lightning modification. Equipment and seeding methods. Identification of lightning discharges. Theoretical consideration for lightning suppression. (Figures)

The Influence and Implications of Windbreaks on Agriculture in Dry Regions, by NORMAN J. ROSENBERG 327

Nebraska windbreak studies. Influences of windbreaks. Wind reduction in the sheltered zone. Shelter effect on radiation, air temperature, soil temperature, and atmospheric humidity. Moisture conservation in sheltered areas. Physiological regulation of transpiration by sheltered plants. Aerodynamics and CO_2 supply. (Figures and Tables)

Microclimate Before and After Irrigation, by LEO J. FRITSCHEN and PAUL R. NIXON 351

Physical processes in the microclimate. Small oases. Large oases. Traverse of irrigated and desert lands. Application of data. (Figures and Tables)

Ecological Implications of Weather Modification, by R. H. WHITTAKER 367

Effects on natural communities. Community and ecosystem. Community production. Population response to weather modification. Community gradients. Population shifts in response to weather modification. Magnitude of effects. Recommendations in relation to natural communities. Weather modification and human ecology. (Figures)

Index 387

I. The Problem of Biometeorological Inference

Biometeorological Inference and Plant-Environment Interrelations

WILLIAM P. LOWRY, *School of Science, Department of Statistics, Oregon State University, Corvallis, Oregon*

BIOMETEOROLOGY is the branch of ecology concerned with the interrelations between the chemical and physical factors of the atmospheric environment and living organisms (AMS, 1961; NAS-NRC, 1962; Sargent, 1963). Inference may be defined as the process of arriving at a conclusion by reasoning inductively from specific facts. Biometeorological inference, then, means the process of combining the facts about the atmospheric environment and those about an organism to reach conclusions about their interrelations. This paper, a synthesis of two others, is a critical examination of a particular scientific endeavor (Lowry, 1963, 1966).

There appear to be two basic plans which scientists use in dealing with these sets of facts. One plan designates a set of environmental conditions and observes the organism's reactions. The other plan starts with organismic reaction and analyzes concomitant sets of environmental factors. Both goals are the exposition of the true nature of certain interrelations between environment and organism, but in both cases the exposition has as an intermediate step the statement of a hypothesis, or model, about how organism and environment should interact. Between the hypothesis and the complete exposition lies experimental testing of the model.

These well-known concepts and patterns are restated to emphasize that the work described here has produced not a definitive explanation, but only a portion of an inferred generalization . . . that is, the basic structure of a model. Testing and further elaboration are needed.

The Problem

This paper is an attempt to explain what sequence of meteorological events produces an abundant cone crop in Douglas fir, *Pseudotsuga menziesii* (Mirb.) Franco. The approach used falls under the second plan mentioned above, in which a set of environmental conditions is sought which produces a specified organismic reaction; it combines facts about an organism and its atmospheric environment in such a way as to yield a tentative explanation. The question is what, not how, interrelations are involved; so, even if the inference is found experimentally to be valid, it remains for the mechanisms of interaction to be explained before the exposition is completed.

The Data

Figure 1 gives the record of cone crop abundance, the basic dependent variable in this study. This information was supplied by Dr. J. W. Duffield in 1957 and is the result of a 48-year survey conducted by the Weyerhauser Company and the U. S. Forest Service. Duffield's suggestion that the record might be used in seeking an explanation of weather effects on cone crop was the impetus for this

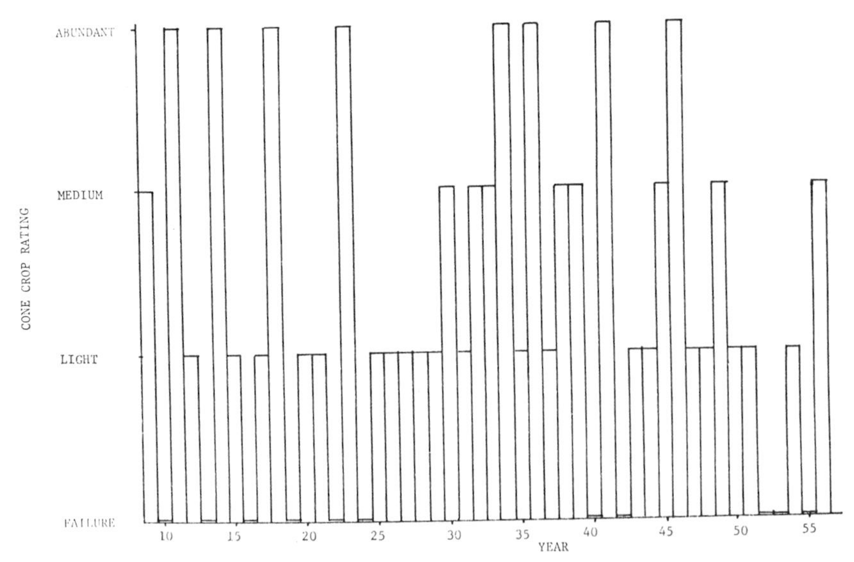

Fig. 1. Rating of Douglas fir cone crops. Western Washington and western Oregon, 1909–1956. Source: Pacific Northwest Experiment Station (U. S. Forest Service) and Weyerhauser Timber Company.

study, and the nature of the information has dictated the approach to a great extent.

The cone crop record attempts to express relative abundance for Douglas fir over the region of western Washington and western Oregon. Sampling procedures were apparently objective and homogeneous, but their details are unknown to me as were the criteria for assignment of a given year to a particular abundance class. These limitations notwithstanding, the information appears satisfactory for present purposes and is probably the best available record of comparable length.

The nature of the cone crop record largely determined the nature of the meteorological records to be combined with it. The meteorological records should be of comparable length; they should be generally representative of the same area; they should be the product of a homogeneous observational program; and they should contain time units which are biologically meaningful. These requirements are met for the most part in the only readily available meteorological records dating back to the early 1900's; they include monthly values of mean temperature and total precipitation from various stations in the area. The question of whether or not to achieve areal representation by employing records from one or from several stations was resolved by the arbitrary decision to use data only from Salem, Oregon, a station centrally located in the area.

The necessary requirements for an adequate biometeorological data system include: knowledge of the nature of the environment and the organism; knowledge of the instruments available and of their interactions with the environment and the organism; a scheme for characterizing the environment and the organism; and a plan for obtaining measurements compatible with the scheme for characterization. Since the measurements were already made, and since we have the required knowledge about the natures of organism and environment as they apply to this problem, it is necessary only to examine the schemes for characterizing organism and environment.

The variety of schemes for characterization is limitless, but the most successful seem to have certain features in common:

1. They accurately reflect the working hypothesis.
2. They are quantitatively based on scales which are not arbitrary or subjective.

3. They place the thing characterized in its spectrum of possible states.
4. They are internally consistent in the logical sense.
5. They are compatible in that, for instance, all variables involving energy are expressed in units of energy.
6. They contain provisions for all reasonably pertinent factors (Lowry, 1963).

How do the cone crop record and the temperature and precipitation records compare with this list?

Assuming the cone crop was classified in the late summer of each year of record, we cannot be sure the scheme accurately reflects the potential cone crop as it existed just prior to pollination, that is, the true reaction of the organism under scrutiny (Lester, 1963). Although the scheme appears to place each year in a spectrum, it is not quantitative. One may assert the scheme is not internally consistent because it appears that a prior conception of abundance was assumed before abundance data were obtained. Had a scale been applied afterwards it is unlikely the relative frequencies would have been in the pattern shown in Figure 1. Since these are essentially the only available records, however, we must use them.

We have assumed that the temperature and precipitation records from Salem are sufficiently representative of the area for which the cone crop was classified. Both records are quantitative in the proper sense and are internally consistent. Because the records reflect heat and moisture explicitly and light implicitly, they provide all reasonably pertinent meteorological factors affecting cone crop abundance.

The schemes for characterizing the organism of concern and the atmospheric environment are certainly less than optimum, but can be made workable if we remember the nature of their shortcomings.

Procedures and Results

With this biological variable in four non-quantitative classes and two environmental variables on continuous scales, it seemed appropriate to express for statistical analysis all three on four-point linear scales. Accordingly, the cone crop was designated as the variable C having values 3 for abundant, 1 for medium, −1 for light, and −3 for failure. Monthly mean temperature and monthly total precipitation were designated T and P, placed in quartiles within each of the twelve months, and assigned the same four values, with 3 being associated with quartiles of highest temperature and greatest total precipitation. It is likely the conclusions to follow would not have been different had other schemes for quantification been employed, and none of the criteria for adequacy of characterization appear to have been compromised.

The principal statistic employed in this study was:

$$S_p = \sum_i C_i P_j \qquad \text{or} \qquad S_t = \sum_i C_i T_j \ ,$$

where i specifies the year of the cone crop, and $j = 0, 1, 2, 3, \ldots, 30$, the number of months prior to October of the cone crop year that takes on one value for each sum. Figure 2 shows how one value of S is calculated for each of the environmental variables for each of 30 months, and how S is the sum of 48 similar products. The index, S, will have a large positive value when the biological and meteorological variables are positively associated, or correlated, and a large negative value for negative association. With relative frequencies of each value of C, P, and T known (Fig. 3), and therefore with joint sampling distributions of the statistic known, one may assume

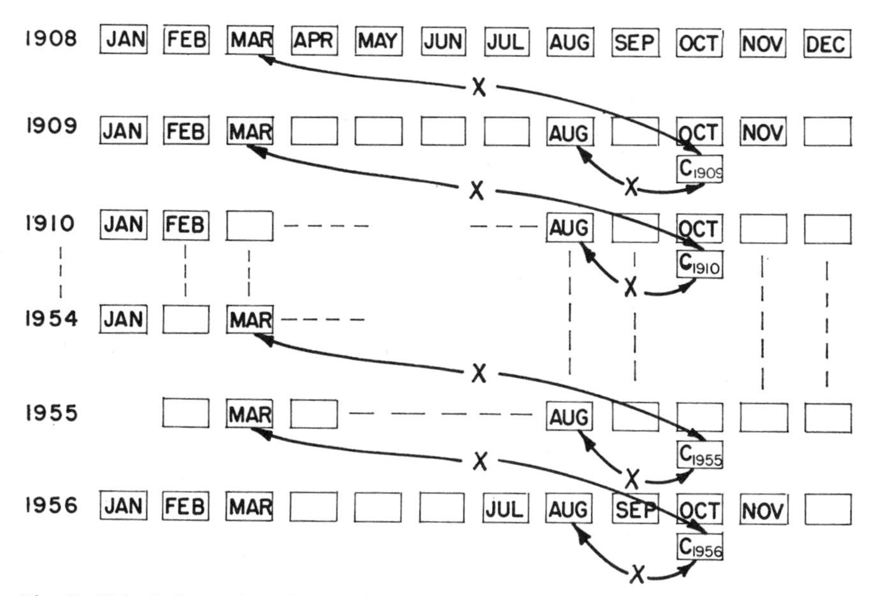

Fig. 2. Calculations of statistic S for months 2 and 19 prior to October cone crop harvest.

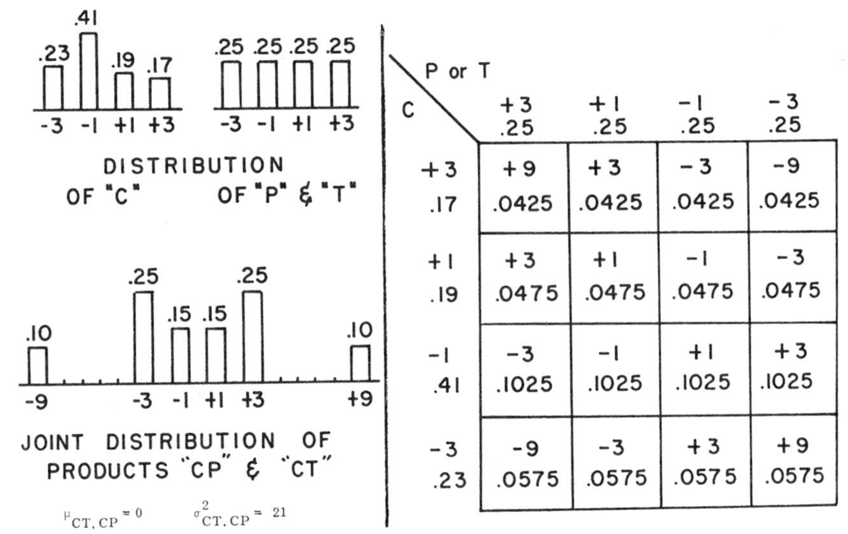

Fig. 3. Sampling distribution for the products *CT* and *CP*.

the null hypothesis of no association and calculate critical values for the 5-percent and 1-percent significance levels according to:

$$S_{(.05)} = \pm\ 1.96\,(n)^{1/2}\ (\sigma)_{CP,\,CT}$$

and

$$S_{(.01)} = \pm\ 2.58\,(n)^{1/2}\ (\sigma)_{CP,\,CT}\ ,$$

where n is the sample size and $(\sigma)_{CP,CT}$ is the standard deviation of the joint sampling distribution of C and P, or C and T.

Figure 4 shows the results of analysis with $n = 48$, together with an interpretation in the form of values beyond the critical limits. It is reasonable to ask, since the two sets of values of S are each nearly normally distributed, whether the statistically significant values in each of the two sets have any biological validity in terms of causal relationship. An approach to answering this question lies in dividing the 48-year record in two, performing the same analysis on each, and seeing which patterns of significance, if any, persist in all analyses. The decision of how to divide the record was difficult.

If the record were divided into its first and its last 24 years, the latter half of the record undoubtedly would contain information from more high-elevation sampling sites than the earlier half. If alternate years were placed in the two subsamples, the strong pos-

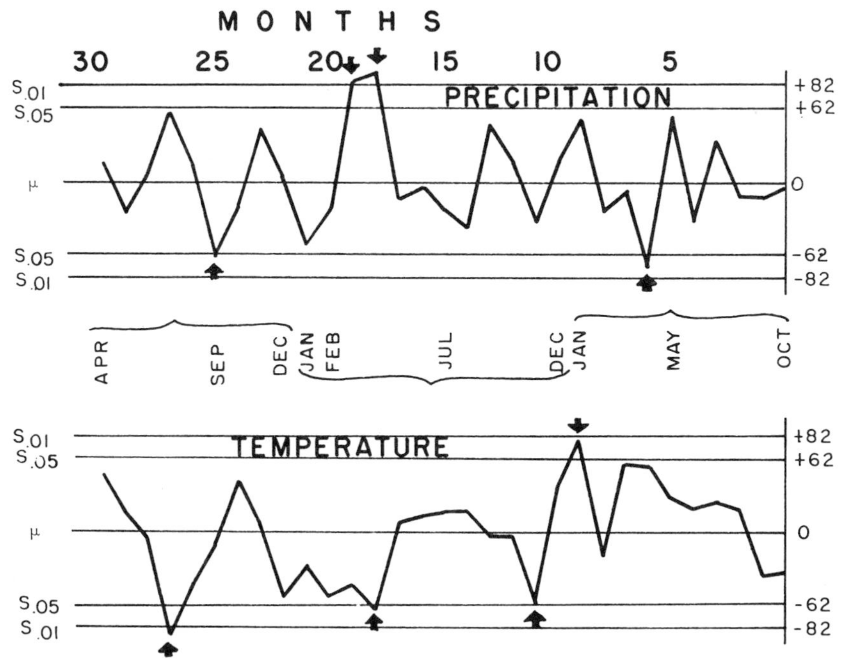

Fig. 4. Values of S for precipitation and temperature versus number of months prior to October of the conecrop year. Arrows indicate values beyond the 5 percent significance level.

sibility of a two-year periodicity in plant behavior might lead to inaccurate results. Complete randomizing of the record yielded an unsatisfactory pairing which appeared to have in it too much of the faults of the first two approaches. Finally, each pair of years taken chronologically was randomly assigned, and the study proceeded.

One final question remained. How could the possibly adverse effect of low temperatures in the spring of the harvest year be examined? To answer this, a one-tailed test of significance was performed for $j = 0, 1, \ldots, 12$ on each of the following statistics: (1) conditional probability the monthly mean temperature was in the lowest quartile, given that the cone crop was a failure; (2) conditional probability the monthly mean temperature was below its median, given that the cone crop was either light or a failure; and (3) conditional probability the monthly mean temperature was below its median, given that the cone crop was a failure.

None of these tests account for the possible effect of a relatively short period of very cold temperature, since such an event might easily be masked in a monthly mean. Unlike the techniques involving a broad search for clues by means of statistic *S*, the test involving the conditional probabilities is concerned with a specific mechanistic hypothesis already suspected because of information previously available. Thus, the specific hypothesis requires more detailed data than does the broader search for clues.

We set out to assign biological validity to those times and variables for which statistical significance persisted through analyses of the 48-year sample and both the 24-year samples. By the nature of the procedure, the sum of the two values of *S* for subsamples equals the value of *S* for the sample from which they were drawn. Biological validity was assumed, therefore, when *S* for the sample and one subsample were statistically significant, *S* for the other subsample was greater than one standard deviation, and the algebraic sign was the same for all three. Biological validity was also assumed for the one case of statistical significance on spring damage due to low temperatures.

Figure 5 shows on a single time scale the results of the various statistical tests just described, and Table 1 includes the combination of all the results designated as having biological validity. This combination is a tentative answer to the question motivating the study.

Discussion

What is the nature of this tentative answer? Where does it fit in our overall scientific scheme of investigation? First we should consider an example of the kind of interpretation required at this point. Note that an abundant cone crop apparently requires high precipitation in the spring preceding the year of harvest. Since in the Douglas fir region spring is ordinarily a time of completely saturated soil or maximum snow pack, this conclusion needs interpretation. It may be that the biophysical connection is with cloudiness or with absolute humidity, for example, rather than with actual precipitation. If it is with cloudiness, this may in turn reflect either the active role of light at this time or perhaps the higher night temperatures associated with cloudiness. By the algebraic sign, a correlation with light energy would have to be interpreted as a positive correlation with low light intensity. This may be accept-

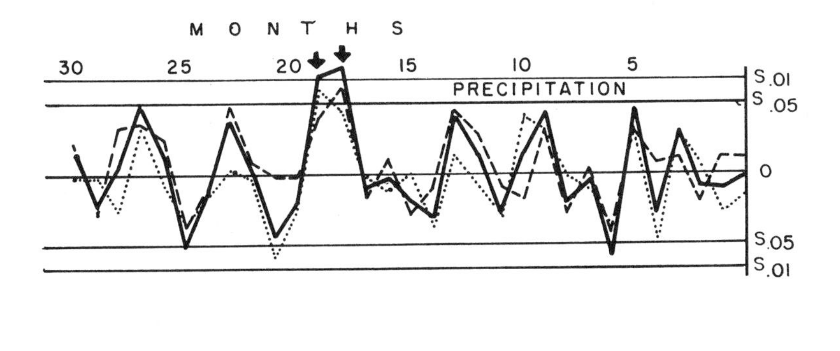

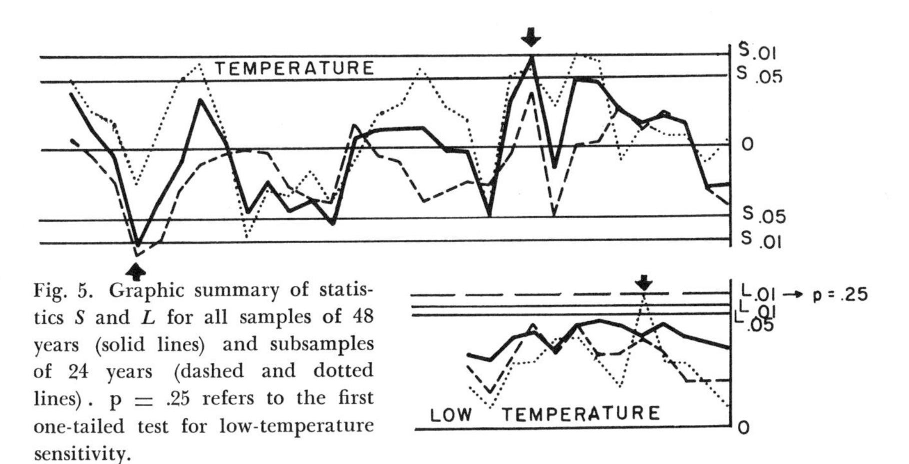

Fig. 5. Graphic summary of statistics *S* and *L* for all samples of 48 years (solid lines) and subsamples of 24 years (dashed and dotted lines). p = .25 refers to the first one-tailed test for low-temperature sensitivity.

Table 1. Combination of apparent requirements for abundant cone crop. These represent the associations designated as having biological validity and correspond to the values indicated by arrows in Figure 5.

Month no.	Month	Requirement
27	July	Cool
19	March	High precipitation
18	April	(Moist, cloudy)
9	January	Warm
4	June	Not cold

able, however, since the absence of a strong correlation of cone crop with air temperature during this period leads to the suggestion of a requirement that temperatures in the meristematic tissue itself must not be outside an intermediate range. Higher night temperatures would keep the tissue in this optimum range during more hours of each day. Thus, the two interpretations of the role of cloudiness may be mutually supporting.

Discussion of possible mechanisms involving the active role of atmospheric humidity will not be undertaken here. But the answer to our basic question gives us reason to suspect that the processes of reproductive physiology in Douglas fir are particularly sensitive to the atmospheric environment during the second spring preceding cone maturity and, although precipitation itself may not be the controlling variable, there would be no difficulty in constructing reasonable hypotheses involving variables related to precipitation.

The choice of examining 30 months prior to an October harvest was arbitrary. Presumably the tree matures its cone crop in one year. Our tests yielded evidence, however, that an environmental influence exists as long as 27 months prior to harvest.

Conclusions

Table 1 is the first product of the process of biometerological inference in the study under discussion. It is a set of clues as to where and when to look for critical plant-environment interactions in the myriad possible places and times one might look. It appears to have the virtues of greater objectivity, longer records, and consideration of more months prior to cone maturity than similar studies on the subject (Daubenmire, 1960; Garman, 1955; Lester, 1963; Maguire, 1956). But despite these virtues, and even after interpretation, validation of the answer requires additional statistical testing and experimental field testing.

The results of this study have provided sufficient basis for experimental field testing to be incorporated in a study of precocious flowering in juvenile Douglas fir at Oregon State University. In the testing, four series of three-year-old trees will be observed under semicontrolled plantation conditions simulating those described above. If possible, additional statistical tests will be undertaken at Oregon State to examine the validity of these prescriptions and to seek more detailed information on the nature of the apparent environmental requirements for an abundant cone crop.

Although both field testing and statistical testing may provide clear evidence supporting our present ideas, and although field testing may even lead to acceptance of semicontrolled environments as operational procedures in genetics research, still the goal of a true model of the interactions under discussion will not be complete without postulation of the mechanisms connecting organism and environment, whether biochemical or ecological. We have now a provision for focusing attention, effort, and discussion on a manageable set of ideas about the sequence of requirements for the success of a very complex process.

What does our critical examination tell us as we prepare to extend the statistical portions of the inference? Having examined the inputs with a critical eye, and having written down the obvious shortcomings, how can we improve the inputs?

For the present problem we should use cone crop observations of small geographic areas which provide quantitative measurements under a known sampling scheme, and which express abundance of conelets before pollination in order to screen out effects of abortion. In order to obtain more data it may be possible to combine several recently obtained short records in which these sampling difficulties have been overcome.

If cone crop records representing smaller areas are used, it becomes appropriate to use meteorological data from individual stations representing the same areas. If the results of such supplementary studies support the results presented here, we would be in a position to explore relations using time units shorter than a month. These additional applications of the process of biometeorological inference may modify, strengthen, and clarify the pathway along which we conduct our search for this particular set of critical plant-environment relations.

REFERENCES

American Meteorological Society (AMS), 1961. *Proposal to the National Science Foundation to Establish a Study Group on Bioclimatology within the American Meteorological Society.* Boston. (Mimeograph)

Daubenmire, R. F., 1960. A seven-year study of cone production as related to xylem layers and temperature in *Pinus ponderosa. Am. Midland Naturalist, 64:* 187–193.

Garman, E. H., 1955. Regeneration problems and their silvicultural significance in the coastal forests of British Columbia. *British Columbia Forest Service, Tech. Bull., 41:* 1–67.

Lester, D. T., 1963. Conelet production and floral initiation in red pine in relation to climate. *Univ. Wisconsin Forestry Note No. 100.* (Mimeograph)

Lowry, W. P., 1963. Biometeorological data collection. *Phytopathology, 53:* 1200–1202.

Lowry, W. P., 1966. Apparent meteorological requirements for abundant cone crop in Douglas fir. *Forest Sci., 12:* 185–192.

Maguire, W. P., 1956. Are ponderosa pine cone crops predictable? *J. Forestry, 54:* 778–779.

National Academy of Sciences—National Research Council (NAS-NRC), 1962. Section on Biometeorology. *The Atmospheric Sciences 1961–1971;* vol. 1, pp. 55–57. Publication 946, NAS-NRC, Washington, D. C.

Sargent, F., 1963. The nature and nurture of biometeorology. *Am. Inst. Biol. Sci. Bull., 13:* 20–23, and identically in *Bull. Am. Meteorol. Soc., 44:* 483–488.

II. Ground Level Climate and Plants

Phenological Patterns and Their Use as Climatic Indicators

JOSEPH M. CAPRIO, *Plant and Soil Science Department, Agricultural Experiment Station, Montana State University, Bozeman, Montana*

PLANT SPECIES AND PLANT GROWTH have been used in various ways as indicators of ground level climate. Early climatic classification was, in fact, based upon natural vegetative cover, and information on climatic change is being sought in the study of tree rings, nature's historical recordings of plant growth (Fritts, 1965; Koppen, 1900).

Plant development may also be used as an indicator of ground level climate. Plant development means the passage of plants through various phases in their advancing seasonal maturity. Such studies are usually grouped under the heading of phenology, which is the science of periodic biological events and their relation to seasonal climatic changes.

This paper makes reference, primarily, to a single phenological event, that of the first bloom date of the common purple lilac, *Syringa vulgaris* L.

Patterns of Geographic Progression

The advance to higher elevations of the beginning of blooms of the common purple lilac, as determined in this study by map analysis and its relation to a selection of clones of other plants, is compared in Figure 1. The graph is based on phenological information on clonal transplants published by Clausen *et al.* (1940). Included in this group of plants are ecotypes and ecospecies of the genera *Potentilla, Horkelia, Achillea,* and *Artemisia.* Many species studied by this group, although blooming at later dates than the lilac, tend

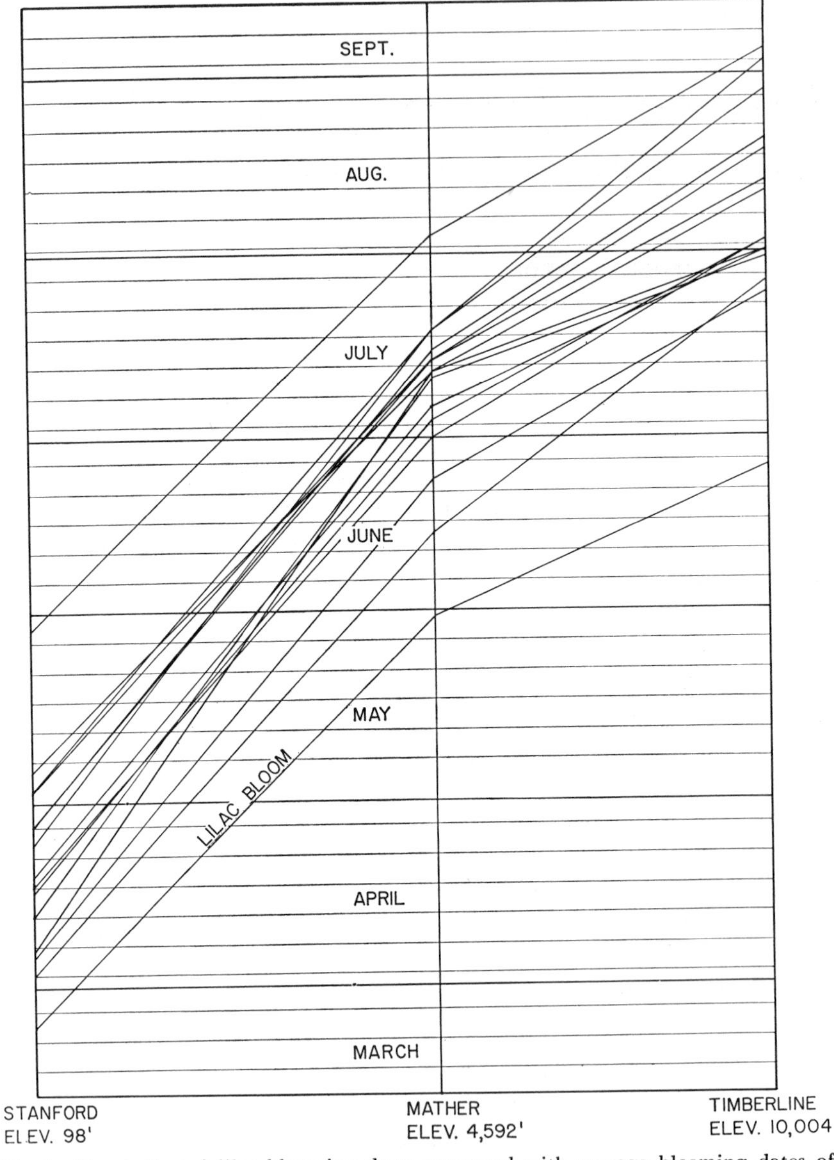

Fig. 1. Map-indicated lilac blooming dates compared with average blooming dates of other plants (not labeled) at Stanford, Mather, and Timberline, California, located near 38°N latitude (Data for other plants based on Clausen *et al.*, 1940).

to progress upward to higher elevations in their bloom at about the same speed as the lilac. The progression of lilac blooms is undoubtedly related to the geographic progression of the development of numerous other plant species growing throughout the mountainous West.

Phenological maps have been published for the area east of the Rocky Mountains, especially for agriculturally important plants, but little is known about the progression of plant development in the mountainous West largely because the great variation in topography makes it difficult to detect any general pattern throughout the area. To circumvent the confounding influence of elevation, a manual mapping procedure was developed which considers a three-dimensional pattern, then stratifies the data by using a separate map for each 100-foot elevation interval. The details of the construction of these equal-elevation maps are described elsewhere (Caprio, 1966).

Figure 2 shows the pattern of isophanes (isophenes) at 0-, 3,000-, and 6,000-foot elevations. Sea-level isophanes were drawn by projection from higher elevations assuming constant isophanal gradients. The north-south orientation of isophanes at sea level, particularly in California, is a conspicuous feature of this map. Lilacs begin to bloom about March 31 at sea level, for example, along the entire length of California. The tendency of the isophanes to reach a northern extreme in the central part of the region is another characteristic of the sea-level isophanal pattern. The line (not shown in Fig. 2) connecting the points at which isophanes reach their northernmost limits is called the "Early Ridge".

The pattern at 3,000 feet is somewhat similar but the isophanes are farther apart than they were at sea level along the California coast. Again there is a conspicuous peaking in the central part of the region, the Early Ridge, and a tendency for isophanes to become less curved and assume a more latitudinal orientation. At 6,000 feet the isophanes are even less curved and more latitudinally oriented, but still the Early Ridge is evident near the center of the region. The Early Ridge appears to move eastward at higher elevations, particularly in the northern part of the region.

From equal-level isophanal maps which have been drawn for every 100-foot interval of elevation it is possible to construct maps which show those elevations where lilacs normally begin to bloom on any

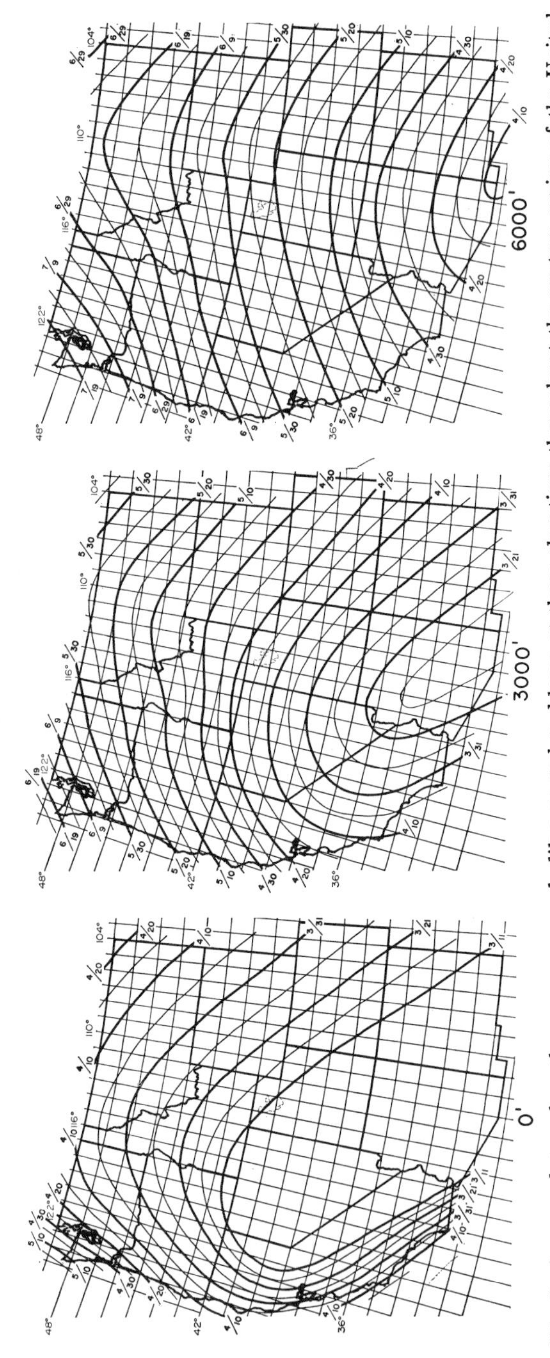

Fig. 2. Average dates when the common purple lilac started to bloom at three elevations throughout the western region of the United States (1957–1961).

given date. The map labeled March 16 in Figure 3 indicates those elevations at which lilacs begin to bloom on March 16. Any location at 2,400-foot elevation along the line labeled 24, for example, has an average beginning bloom date of March 16. The map for April 15 is interpreted similarly. For example, any place located at 4,200 feet elevation along the line marked 42 would have an average first bloom date of April 15. According to this map, lilacs begin to bloom on April 15 along the central coast of Oregon. The May 15 map indicates that lilacs on this date are just beginning to bloom at the northwestern tip of Washington near sea level whereas in Arizona and New Mexico they are beginning to bloom at elevations above 8,000 feet in the southern parts of the states. The June 14 map is of particular significance because phenological stations do not have mean dates of lilac bloom much beyond mid-June. Therefore, the elevations indicated here closely approximate the extreme northern limits of lilacs. While lilacs can develop and bloom at 9,000 feet in Colorado, for example, their highest extent in northwestern Washington is about 3,000 feet. Beginning lilac bloom generally does not occur before the middle of March. Therefore, the first map in this series, dated March 16, indicates the approximate southern limits for the common purple lilac.

The data for a five-year period (1957–1961) were also analyzed statistically for different zones according to the following equation:

$$Y = aX_1 + bX_2 + cX_3 + d, \text{ where}$$

$$Y = \text{date of bloom (March 1 = 1)}$$

$$X_1 = \text{latitude}$$

$$X_2 = \text{longitude}$$

$$X_3 = \text{elevation}$$

The letters, a, b, c, and d are constants determined by the regression analysis. The zones, identified by circled numbers in Figures 4 through 7, were determined by geographic considerations and also by the availability of phenological reports. All zones are geographically distinct except that Zone 7 also includes all data from Zone 1.

This equation could not be applied for Zones 15 and 16 in California because of the complex isophanal pattern in that part of the

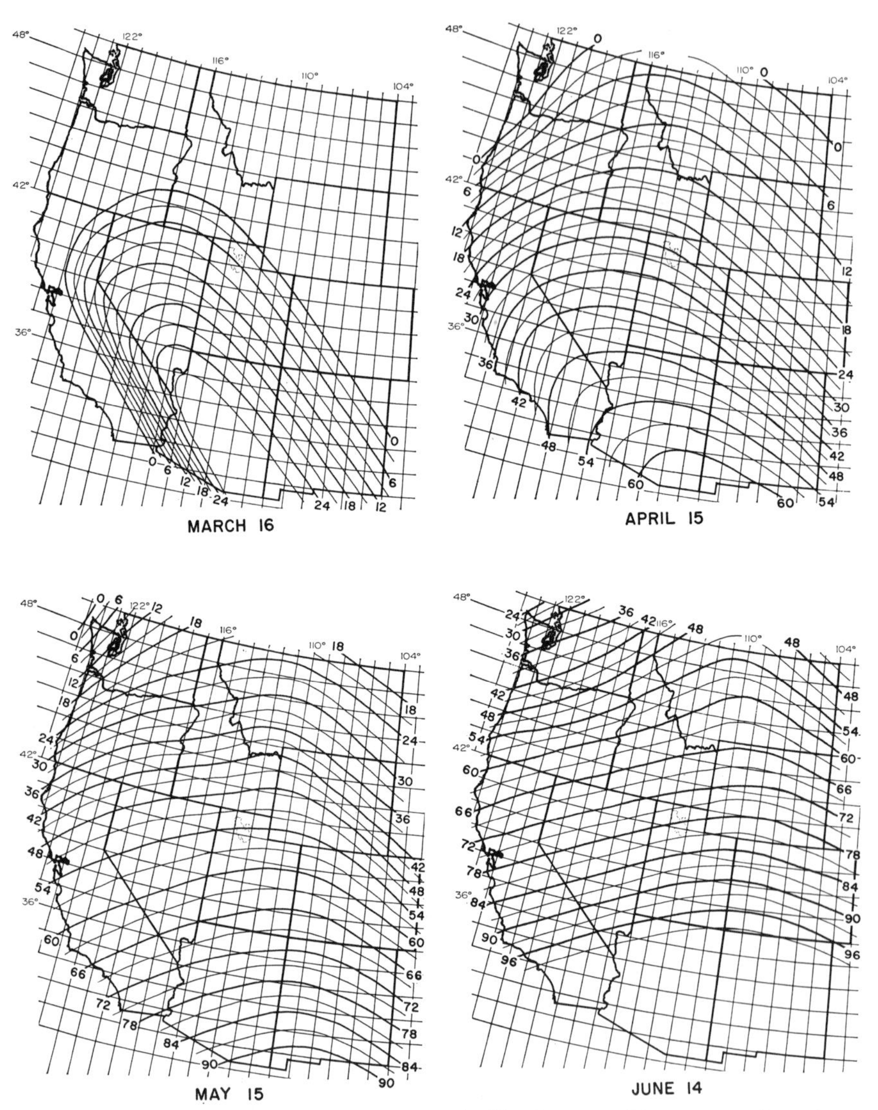

Fig. 3. Elevations at which the common purple lilac began to bloom on various dates throughout the western region of the United States (1957–1961). Elevations indicate hundreds of feet. Each point on the map at which the elevation coincides with the curved lines indicates the lilac's beginning bloom on the date shown at the bottom of the charts.

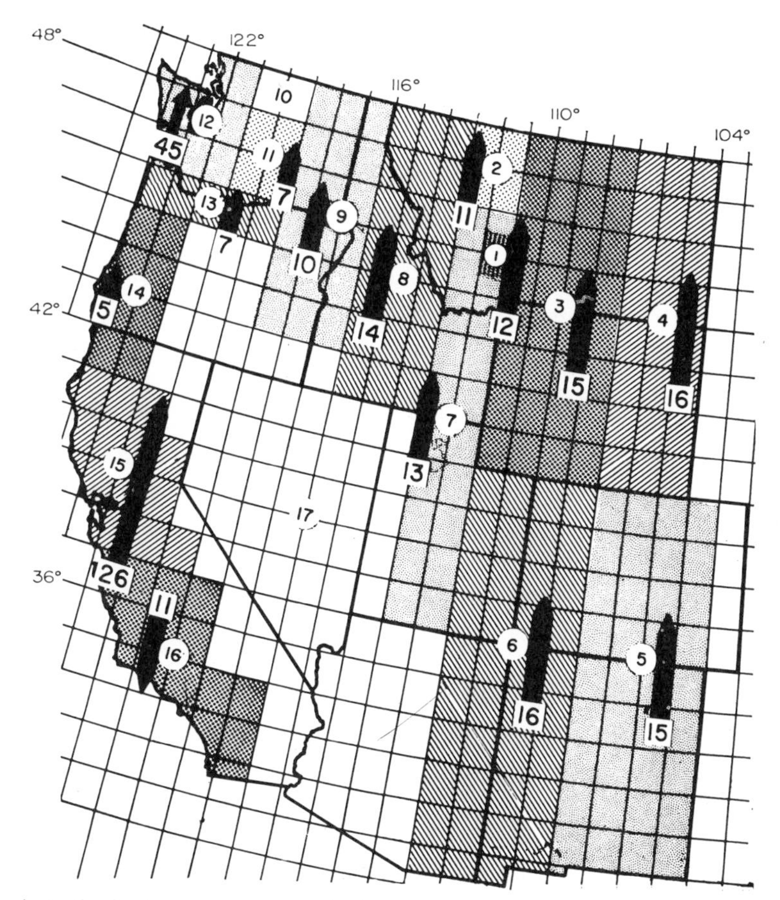

Fig. 4. Latitudinal movement of beginning lilac bloom in minutes per day (indicated by boxes). Shading and circled numbers indicate geographic zones.

western region. However, the relationships were amenable to the following equations:

$$\text{Zone 15: } Y = aX_1 + bX_2 + cX_3 + dX_3^2 + eX_1X_3 + f$$

$$\text{Zone 16: } Y = aX_1 + bX_2 + cX_3 + dX_3^2 + eX_2X_3 + f$$

The letters *a, b, c, d, e,* and *f* are constants determined by regression analysis.

The quadratic elevation term provides for nonlinear relation to higher elevations and the additional terms X_1X_3 and X_2X_3 provide for interaction between latitude and elevation and between longitude and elevation. While this statistical approach may be more objective than the manual mapping procedure, the mapping method may provide the more accurate estimates of bloom dates since these simple equations are relatively inflexible, considering the climatic complexity of such extensive geographic areas.

Table 1 gives pertinent information on the derived equations. The reciprocal of the derivatives of these equations, presented in Table 2, indicates the rate at which the bloom progresses latitudinally (north and south), longitudinally (east and west), and upwards in elevation.

In Figure 4 the length of the bars is proportional to the north and south speed of beginning lilac bloom at a given elevation according to the equations. When speed is too great to indicate in proper proportions, an arrow is used. The speed of progression in minutes per day is written under each of the bars. Zones are identified by circled numbers. All movement is northward except in California where there is southward progression of lilac bloom. According to Hopkins' Bioclimatic Law (1918), the movement is fifteen minutes per day northward. Hopkins states that ". . . the time of occurrence of a given periodical event in life activity in temperate North America is at the general average rate of 4 days to each 1 degree of latitude, 5 degrees of longitude, 400 feet of altitude, later northward, eastward and upward in the spring and early summer, and the reverse in late summer and autumn." There are large deviations from his values, particularly along the West Coast. The speeds of northward movement in the eastern half of the region are very close to Hopkins' fifteen minutes per day. Northward movement of the lilac bloom phase is slower in Oregon but more rapid in western Washington. This is in agreement with mapped isophanes which tend to parallel the Washington coast at lower elevations with a steep gradient in an east-west direction. The negative value in southern California indicates that lilacs develop later near the coast than in the warmer interior. This is probably due to the northwest-southeast orientation of the coast, which causes cooler temperatures to prevail on approaching the coast from the north. Northward movement in the foehn areas of Washington and Montana (Zones 11 and 2) is indicated as being rather slow.

Figure 5 indicates the statistically derived east and west movement

Table 1. Statistical analysis of the relation between average date of beginning lilac bloom and latitude, longitude, and elevation.

Zone no.	No. of observations	Multiple R*	Standard error of est. (days)	Coefficients of equations: Latitude (a)	Longitude (b)	Elevation (c)	(Elevation)² (d)	(Lat) (Elev) (e_1)	(Long) (Elev) (e_2)	Constant of equation (f)
1	28	.887	1.9	+4.9753	−7.2477	+.7305 (10^{-2})	—	—	—	+631.5
2	13	.764	2.6	+5.6961	−5.2191	+.8763 (10^{-2})	—	—	—	+360.7
3	67	.778	4.4	+4.0725	−1.1047	+.8686 (10^{-2})	—	—	—	−19.6
4	79	.797	4.0	+3.7266	−1.3823	+.7720 (10^{-2})	—	—	—	+30.0
5	76	.954	4.7	+3.9640	−2.6456	+.8974 (10^{-2})	—	—	—	+145.9
6	31	.958	4.7	+3.8306	+.1356 (10^{-1})	+.1166 (10^{-1})	—	—	—	−149.2
7	85	.950	4.2	+4.7311	+.3173	+.1350 (10^{-1})	—	—	—	−227.3
8	49	.868	4.9	+4.2578	+4.5421	+.1208 (10^{-1})	—	—	—	−678.6
9	63	.955	4.3	+5.8625	+.4196	+.1539 (10^{-1})	—	—	—	−287.6
11	16	.975	2.8	+8.8297	−1.2303	+.1075 (10^{-1})	—	—	—	−227.5
12	34	.821	5.3	+1.3471	+4.8032	+.1704 (10^{-1})	—	—	—	−600.2
13	31	.876	5.5	+8.9659	+4.0490	+.1590 (10^{-1})	—	—	—	−859.9
14	40	.849	6.1	+11.2331	+9.2409	+.2055 (10^{-1})	—	—	—	−1595.6
15	69	.913	6.8	+.6876	+3.2634	−.3323 (10^{-1})	+.6079 (10^{-6})	+.1053 (10^{-2})	—	−403.1
16	41	.814	6.1	−5.4018	+3.9309	−.1228	+.3494 (10^{-6})	—	+.1073 (10^{-2})	−257.8

* Multiple correlation coefficient.

Table 2. Mean geographic coordinates and statistically derived geographic movement of beginning lilac bloom.

	Mean geographic coordinates			Movement in		
Zone	Latitude	Longitude	Elevation	Latitude (min/day)	Longitude (min/day)	Elevation (feet/day)
1	45.93	111.29	4,612	+12.1	−8.3	137
2	47.97	111.65	3,551	+10.5	−11.5	114
3	45.49	108.98	4,218	+14.7	−54.3	115
4	44.56	105.37	4,185	+16.1	−43.4	130
5	37.44	104.78	5,841	+15.1	−22.7	111
6	36.53	108.41	5,765	+15.6	+4424.5	86
7	43.32	111.72	4,928	+12.7	+189.1	74
8	45.94	114.59	3,518	+14.1	+13.2	83
9	46.04	117.35	2,501	+10.2	+143.0	65
11	46.94	119.79	1,086	+6.8	−48.8	93
12	47.41	122.67	456	+44.5	+12.5	59
13	45.51	121.81	883	+6.7	+14.8	63
14	43.20	123.14	1,021	+5.3	+6.5	49
15	39.04	121.83	1,561	+25.7[a]	+18.4	102[a]
16	34.90	118.60	2,245	−11.1	+9.4[a]	166[a]

[a] Value at mean geographic coordinates of phenological stations.

of isophanes at a given elevation. According to Hopkins' Law, plant development at a given elevation progresses eastward at the rate of 75 minutes per day. The bars and arrows point in the direction of movement; lilacs bloom later at a given elevation in the area towards which the bars and arrows are pointing. The bars are drawn to proportion; the arrows are not. Lilacs bloom first at a given elevation in the interior and then progress westward towards the coast. This movement towards the coast, however, is relatively slow. Movement is towards the east in the Great Plains, indicating that lilacs bloom first in the central part of the region at a given elevation and then progress eastward. This is in agreement with the manually determined configuration of isophanes which show the Early Ridge located in the central part of the area. At a given elevation the earliest maturing areas are those in the central part of the western region and lilac beginning bloom (at a given elevation) progresses

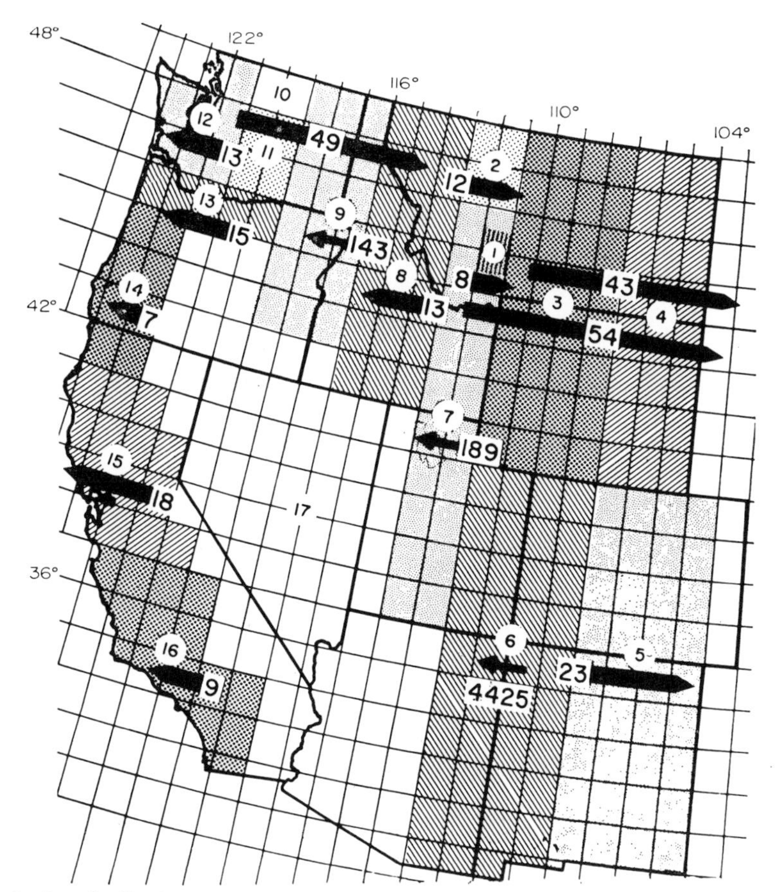

Fig. 5. Longitudinal movement of beginning lilac bloom in minutes per day. Shading and circled numbers indicate geographic zones.

from the central to the eastern and western limits of the region. Rapid east and west movement in central parts of the western region indicates that isophanes assume an orientation more parallel to east and west lines, which is in agreement with the manually drawn isophanes. It is interesting to note that bloom in the two foehn areas is later with movement eastward from the Cascade and Rocky Mountain ranges.

The derived rates of progression of lilac beginning bloom to higher elevations are given in Figure 6. According to Hopkins' Law, the rate of progression to higher elevations is 100 feet per

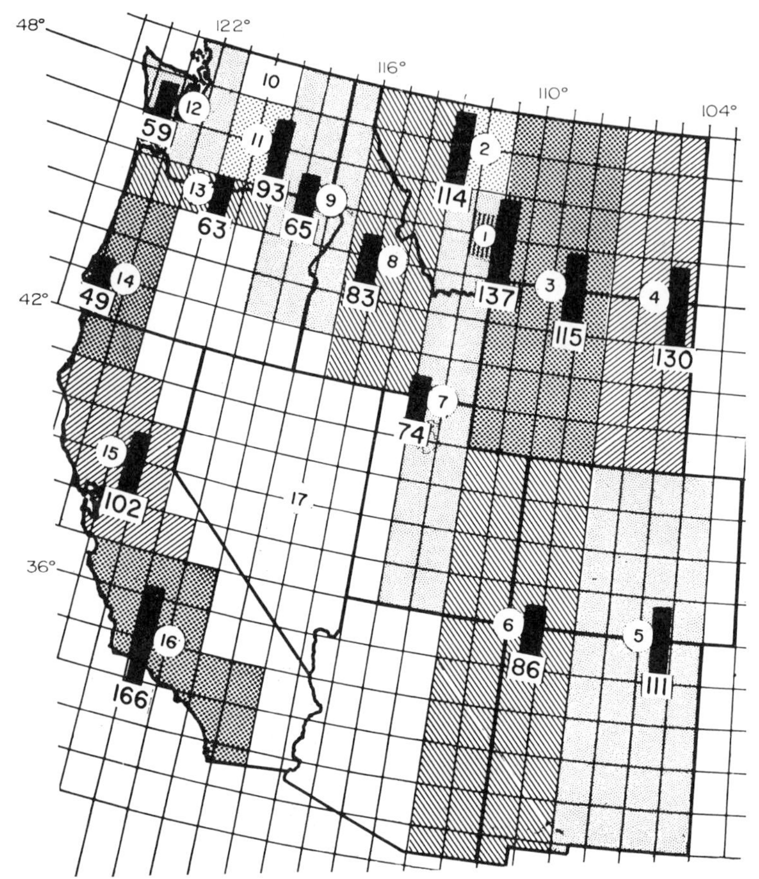

Fig. 6. Movement of beginning lilac bloom upward in elevation in feet per day. Shading and circled numbers indicate geographic zones.

day. Computed rates are greater than this in the Great Plains area. A complex pattern prevails along the West Coast. In southern California lilac beginning bloom progresses rapidly to higher elevations. Figure 6 indicates the rate of progression upward at mean location of phenological plants for each zone. For Zones 15 and 16, this is 1,561 and 2,245 feet of elevation, respectively. Rates of progression upward near sea level, according to the equations (not shown in Figure 6), are more than 200 feet per day in Zones 15 and 16. In contrast, the movement to higher elevations is slower in eastern Oregon and Washington. The reason for these differences in rates

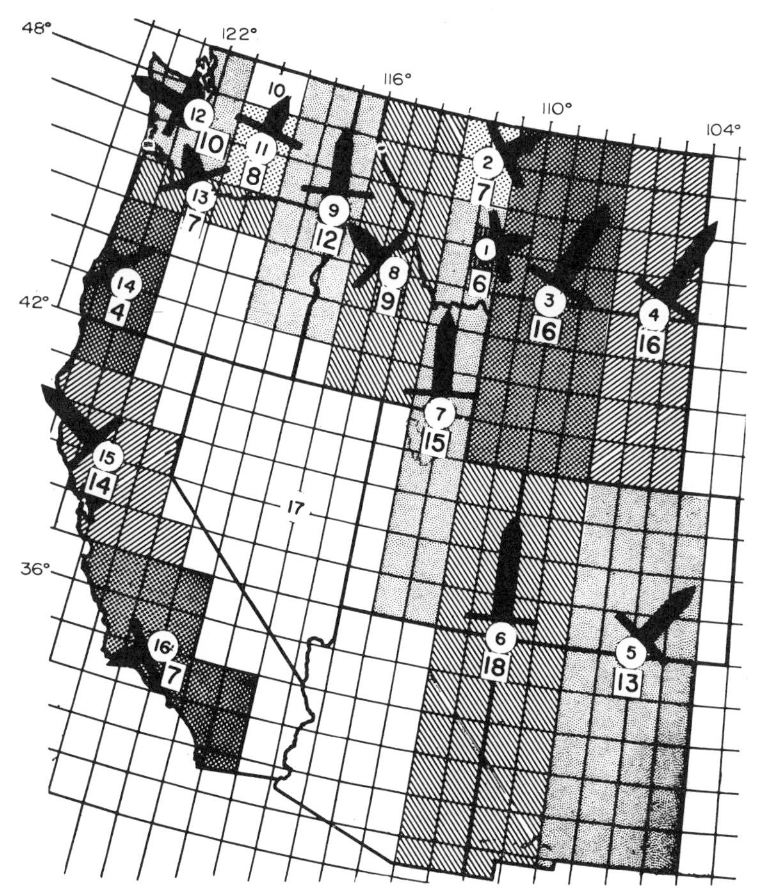

Fig. 7. Orientation of isophanes and movement of beginning lilac bloom perpendicular to isophanes in miles per day (indicated by boxes). Each bar points in the direction of movement and the length of the bar is drawn in proportion to the speed. The line at the base of the bar is drawn parallel to the isophanes. Shading and circled numbers indicate geographic zones.

of progression to higher elevations along the Pacific Coast will be discussed later.

The computed orientation of isophanes and the speed of progression of lilac bloom at a given elevation in a direction perpendicular to isophanes are indicated in Figure 7. The large pointed bar indicates the horizontal direction of plant progression. The values change according to location and elevation in Zones 15 and 16 in California; values indicated for these zones are for the mean location and elevation of all the phenological plants studied in each zone. The length of the bar is proportional to the speed, which is indicated at the base of the bar by a number indicating miles per day. The progression in all zones has a component towards the north except in southern California (Zone 16) where the direction is to the southwest. Generally the direction is towards the northeast in the eastern part of the region and the northwest in the western part of the region. The orientation of isophanes, indicated by the line at the base of the bar, corresponds closely to those of the manually drawn maps (Fig. 1). They are oriented southeast-northwest in southern California, southwest-northeast along most of the coast, and northwest-southeast in the Great Plains. Note the northwest-southeast orientation of isophanes in the foehn areas. It may be a general rule in middle latitudes of the Northern Hemisphere that windward of mountain systems isophanes are oriented from southwest to northeast, and leeward of these mountain systems the orientation is from northwest to southeast. The rule may be

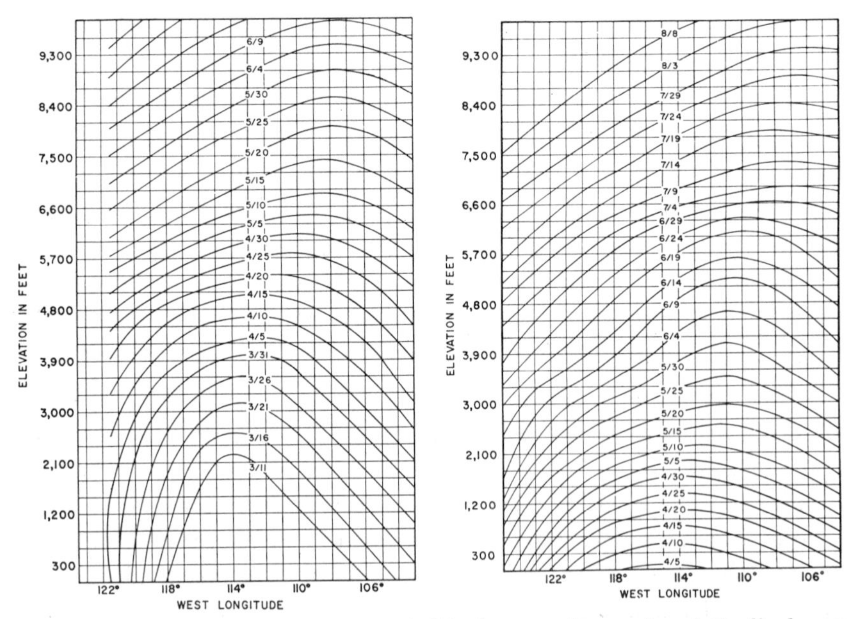

Fig. 8. Average dates when common purple lilac began to bloom along latitudinal cross sections (1957–1961). Left: 36°N; right: 48°N.

applicable both for entire regions such as the western region and for more local situations.

Since the manually drawn map analysis represents a three-dimensional system it is possible to construct cross sections of isophanes for different parts of the region.

The east-west oriented cross sections at 36°N and 48°N latitude are shown in Figure 8. The cross section at 36°N cuts through California just to the south of Oakland and through southern Nevada, northern Arizona, and New Mexico. Isophanes approach lower elevations vertically along the California coast, indicating little change in lilac blooming date with increasing elevation. The isophanes curve upward from west to east, reaching a peak at the Early Ridge, and then deflect downward farther to the east.

The east-west cross section for 48°N latitude cuts near the northern boundaries of Washington, Idaho, and Montana. The isophanal pattern resembles that for 36°N latitude, but isophanes at lower elevations near the coast approach the surface at a lower angle and are closer together.

A comparison of the actual reports of lilac bloom from different stations and the smooth isophanal patterns reveals local zones of departure; that is, areas where there is a relatively large proportion of stations having mean lilac beginning bloom either earlier or later than indicated by the regional equal-level isophanal maps. Figure 9 shows zones of departure and how early or late they are. Most departures are about five days earlier or later than the date indicated on the map. In general, places where bloom begins earlier than one would expect from the smooth regional map analysis occur in those areas which are to the lee of mountain ranges. The foehn areas in Washington and Montana are two examples. Blooms which occur later than indicated by map analysis in parts of southwestern Arizona and southeastern California may be attributed to the lack of adequate winter chilling and the resultant delay in foliation and blooming. The early zone extending from Nevada to Oregon and into California is one for which there are only few reports and its extent, therefore, is rather vague. It is indicated on the map by dashed lines.

The length of the lilac blooming stage throughout the region

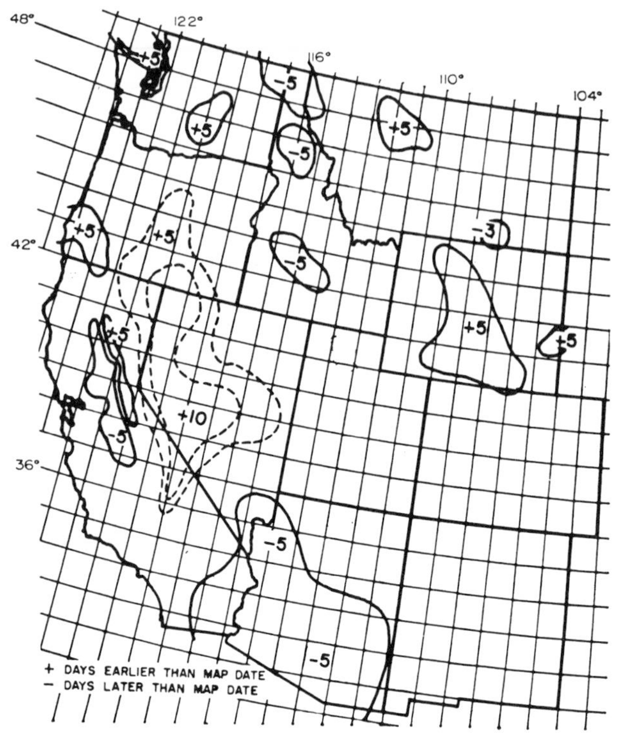

Fig. 9. Zones of departure of actual beginning lilac bloom date from map-indicated average date (1957–1961).

varies from a maximum exceeding 30 days in a narrow strip along almost the entire Pacific Coast to less than 18 days in eastern parts of Colorado, New Mexico, Montana, and Wyoming.

Pattern of Thermal Advance

Numerous studies have indicated that the development of plants is highly correlated with the thermal environment. It might be expected, therefore, that the isothermal pattern throughout the region would tend to conform somewhat to the equal-level patterns of the isophanal analysis. Figure 10 shows lilac isophanes at 4,800 feet and, on the right, the April isotherms at 850 millibars (about 4,800 feet of altitude) published by the U. S. Weather Bureau (1949). There is a marked similarity in the isophanal and isothermal patterns.

To understand more about the relationship between the thermal environment and plant development, the pattern of lilac bloom was compared with the pattern of upper air temperatures at 0300 GMT (7:00 P.M. PST and 8:00 P.M. MST) published by the U. S. Weather Bureau (1957, 1958). Figure 11 shows the isophanal patterns of beginning lilac bloom in its relation to upper air measurements at Albuquerque, New Mexico. Elevation is indicated along the ordinate and temperature along the abscissa. Temperature stratification is given for each month from March through June. The temperature on March 15 at 10,000 feet over Albuquerque, for example, was approximately −1°C. The elevation of Albuquerque is 5,311 feet. Plotted lines of mean monthly upper-air temperature provide a time scale going from left to right which is used to plot the average date of lilac bloom. Temperatures are projected linearly by a dashed line to the surface. Lilacs near 5,300 feet elevation bloom in the Albuquerque area at a temperature of about 16.6°C. Lower temperatures prevail when lilacs normally begin to bloom at higher elevations.

Temperature distribution at Santa Maria, California, and the average date of beginning lilac bloom at different elevations in that area are given in Figure 12. It was shown (Fig. 8) that lilacs tend to develop at about the same date in the lower several thousand feet near the coast of southern California. The reason for this appears to be related to the thermal stratification of the atmosphere in that area. Near isothermal conditions exist in the lower several thousand feet in southern California during the early spring period. Temperatures prevailing at the time when lilacs begin to bloom are also indicated as decreasing with increasing elevations in the Santa Maria area but relatively less than in the Albuquerque area. Albuquerque and Santa Maria seem to represent two extremes in the rate at which temperature falls with elevation at the time when lilacs begin to bloom.

The typical temperature distributions with increasing elevations on dates when the analysis indicates lilacs are at the beginning bloom phase are shown in Figure 13. The line on the right is characteristic of the southeastern area where lilacs bloom at high temperatures and where the rate of temperature drop with increasing elevation at the time when lilacs begin to bloom is greatest–

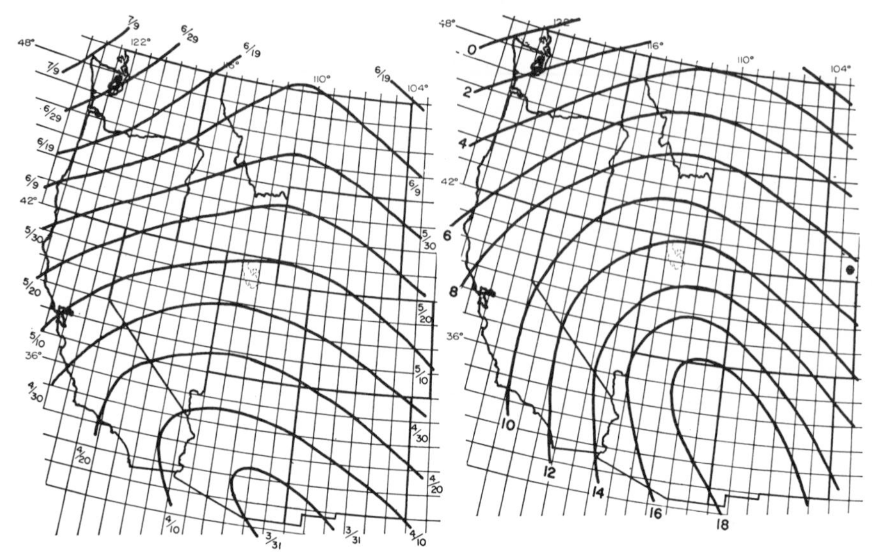

Fig. 10. Left: Average dates when the common purple lilac begins to bloom at 4,800 feet of elevation. Right: Average April temperatures (°C) at 850 millibars (mbs) or about 4,800 feet of elevation.

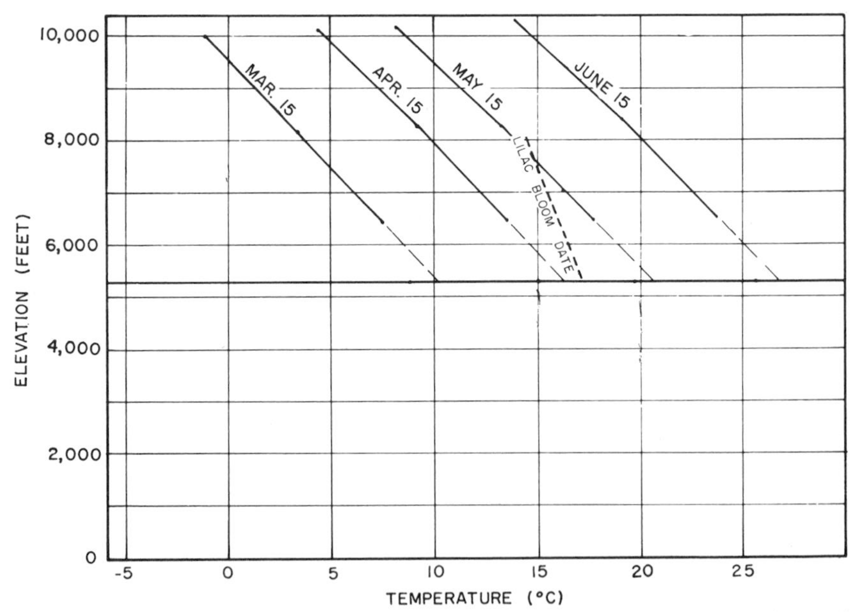

Fig. 11. Mean temperature of the atmosphere above Albuquerque, New Mexico, and average date and temperatures at which lilacs begin to bloom at corresponding elevations.

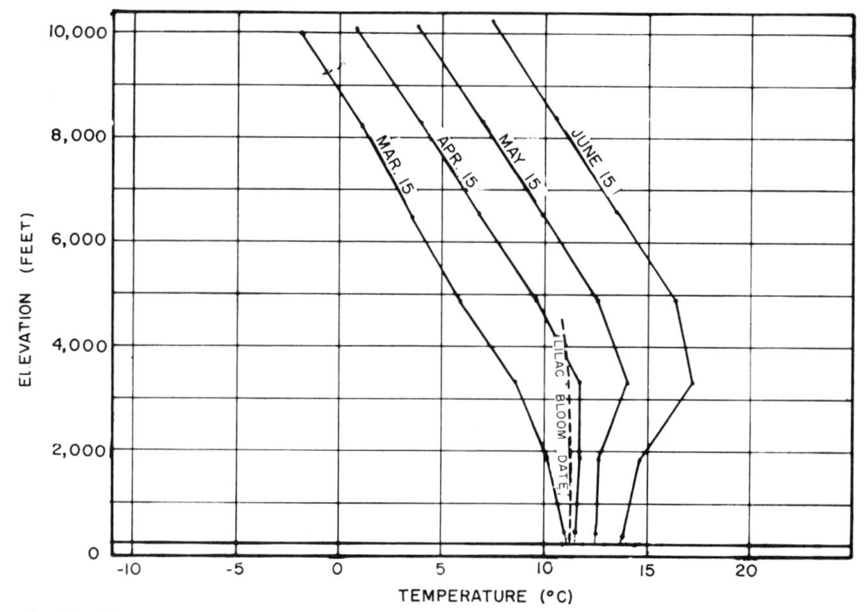

Fig. 12. Mean temperature of the atmosphere above Santa Maria, California, and average date and temperatures at which lilacs begin to bloom at corresponding elevations.

averaging about 1.5°F per 1,000-foot increase in elevation. The central line is typical of much of the area throughout the western region where the temperature drop at the time of beginning lilac bloom averages about 0.9°F per 1,000 feet. The line on the left is typical of locations along the West Coast where it is relatively cool at the time when the analysis indicates lilacs are at beginning bloom phase and where temperatures at higher elevations at the time of beginning bloom are not much different from those at lower elevations, being roughly 0.3°F cooler every 1,000 feet. The apparent tendency for lilacs to bloom during colder conditions at higher elevations may have important agricultural implications.

On an average, a given mean temperature (thermal wave) moves to higher altitudes throughout the western region at the rate of about 65 feet per day. California is an exception since an inversion develops there at the end of the winter. The rapid advance of lilac bloom to higher elevations in coastal southern California is probably related to this anomalous temperature stratification. The plant wave moves to higher elevations at an average of about

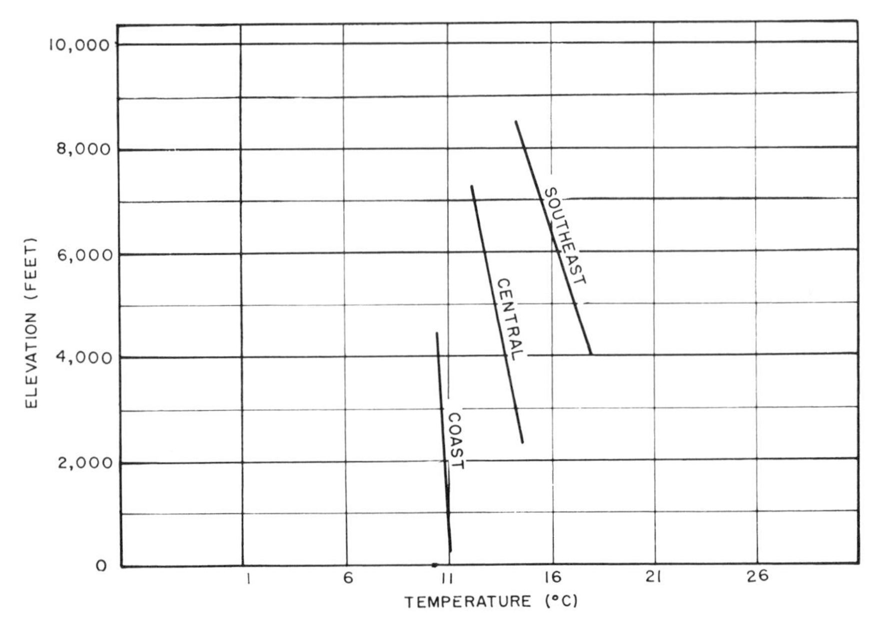

Fig. 13. Typical mean atmospheric temperatures prevailing at the time when lilacs normally begin to bloom at corresponding elevations in the coastal, central, and southeastern areas of the western region.

100 feet per day but wide variations are noted within the western region (Fig. 6). Since the thermal wave progresses to higher elevations at a rather uniform rate over much of the West, it appears that the lilac bloom wave moves somewhat independently of the thermal wave. The difference in the rate of progression of these two waves to higher elevations may reflect some feature of climatic difference within the region. The coast is generally cloudy during the late winter and spring growth period until lilac bloom, and the Great Plains area tends to be less cloudy during this phenological period. The difference in movement of thermal and plant waves may be related to the intensity of solar radiation, the plant wave progressing to higher elevations at a relatively greater speed than the thermal wave in those areas which are least cloudy. The relatively rapid movement of the plant wave to higher elevations in the foehn areas of Montana and Washington is in agreement with this interpretation. The slower movement of the plant wave to higher

elevations on the windward side of major mountains computed in this study also agrees with this interpretation. A study of lilac bloom in Hungary has reported that the movement to higher elevations on the north slopes of mountains is slower than on the south slopes. This also suggests that radiation may be linked to the differential rate of movement of plant phases to higher elevations (Mandy, 1940).

Since plant-geographic relations can be highly influenced by variability of climate and topography, and because upper atmospheric temperatures rather than temperatures at the plant site are used, further studies are needed to confirm the relative rates of plant and thermal progressions suggested by this analysis.

Uses of Phenological Data

The surface distribution of the mean date when lilacs begin to bloom has been mapped in Montana. The pattern is strongly influenced by topography. Lilac blooms are generally earlier at lower elevations, where they occur prior to the middle of May. Areas having blooms before May 15 occur both east and west of the Continental Divide. A map showing the average date of the last spring freeze was also drawn for Montana. The pattern of the last freeze and the pattern of the time of beginning lilac bloom are not similar. There are extensive areas in the eastern part of the state where the average date of the last freeze occurs prior to May 15, but none are indicated west of the Continental Divide.

The difference between the average date of last freeze and the average date of beginning lilac bloom is being used as an index of freeze hazard. If the last freeze normally occurs before lilacs come into bloom, there is little freeze hazard to bloom, but if the average last freeze normally occurs after lilacs begin to bloom, there is a high freeze hazard. Large areas in the eastern part of Montana are characterized by a low freeze hazard. West of the Divide the only extensive area indicated as having a low freeze hazard is in the vicinity of Flathead Lake. The rest of the area is largely one of a high freeze hazard; plants develop early but freezes continue late. Another important feature of this freeze hazard map is that it tends to reflect elevation. The last spring freeze in Montana occurs at a late date at higher elevations relative to the time when lilacs begin to bloom.

The precise cause of differences in the speed of the plant waves and thermal waves is uncertain, but it may be related to the radiation environment. Consider a unit of radiational effect to be that amount of radiation which will cause the plant wave (beginning lilac bloom in this case) to keep exact pace with the normal thermal movement to higher elevations in the spring of the year. Cloudy areas such as western Washington would have a value of about one unit while sunnier areas such as the Great Plains would have greater values. Normally, freeze hazard would increase most with elevation in the areas with higher units of radiational effect. This approach becomes more complex if temperatures do not increase at the same rate at the different elevations.

Different temperatures have been shown to prevail in different parts of the region at the time when lilacs begin to bloom. The time of lilac bloom, therefore, does not indicate temperature of the atmosphere at the time. In any given area, lilacs appear to begin blooming under different thermal conditions at different elevations. In an area of varied elevations, therefore, lilacs cannot be expected to be indicative of the thermal environment existing at that time unless some correction is made for elevation. The time when lilacs begin to bloom is not dependent solely on ambient temperatures preceding bloom. One of the main limitations in using data recorded in shelters is that temperatures are not indicative of the radiant heat exchange of plants. Two locations with the same shelter temperature but with different radiation regimes are likely to have different rates of plant development.

Of what value, then, are phenological maps? They do serve as indexes of regional differences in plant development rates. Schnelle, in his book on phenology (1955), stressed the importance of phenological information in estimating the nature of the climate between meteorological stations. Among the advantages of using plants as a source of meteorological information, according to Schnelle, are their economy and availability. He strongly supported the use of phenological methods in topoclimatology, that is, climatology in areas of variable terrain, which is generally concerned with climatic mapping on scales of about one to 25,000.

Two methods of utilizing phenological data for climatic purposes will be considered:

1. In the geographic anomaly technique, departures of blooming date from the general geographic isophanal pattern are taken as indicative of climatic departures. The geographically mapped isophanal pattern developed in this study is an example. Zones of early and late bloom departures from the dates indicated by the regional maps are likely to reflect climatic departures from the broad regional pattern. This technique can be also used when analyses are made for smaller areas. Relations, derived statistically, between date of bloom and geographical parameters can serve as a similar base. Departures of blooming date from the geographic patterns, derived statistically, are likely to reflect climatic departures. Assuming that there is an adequately dense phenological network, this approach can be applied on a microclimatic scale. Usually, the assumption is that those areas of earlier bloom are locations of more favorable heat relations.

2. The method in which historical records of a phenological event are related to a climatic parameter for one or more locations in a general area is another way of using phenological data for climatic purposes. Estimates of the climate of specific locations are made from recorded phenological data. For example, if mean temperature is 60°F at the normal time for a plant to reach a given stage of development in a certain area, an estimate of the date when the mean temperature reaches 60° at the second location may be made by utilizing phenological data. Instead of a specific mean temperature at the time of a phenological event, the accumulation of degree-days or some other climatological factor may be more pertinent. Empirical equations are derived which relate phenological events to meteorological conditions. Plant-climate relations may change within the region, especially with changing elevation, so one should deal with a relatively homogeneous climatic area.

The use of phenological information in climatology is referred to in Europe as "phenological climatology". This information is being used successfully to estimate climatic conditions between points of meteorological measurements. The availability of phenological information also makes possible greater use of climatological data, particularly for agricultural applications.

Limitations of Application of Phenological Data

While phenological data can be used to understand more about the climatic environment, there are limits to the method.

Little success has been achieved by using a single equation to relate plant development over an extensive area with the climatic environment.

Even when using clonal material, it is inadvisable to draw conclusions from reports of a single plant, because plants as individuals often act erratically due to disease or some other peculiar circumstance affecting their growth. Therefore, when interpreting phenological records it is advisable to use a mass of data rather than information from a single plant. The massive data approach was used in this study to determine the pattern of beginning lilac bloom throughout the western region.

Soil differences can affect plant development and may have to be taken into account in localized areas. Studies from Europe indicate that plant development can be advanced or retarded more than one week by different soils; soil texture and color are known to influence the rate of plant development (Illichevsky, 1933; Schnelle, 1955). Soil fertility can also influence the rate of plant development. Nitrogen fertilization, for example, often extends the vegetative period and phosphorus usually brings on earlier maturity.

The method of soil cultivation and variable soil moisture are known to affect the developmental rate of plants. The flooding of areas adjacent to rivers has been reported to delay the development of plants growing in such areas (Illichevsky, 1933). Drought during the later part of the life span usually hastens maturity; maturity tends to be delayed if moisture is lacking at seeding time or during the early growth period (Holmes and Robertson, 1959).

Applications of certain chemicals on plants have been reported to influence the rate of maturity. Gibberellin applied on lemons delays their maturity (Coggins *et al.*, 1964). Griggs *et al.* (1965) reported that the growth-retarding compound, B-9, will delay the bloom of Bartlett pears and thus protect them from late freezes. Parthenocarpic Calamyra figs induced by kinen are reported to mature about one week earlier than those naturally pollinated (Crane and Overbeek, 1965).

The development of many plants is influenced by photoperiodic and thermoperiodic effects (Salisbury, 1963). It is known that the age of some plants can influence their rate of development. Small trees, for example, tend to flower somewhat earlier than old and tall trees (Illichevsky, 1933). Density of planting can have a bearing on the time of maturity and is often noticeable in agronomic field tests. Environmental influences prior to the current growing season may also influence plant development; this effect of preconditioning has been discussed by Rowe (1964).

Conclusions

Phenological information is being used to help understand more about climate, in spite of its limitations. Most non-climatic effects are usually of little consequence compared with the greater effects attributable to climatic differences. Plant reports from weather stations are used to obtain an index which shows how the climate varies between the stations. Indications of microclimatic differences may also be obtained by observing the development of plants near the ground.

The following questions may be raised from relations suggested by this lilac bloom study. Do most plants usually take longer to complete given stages of development in marine-type climates than in continental-type climates? What is the significance of the apparent difference between regions in the rate at which the temperature drops at higher elevations when lilacs begin to bloom; and is this largely a function of cloudiness? Do isophanes in foehn areas generally slope from northwest to southeast in middle latitudes? Are isophanes on the windward side of mountains generally oriented from southwest to northeast? Why do lilacs reach a given stage of development along the West Coast under much lower ambient temperatures than in other areas? Will consideration of heat units accumulated during the current growing season largely explain this or are other factors such as preconditioning also important?

The blooming of lilacs at lower temperatures along the Pacific Coast cannot be interpreted to mean, *a priori,* that there are fewer heat units accumulated there up to the time of bloom than in other areas. Temperatures increase more gradually along the coast than in the interior during the spring, so heat units can accumulate over a longer period of time along the coast. Perhaps it will not be possible to express precisely the time when lilacs bloom through meteorological parameters. When considering air temperature alone, the heat unit requirements differ geographically so that an equation derived from data at one location does not explain the behavior of the plant in all geographic areas.

Berg (1952) believes that it is not possible to represent phenological data as a function or a sum of functions of the different meteorological elements. Phenological data, he stated, is one sort of climatic element, and as such has equal rights and is equally as meaningful as the other climatic elements. Just as one studies temperature maps to understand climate, he believes one should study phenological maps. Perhaps this is so, but future endeavors to relate plant development to meteorological parameters might prove more successful than those of the past.

A much greater use of phenology in climatological applications may be made as more is learned about the relationship between the environment and plant response. The establishment of a rather dense phenological network of genotypes of several plant species throughout the United States could make an important contribution towards understanding more about the climate and its relationship to plant development.

Author's Note: Data on *Syringa vulgaris* L. have been collected throughout the western region of the United States since 1957 under Regional Project W-48 entitled *Climate and Phenological Patterns for Agriculture in the Western Region.* This project is supported by funds from the United States Department of Agriculture.

The author gratefully acknowledges the assistance of Michael Bolin and Kenneth Sievert for lettering and inking the figures for publication, of Mrs. Jean Faldetta and Miss Laura Heath for assistance in data processing and statistical analysis, and of personnel of the Computer Laboratory and Art Service at Montana State University for their help in preparing figures and in computer programming.

REFERENCES

Berg, H., 1952. Bedeutung und grenzen der phanologie fur die klimatologic. *Ber. Deut. Wetterdienstes, 42 (11):* 358–361.

Caprio, J. M., 1966. Pattern of plant development in the western United States. Western Regional Research Publication. *Montana Agr. Exp. Sta. Bull., 607.* Bozeman, Montana.

Clausen, J. J., D. D. Keck, and W. H. Hiesey, 1940. *Experimental Studies on the Natures of Species. I.* Effect of varied environments on western North American plants. *Publication No. 520.* Carnegie Institution, Washington, D. C.

Coggins, C. W., R. M. Burns, H. Z. Hield, and R. G. Platt, 1964. Gibberellin delays lemon maturity. *Calif. Agr., 18 (1):* 15.

Crane, J. C., and J. Overbeek, 1965. Kinin-induced parthenocarpy in the fig, *Ficus carica* L. *Science, 147 (3664):* 1468–1469.

Fritts, H. C., 1965. Tree-ring evidence for climatic changes in western North America. *Monthly Weather Rev., 93 (7):* 421–443.

Griggs, W. H., B. T. Iwakiri, and R. S. Bethell, 1965. B-Nine fall sprays delay bloom and increase fruit set on Bartlett pears. *Calif. Agr., 19 (11):* 8–11.

Holmes, R. M., and G. W. Robertson, 1959. Heat units and crop growth. *Canada Dept. Agr. Publ. No. 1042.* Ottawa, Canada.

Hopkins, A. D., 1918. Periodical events and natural laws as guides to agricultural research and practice. *Monthly Weather Rev., Suppl. 9.* U.S. Dept. Agriculture, Washington, D.C.

Illichevsky, S., 1933. Plant-flowering and local factors. *Acta Phaenologica, 2:* 20–29.

Koppen, W., 1900. Versuch einer klassifikation der klimate, vorzugsweise nach ihren beziehungen zur pflanzenwelt. *Geog. Ztschr., 6:* 593–611, 657–679.

Mandy, G., 1940. Orgonafajtak viragzasanak fonologiai felvetele 1949-ben. *Idojaras, 53 (11–12):* 367–374.

Rowe, S. J., 1964. Environmental preconditioning with special reference to forestry. *Ecology, 45 (2):* 399–403.

Salisbury, F. B., 1963. *The Flowering Process.* The Macmillan Company, New York.

Schnelle, F., 1955. *Pflanzen phanologie, Akademische Verlagsgesellschaft.* Geest and Portig, Leipzig, Germany.

U. S. Department of Commerce, 1949. Upper air average values of temperature, pressure and relative humidity over the United States and Alaska. *Weather Bureau Tech. Paper No. 6.* Environmental Sciences Service Administration, U.S. Dept. Commerce, Washington, D.C.

U. S. Department of Commerce, 1957. Averages for isobaric surfaces, height, temperature, humidity, and density. *Weather Bureau Tech. Bull. No. 32, Part I.* Environmental Sciences Service Administration, U. S. Dept. Commerce, Washington, D.C.

U. S. Department of Commerce, 1958. Extremes and standard deviations of average heights and temperatures. *Weather Bureau Tech. Bull. No. 32, Part II.* Environmental Sciences Service Administration, U. S. Dept. Commerce, Washington, D.C.

Growth Rings of Trees: A Physiological Basis for Their Correlation with Climate

HAROLD C. FRITTS, *Laboratory of Tree-Ring Research, The University of Arizona, Tucson, Arizona*

EARLY IN THE TWENTIETH CENTURY, A. E. Douglass was able to show that the widths of annual rings in trees from semiarid sites correlate with variations in climate (Douglass, 1928). The sequence of wide and narrow rings was so predictable that he was able to recognize and crossdate the same pattern in tree stumps from nearby areas and to determine the actual year in which the trees were felled (Douglass, 1919). These discoveries were followed by a vigorous program of tree-ring research that led to the development of a new discipline called dendrochronology. This discipline may be broadly defined as the study of yearly growth patterns in trees and their use in dating past events and in evaluating fluctuations in past climate.

In recent years, dendrochronology has matured into a sophisticated science. Tree-ring relationships are readily measured and tested by quantitative means, and results are understandable in terms of modern physiological principles. In this paper I describe the characteristics exhibited by a group of ring widths represented in the annual growth layers of the main stem from the center to the bark of the tree. I also attempt to account for some differences in these characteristics which are explainable in the light of modern concepts of tree physiology and recent results from studies at the Laboratory of Tree-Ring Research.

Characteristics of Tree-Ring Series

A growth ring is formed inside the bark by division of cambial cells which produce large, thin-walled wood or xylem cells (earlywood) at the beginning of the growing season and small, thick-walled wood cells (latewood) toward the end of the growing season. The abrupt change in cell size between the last-formed wood of one year and the first-formed wood of the next year usually delineates the boundary between annual growth increments (Record, 1912; Bannan, 1962). In the main stem of the tree these boundaries usually approximate a series of overlapping, superposed conical surfaces. However, in certain cases the surface may be better described as a cylinder, paraboloid, or neiloid (Husch, 1962).

Thus, each year's increment produces a continuous or sometimes discontinuous layer surrounding the previously formed wood, except in the newly formed twigs at the stem apex where the year's increment becomes the first layer of wood. Each successive layer appears to be a ring when viewed in a transverse section and surrounds an increasing number of previously formed rings toward the stem base.

The actual dimensions for this series of superposed conical surfaces are a function of the tree's heredity and environment acting throughout the life history of the developing and aging individual (Kramer and Kozlowski, 1962; Mason and Langenheim, 1957). Therefore, measurements of any one dimension of this series of conical surfaces, such as the widths of rings along a transverse section at the stem base, represent the product of a variety of gradients acting through time within the existing structure of the tree (Duff and Nolan, 1953; Fritts *et al.*, 1965c; Smith and Wilsie, 1961).

The foliage of the crown is the principal manufacturer of growth regulators and food, as well as the primary transpiring surface (Kramer and Kozlowski, 1962). As new layers of wood are added above and outside the existing layers, the tree crown is also growing and lower branches are dying; hence, the mean crown position is farther up the main stem. With the increased height of each year's terminal growth, food and growth regulators must travel a greater distance down the stem to a given cambial area. Also, in a tree with a constant growth rate, the same ring width for any two rings represents a larger volume in the outer, more recently formed, ring.

It has been shown (Fritts *et al.,* 1965c) that these changes with age and stem height cause changes in ring characteristics, especially in the lower stem portions of trees growing on semiarid sites. Near the center, as shown on a transverse basal section of the main stem, rings are generally wide. Toward the outside, they become narrower and are likely to exhibit more relative variability in width from year to year. This change is attributed to increasing competition within the tree for materials manufactured in the crown. As the distance from the crown increases, materials, such as carbohydrates and hormones, moving from the crown to the lower portions of the stem may be largely consumed or concentrations reduced in transit. This is especially marked during dry, warm years when the net production of food and growth-controlling substances by the crown may be low (Kramer and Kozlowski, 1962). In addition, the ratio of green to non-green living tissue decreases with age (Kramer and Kozlowski, 1962). Also, cambial initiation occurs last in the basal cambium while growth cessation may occur there first (Larson, 1962). As a result of these changes, both the relative growth rate and the length of the growing season may fluctuate more widely from one year to the next as the tree increases in size. This produces more variable but narrower rings. These same phenomena may also explain the higher frequency of partial rings in the outer portions of the stem base as well as the decreased number of intra-annual bands of latewood sometimes referred to as false rings (Fritts *et al.,* 1965c).

A transverse section through the upper crown portion of the same stem frequently exhibits less pronounced changes in ring characteristics. Because of the proximity of the crown and decreased terminal growth rates in the older tree, food and hormone supplies do not change as markedly through time. The rings in this portion of the stem resemble their counterparts in the outer stem base which were formed during the same period. However, the correlations of ring-width changes from year to year with ring-width changes in other trees, and with the associated variation in macroclimate, are frequently not as high in the upper as in the lower portions of the stem (Fritts *et al.,* 1965c).

The basal stem section thus not only provides the longest and oldest ring-width chronology in a tree, but the patterns in ring width provide the most reliable estimator of past variations in moisture and temperature which have limited the processes controlling growth.

In order to properly relate ring patterns of the basal section to yearly climatic variation, it is necessary to remove from consideration the gradually changing differences associated with the age, crown position, and mean growth of the tree (Fritts *et al.,* 1965c; Schulman, 1956). This is accomplished by fitting a regression line or curve to each ring-width series and dividing the actual ring width by each yearly value of this fitted curve (Fritts, 1963; Matalas, 1962; Schulman, 1956). This transforms ring-width values from nonstationary time series to tree-ring indexes which exhibit a mean of 1.00 and a variance that is independent of tree age, position within the stem, and mean growth of the tree (Matalas, 1962). Since the mean index for all radii is the same, indexes have the added advantage over ring-width measurements in that they receive equal weight when averaged and manipulated whether they come from fast- or slow-growing portions of a tree.

These same characteristics of ring-width series may also vary with species and with differences in site. Some results from a study of replicated tree-ring samples from *Pseudotsuga menziesii* (Mirb.) Franco, *Pinus ponderosa* Laws., and *Pinus edulis* Engelm. in northern Arizona are summarized in Figure 1 (Fritts *et al.,* 1965a). A transect was studied along a gradient from the mesic forest interior on the shoulder of the San Francisco Mountains to the semiarid forest border approximately 18 miles northwest of the mountain mass where trees are widely spaced and interspersed with grassland. At the forest interior site (represented by J in Fig. 1), precipitation is high and less limiting to processes in the trees. There is a dense forest cover. The average ring width is large. The ring-width patterns from these sites show less relative variation from year to year but there is proportionately more variation in ring width from tree to tree in any given year. The ring-width chronologies from such trees are referred to as "complacent" for they do not correlate with each other and do not exhibit a close relationship with macroclimatic variation. Since there is almost always sufficient moisture for some growth, partial rings or local absence of rings are infrequent except in suppressed trees.

Near the semiarid forest border (L, Fig. 1), there is less effective and more variable precipitation, and there are more days when moisture is limiting to processes within the tree. Rings are narrower and arboreal dominance in such sites is less, but there is more relative variation in ring width from year to year. Partial rings are more abundant, ring-width patterns are more closely cor-

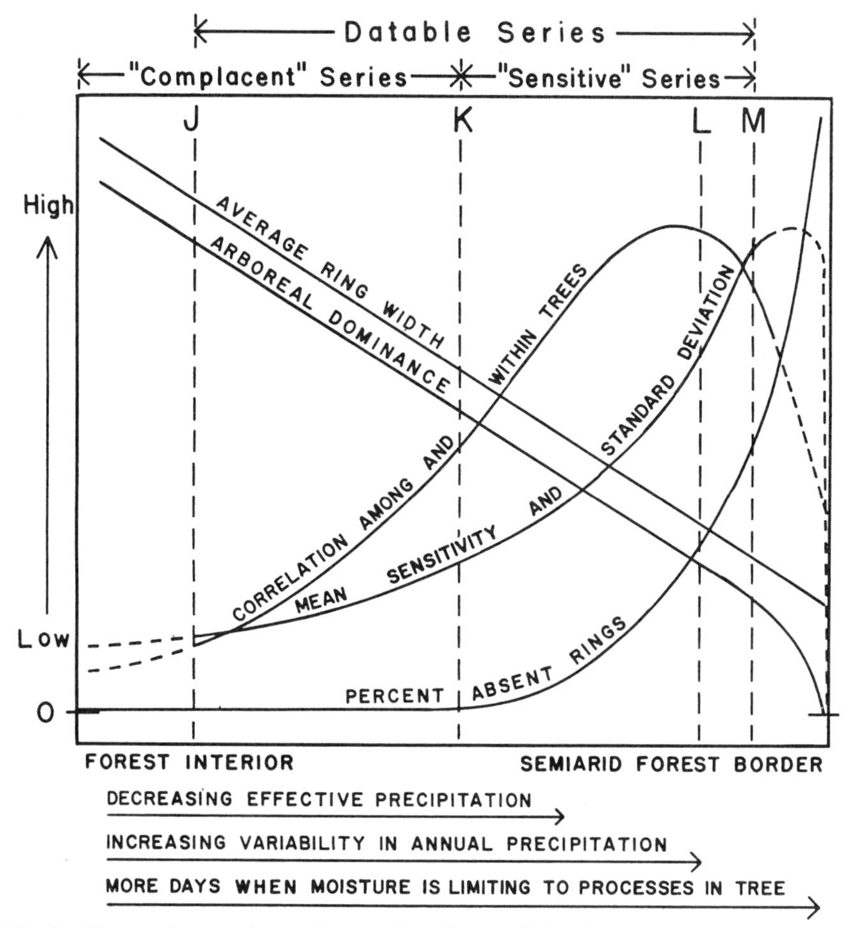

Fig. 1. Changes in tree-ring and vegetation characteristics that can be observed along a gradient from the forest interior to the semiarid lower forest border. Climatic differences are indicated below the figure and dendrochronological categories above. J to M delineate the area of datable tree-ring series; K is the approximate boundary between trees with "complacent" and with "sensitive" series; L marks the area where tree-ring widths correlate best among trees and exhibit the closest relationship with climatic variation (Fritts *et al.*, 1965a).

related among and within trees, and the patterns relate more closely to climatic variation. Such trees produce "sensitive" ring-width chronologies.

These changes, which were measured along this environmental gradient, document the fact that rings from trees of the semiarid forest border can be used best to estimate climatic variation, for climate is most frequently limiting to the growth-controlling processes in the trees.

This relationship is illustrated further in Figure 2 by the three tree-ring chronologies for *Pinus aristata* Engelm. in the White Mountains of California. Each of these chronologies was derived from ring-width measurements taken along twenty radii (two radii in each of ten trees). Each ring-width series was converted to index values, which were averaged for each group. The yearly averages are plotted against time in the left portion of the figure. The lowest chronology in the figure exhibits little variability from year to year. The trees came from a relatively dense and moist forest stand where

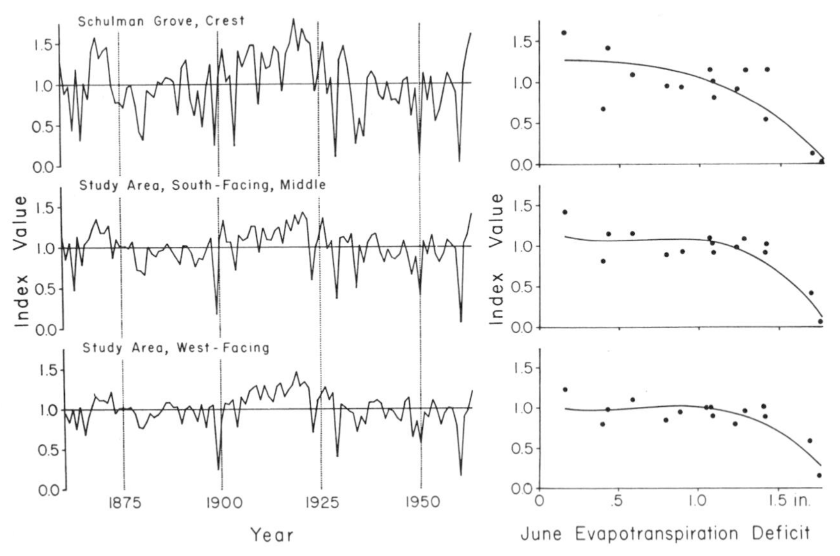

Fig. 2. Tree-ring width chronologies (index values) for *Pinus aristata* from three contrasting sites plotted against year of formation (left) and against evapotranspiration deficits in June (right). The three curves drawn on the right represent a least squares fit of a third-degree polynomial to the relationship, and the major deviations of the points from this curve reflect the additional effects of winter temperature and autumn moisture on the subsequent season's ring growth.

there is abundant snow accumulation. The standard deviation for this 104-year chronology is 0.199. The middle chronology came from a more arid site on a south-facing slope and exhibits more variability as shown by a standard deviation of 0.241. The upper chronology was obtained from gnarled and stunted trees growing on a dry, windswept, and rocky ridge. The ring-width indexes from these trees are extremely variable as shown by a standard deviation of 0.376.

The plotted points on the right of Figure 2 represent index values for the last 15 years of each chronology plotted against evapotranspiration deficit in June. This parameter was calculated from daily weather records using a computer program written by H. H. Engelbrecht (after Thornthwaite and Mather, 1955). Daily precipitation and mean daily temperature values used were recorded at the White Mountain Research Station located approximately seven miles north of the sampled stands and at about the same elevation. Extensive regression analysis following Fritts (1962a) and Fritts *et al.* (1965b) showed that June evapotranspiration deficit was the climatic factor most closely related to tree-ring growth in all three of these sites. The regression line in Figure 2 is a least squares fit of a third-degree polynomial and the major deviations from the line reflect the limiting effects of a cold, dry winter and a warm autumn on the subsequent year's growth. (Cold winters and dry, warm autumns produce negative ring-width departures while warm winters and moist, cool autumns produce positive departures.)

The rings for trees from the more moist sites shown in the chronologies at the bottom and middle of Figure 2 are small only during years of extreme evapotranspiration deficit in June. The rings of the exposed-site trees shown at the top exhibit decreasing widths for years of intermediate to years of extreme June drought as measured by the evapotranspiration deficit. In fact, a straight line could almost provide as good a fit as the polynomial shown in the figure for these exposed-site trees. The three chronologies illustrate that a factor—topographic, edaphic, or altitudinal—which causes soil moisture to become more limiting to the growth of the semiarid-site trees may also increase ring-width variability and enhance the correlation between ring width and the macroclimatic variation.

For the remaining part of this paper, I wish to consider only trees growing on semiarid sites and exhibiting a close relationship between ring widths and climate.

Climatic Relationships

Through several different studies, we have accumulated more than forty replicated samples of tree rings from a variety of species and sites near weather stations with relatively long and continuous records in Arizona, Colorado, California, and Illinois (Fritts, 1962b, 1965; Fritts *et al.*, 1965a, b). The climatic factors and intervals that correlate with ring-width variation were ascertained by a series of stepwise multiple regression analyses (Fritts, 1962a). The curves in Figure 3 are a diagrammatic representation of the correlation results for six species and are ordered according to the approximate elevational range of each species. The abscissa represents the 15 months prior to and including the period of growth which is indicated by "c" on the diagram. The ordinate represents the average correlation of precipitation and temperature during each month with the ring width of that year. Therefore, the distribution of the area under the curve provides an estimate of the relative influence of the two climatic factors, precipitation and temperature, during different portions of the year on the amount of growth occurring in late spring and summer (Fritts, 1965; Fritts *et al.*, 1965b). Frequently, a combination of temperature and precipitation data in a parameter representing evapotranspiration deficit produces the closest relationship.

A comparison of the areas under the curve before the growing season and during the growing season shows that, at least for conifers on semiarid sites, the variation in ring width is more closely correlated with the climate prior to the initiation of growth than with the climate during the growing season. It is also shown that growth of conifers at low elevations relates most closely to the winter component of climate and least to the summer component, while growth of conifers at high elevations relates more closely to the climate of late spring, summer, and the prior summer and early autumn. The rings of deciduous species, such as *Quercus alba* L., relate to conditions during the current growing season and during the latter part of the previous growing season up to the time of leaf-fall.

The primary factor that controls the relative ring width from year

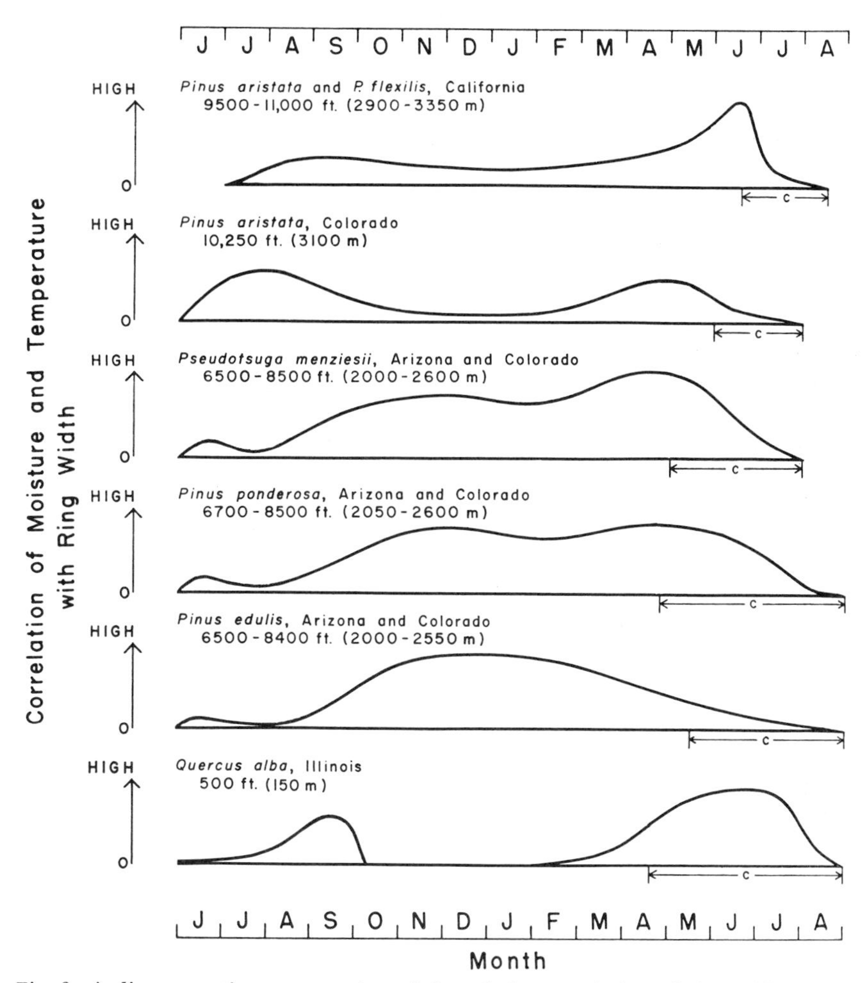

Fig. 3. A diagrammatic representation of the relative correlation of ring widths from semiarid-site trees with moisture and temperature occurring during a 15-month interval prior to and including the growing season. The area under the curve for each monthly interval represents the degree of correlation with the two climatic factors and is proportional to the apparent influence of climate during that period on ring growth. "c" designates the period of cambial activity.

to year is precipitation as it affects soil moisture and the water balance of the tree; but high temperature, probably as it affects evapotranspiration and limits processes such as net photosynthesis, may also be a controlling factor (Fritts, 1962b; Fritts *et al.*, 1965b). Studies on the soil moisture regimes show that the lag in the effect of climate on growth cannot be explained adequately by soil moisture storage (Fritts *et al.*, 1965b). Therefore, it was proposed that climate during the summer, autumn, winter, and spring prior to growth must in some way precondition the tree and indirectly influence the rate of cell production during the growing season.

The chain of events which we have hypothesized to occur and which produce such climatic relationships (Fritts *et al.*, 1965b) is illustrated in Figure 4. The primary climatic factors of low precipitation and high temperatures are shown at the top of the diagram, and the resultant formation of a narrow ring at the bottom. The path of double arrows indicates what we believe to be the primary sequence: increased water stress, reduced net photosynthesis, and low food accumulation as reserves, which result in reduced rates of cambial activity and the formation of a narrow ring. (We now believe that reduced transpiration and the resulting reduction in

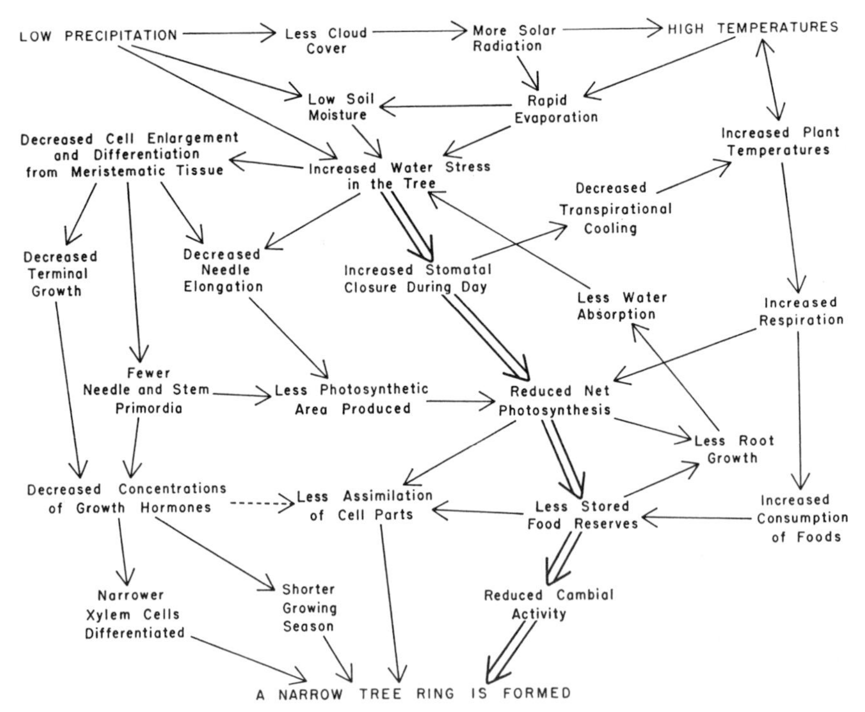

Fig. 4. A schematic diagram of the model hypothesized for the relationship between low precipitation and high temperature and the production of a narrow tree ring (Fritts *et al.*, 1965b).

heat dissipated by evaporation during periods of low soil moisture may be as important in reducing net photosynthesis as the direct effects of high water stress on photosynthesis and respiration.) Some interacting factors affecting this food storage are diagrammed on the right of the figure and some direct effects of climate during the growing season upon growth are shown on the left.

Physiological Evidence

What evidence beyond correlation results is there for such an interacting series of relationships? Since most of the published physiological work has dealt with trees on relatively cool and mesic sites, my students and I were forced to initiate our own investigations. Several *Pinus ponderosa* trees on an exposed south-facing slope at 8,500 feet (2,600 m) in the Santa Catalina Mountains north of Tucson, Arizona, are being studied intensively. Branches are enclosed in polyethylene bags for a period of several months and a whole tree in a polyethylene tent for shorter periods (Decker, 1962; Woodwell and Bourdeau, 1962). The enclosure (Fig. 5) is inflated with a continuous air stream, and the carbon dioxide and water content of the air entering and leaving are monitored. An air conditioning or heat exchange system is used to help maintain the temperature of the enclosure as equal as possible to the ambient temperature. We also measure a number of environmental factors, diurnal changes in stem size using dendrographs (Fritts and Fritts, 1955), and cambial activity by examining anatomical samples (Fritts *et al.*, 1965b).

Some measurements taken from a branch bag experiment conducted by James M. Brown and Carl A. Budelsky during four selected, clear 24-hour periods are shown in Figure 6. Since the radiation load in such mountain environments is high during clear days even in winter, branch temperatures may rise markedly above air temperatures and photosynthetic rates can be high, especially during calm days (Gates, 1965). During early spring, after the winter snow has melted (upper left, Fig. 6), there is sufficient moisture in the soil to allow high rates of photosynthesis. A slight midday depression suggests that under peak radiation loads water deficits or excess heating of the plant tissue occurs, at least in the branch bag. As seasonal temperatures rise and soil moisture is depleted

Fig. 5. Measurement of net photosynthesis, respiration, and transpiration by enclosing a tree in an inflated polyethylene tent and measuring the carbon dioxide and atmospheric moisture entering and leaving the tent. The two stacked rectangular units in front of the tent are the blower and air-cooling systems. Louvers on the side and top control the proportion of ambient and cooled air entering the tent. Towers and cables are necessary to erect and anchor the tent.

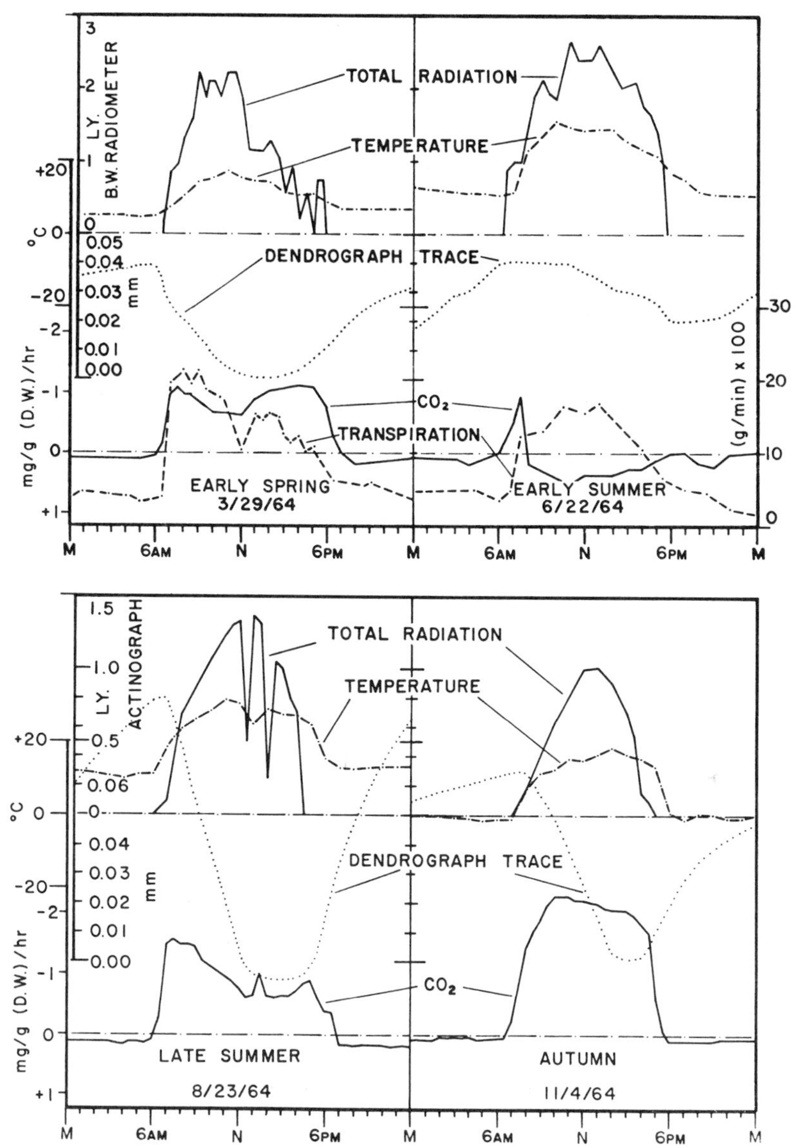

Fig. 6. The daily regime during four selected days of several measured environmental parameters and plant processes for a branch of *Pinus ponderosa* enclosed within a polyethylene bag. Solar radiation was measured with a Beckman and Whitley radiometer and later with a black- and silvered-plate actinograph. Air temperature was measured in the air stream of the outlet from the bag. Transpiration and carbon dioxide exchange are measured as a difference between the inlet and outlet of the bag. The dendrograph trace is from an instrument on the upper main stem of the tree.

throughout the spring period, the midday depressions in photosynthesis become more and more pronounced and transpiration rates decline. By June (upper right, Fig. 6), water has become so limiting and daytime temperatures so high that net photosynthesis is observed in the branch bag only during the cool early morning hours. During the remaining daytime period, the carbon dioxide exchange is positive, indicating higher rates of respiration than photosynthesis. (Under conditions of low soil moisture and high solar radiation, significant heating of plant tissue can be measured in needles inside the enclosure. Thesis investigations by James M. Brown demonstrated that the enclosure effect is largely due to reduced wind speeds. This obviously can force some upward temperature bias inside the enclosure. On the other hand, reduced rates of net photosynthesis persist even during partly cloudy and cooler days when the measured heat load is markedly less. Reduction in net photosynthesis also occurs in the air-conditioned tent. Because of these observations, we believe our results indicate a real phenomenon even though natural conditions may be less extreme in undisturbed semiarid-site trees.) The green tissue of the tree during such a period possibly consumes more food than it produces and cambial growth can occur only at the expense of stored food reserves. Similar but less dramatic summertime observations on *Pseudotsuga menziesii* growing in Washington were recently published (Helms, 1965).

Rains in the summer may replenish the soil moisture supply, allowing faster rates of transpiration and reducing the water stress and heat load on the leaves (lower left, Fig. 6). Rates of photosynthesis comparable to the early spring period can be noted. The summer rains were markedly above average during 1964, so that soil moisture was plentiful well into autumn. With the lower autumn temperatures, abundant moisture, and the reduced heat load, some of the highest rates of daily net photosynthesis ever observed were recorded (lower right, Fig. 6).

The net 24-hour carbon dioxide exchange and some environmental conditions throughout a 15-month period in the same branch bag have been plotted by James M. Brown in Figure 7. During the dry periods in May through July, the monitored branch contributed little photosynthate to the total tree food reserve and during many days it appeared to consume more food than it made. However,

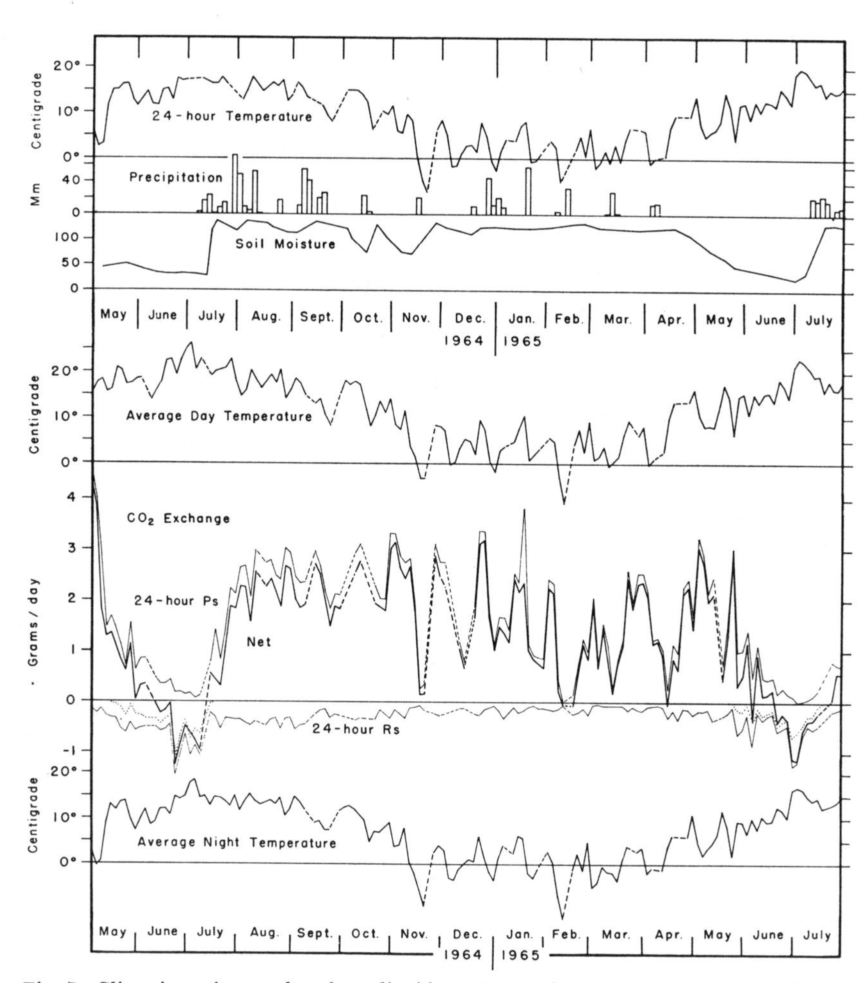

Fig. 7. Climatic regime and carbon dioxide exchange for an enclosed branch of *Pinus ponderosa* from May, 1964, through July, 1965. Data are plotted as three-day averages. Dashed lines connect points through time periods for which no data were obtained. The light lines above and below zero represent the net amount of photosynthesis and respiration measured during the entire 24-hour period. The heavy line represents the daily net carbon dioxide balance or the difference between the total consumed and total released during the 24-hour period. The dotted line below zero indicates the net release of carbon dioxide during the daylight hours.

the summer rains raised the net photosynthetic rates. With high temperatures, the rates of respiration throughout the entire tree were also high; hence the total net gain in foods occurring during summer was probably not so great as in the cooler early spring period. During the summer growing season, a large portion of the current photosynthate and food reserves probably is consumed in the metabolism of the active meristematic tissues.

As the cooler but moist autumn season approached, respiration decreased but photosynthesis remained high. Only during the cold winter days was net photosynthesis markedly reduced. This reduction in net photosynthesis is associated with freezing of the soil or freezing of the trunk at night. This freezing appeared to prohibit water transport to the crown and created a water deficit during the day. The reduction was also associated with subfreezing cloudy days when leaf temperatures were low and directly limiting to photosynthesis. Although some workers report complete suppression of net photosynthesis at high elevations during relatively warm winter days (Tranquillini, 1964), on our semiarid low-elevation sites we observed rapid recovery of photosynthetic capacity within 24 hours after prolonged cold treatment.

During the drier autumn of 1965, soil moisture supplies for the trees were significantly lower than in 1964. We obtained regimes of low photosynthesis and high daytime respiration comparable to, but not as extreme as, the June pattern shown in the upper right of Figure 6.

Recently, I measured ring widths and performed analyses of variance on nine well-watered seedlings of *Pinus ponderosa* from an experiment by Henry Hellmers (unpublished). The seedlings had been treated to controlled temperatures at two different levels for three growing cycles. A 15°C day and an 11°C night throughout the growing period produced a significantly wider ring at the base of the stem than a 23°C day and a 19°C night. In this case, high temperatures without any apparent water stress appear to reduce ring-width growth at the stem base.

It has also been observed that during drier seasons, some semiarid-site conifers produce shorter needles than during more moist seasons. Variations of this sort in needle length have been observed in the field on *Pinus ponderosa, P. aristata,* and *P. edulis.* In the last species, we were able to increase significantly the amount of needle elongation by supplementing the soil moisture around a tree for one growing season (Fritts *et al.,* 1965b). Preliminary regression analysis of these needle-length measurements indicates that needle elongation is directly related to moisture and inversely related to temperature during, and just prior to, the growing season. Since climate does influence needle growth, it can control the photosynthetic area produced in any one season and thus influence the foodmaking capacity and ring growth of the tree for several following years (Fig. 4). (Decreasing efficiency of aging needles may progressively reduce net photosynthetic rates so that the youngest needles probably remain the primary food producers (Freeland, 1952).) This lag in the effect of the climate on tree growth is common and can be measured by the serial correlation exhibited in a series of ring-width indexes. Other lagging effects may be attributed to such phenomena as root growth, flower initiation, and fruit growth which may influence the water balance or compete for food in the tree.

It is apparent from these results that the correlations between ring width and climate in a semiarid region, as shown in Figure 3, have a meaningful biological explanation: climate basically controls the initial foodmaking process of the tree. Low amounts of food reserves are accumulated during years of dry, warm climates and growth in the late spring and summer is slow (Fritts *et al.,* 1965b); hence, the ring is narrow. If moisture is abundant for long periods when the roots and trunk are not frozen and daytime leaf temperatures are above freezing, there will be high rates of photosynthesis and accumulation of abundant food reserves which can maintain high rates of growth during the summer, so that a wide ring is produced.

At low elevations in southwestern North America, summer temperatures and drought are extreme but the winter climate is mild (Fritts, 1965), so that the greatest rates of food accumulation probably occur during the cool autumn, winter, and spring periods. Thus, ring-width growth is most dependent upon and therefore most closely correlated with the climate during the cooler portions of the year. At high elevations or in more northern continental areas, trees are frozen during most of the winter and summer temperatures are mild (Tranquillini, 1964). Trees in these environments probably make and accumulate more of their food during the late spring, summer, and early autumn periods so that the ring widths more strongly correlate with this interval of climate. Soil moisture in spring is partially dependent upon winter snows so that growth in these summer-responding trees may also correlate, but to a lesser extent, with winter precipitation. In the high-elevation *Pinus aristata,* winter temperature is positively correlated with the next summer's growth, which suggests an inhibiting effect of cold winter temperatures on net photosynthesis. (In semiarid western North America, precipitation is usually positively correlated with ring width. Temperature is commonly negatively correlated as it affects evapotranspiration and several physiological processes in the tree. But during midwinter and early spring, temperature sometimes is positively correlated.)

Conclusions

Many differences in the ring-width growth within a tree may be attributed to changing supplies of food and hormones. In moist sites or during periods of favorable climate, there may be sufficient food for the production of wide rings throughout the tree. But in dry sites or during years of low moisture and high temperatures, food competition within the tree is likely to be greater and the cambium at the base of the stem is likely to receive a limited food supply and produce narrow rings. The cambium at the stem base depends upon the entire crown for food and, hence, ring growth reflects the tree's ambient climate. But the cambium in the top of the tree or in the upper branches depends upon a more restricted portion of the crown for its food and hormone supplies. The rings produced by the cambium vary greatly from branch to branch and are less reliable indicators of the climate surrounding the entire tree. Therefore, ring series at the base of semiarid-site trees provide the most reliable, as well as the longest, record of macroclimatic variation.

Tree-ring widths in certain coniferous species growing on semiarid sites appear to represent the integrated effect of climate on food-making and food accumulation in the crown throughout the 14 to 15 months previous to and including the period of growth. Trees on warm, low-elevation sites may most efficiently utilize winter moisture; trees on cool, high-elevation or more northern but arid sites may most efficiently utilize early summer and early autumn moisture. But even with these differences, a significant amount of variance is found to be common among tree-ring series from a wide range of sites, species, and geographic areas in western North America (Fritts, 1963, 1965), emphasizing a common dependence of ring widths on the gross regional patterns in precipitation and temperature. The remaining variance, which is not correlated among sites, may be attributed to local environmental and climatic differences, to variability among and within trees, and to compounding effects of occasional fires, insect or other infestations, and recurring seed years.

It is evident that a large portion of the variability in ring-width patterns from semiarid sites in western North America does reflect the annual climatic differences from year to year. If ring chronologies are derived from a number of trees in semiarid sites and if adequate corrections for age trend are made, these chronologies may be used to reconstruct maps of annual or somewhat longer climatic fluctuations in the past (Fritts, 1965).

Author's Note: The results cited in this paper which were not previously published are from research sponsored by NSF grants GB-1025, G-19949, and GP-2171, and by a Frederick Gardner Cottrell grant from Research Corporation. The author acknowledges the support of the National Geographic Society and National Park Service through the Wetherill Mesa Archaeological project and the support of the Environmental Data Service of the United States Environmental Science Services Administration that sponsored other phases of this program. The Numerical Analysis Laboratory at the University of Arizona provided computing facilities and time. The author drew upon selected unpublished results of research for master of science theses conducted by John W. Cardis and Alan P. Drew and for doctoral dissertations conducted by Carl A. Budelsky and James M. Brown.

REFERENCES

Bannan, M. W., 1962. The vascular cambium and tree-ring development. In *Tree Growth,* edited by T. T. Kozlowski; pp. 3–21. Ronald Press, New York.

Decker, J. P., 1962. Water relations of plant communities as a management factor for western watersheds. *Science, 138:* 532–533.

Douglass, A. E., 1919. Climatic cycles and tree-growth. *Carnegie Inst. Wash. Pub. 289, 1:* 23–29.

Douglass, A. E., 1928. Climatic cycles and tree-growth. *Carnegie Inst. Wash. Pub. 289, 2:* 97–102.

Duff, G. H., and N. J. Nolan, 1953. Growth and morphogenesis in the Canadian forest species I, the controls of cambial and apical activity in *Pinus resinosa* Ait. *Can. J. Botany, 31:* 471–513.

Freeland, R. O., 1952. Effect of age of leaves upon the rate of photosynthesis in some conifers. *Plant Physiol., 27:* 685–690.

Fritts, H. C., 1962a. An approach to dendroclimatology: screening by means of multiple regression techniques. *J. Geophys. Res., 67:* 1413–1420.

Fritts, H. C., 1962b. The relation of growth ring-widths in American beech and white oak to variations in climate. *Tree-Ring Bull., 25(1–2):* 2–10.

Fritts, H. C., 1963. Computer programs for tree-ring research. *Tree-Ring Bull., 25(3–4):* 2–7.

Fritts, H. C., 1965. Tree-ring evidence for climatic changes in western North America. *Monthly Weather Rev., 93:* 421–443.

Fritts, H. C., and E. C. Fritts, 1955. A new dendrograph for recording radial changes of a tree. *Forest Sci., 1:* 271–276.

Fritts, H. C., D. G. Smith, J. W. Cardis, and C. A. Budelsky, 1965a. Tree-ring characteristics along a vegetation gradient in northern Arizona. *Ecology, 46:* 393–401.

Fritts, H. C., D. G. Smith, and M. A. Stokes, 1965b. The biological model for paleoclimatic interpretation of Mesa Verde tree-ring series. *Am. Antiquity, 31(2):* 101–121.

Fritts, H. C., D. G. Smith, C. A. Budelsky, and J. W. Cardis, 1965c. The variability of ring characteristics within trees as shown by a reanalysis of four ponderosa pine. *Tree-Ring Bull., 27(1–2):* 3–18.

Gates, D. M., 1965. Energy, plants and ecology. *Ecology, 46:* 1–13.

Helms, J. A., 1965. Diurnal and seasonal patterns of net assimilation in Douglas fir, *Pseudotsuga menziesii* (Mirb.) Franco, as influenced by environment. *Ecology, 46:* 698–708.

Husch, B., 1962. *Forest Mensuration and Statistics;* pp. 83–95. Ronald Press, New York.

Kramer, P. J., and T. T. Kozlowski, 1962. *Physiology of Trees.* McGraw-Hill, New York.

Larson, P. R., 1962. Auxin gradients and the regulation of cambial activity. In *Tree Growth,* edited by T. T. Kozlowski; pp. 97–117. Ronald Press, New York, and 1965 *Forest Sci., 11:* 412–429.

Mason, H. L., and J. H. Langenheim, 1957. Language analysis and the concept *environment. Ecology, 38:* 325–339.

Matalas, N. C., 1962. Statistical properties of tree-ring data. *Pub. Int. Assoc. Sci. Hydrology, 7:* 39–47.

Record, S. J., 1912. *Identification of the Economic Woods of the United States;* pp. 40–44. John Wiley and Sons, New York.

Schulman, E., 1956. *Dendroclimatic Changes in Semiarid America.* Univ. Arizona, Tucson, Arizona.

Smith, D. M., and M. C. Wilsie, 1961. Some anatomical responses of loblolly pine to soil-water deficiencies. *Tech. Assoc. Pulp and Paper Industry, 44:* 179–185.

Thornthwaite, C. W., and J. R. Mather, 1955. The water balance.

Publications in Climatology 8 (1). Laboratory of Climatology, Drexel Institute of Technology, Centerton, New Jersey.

Tranquillini, W., 1964. Photosynthesis and dry matter production of trees at high altitudes. In *The Formation of Wood in Forest Trees,* edited by M. H. Zimmermann; pp. 505–518. Academic Press, New York.

Woodwell, G. M., and P. F. Bourdeau, 1962. Measurement of dry matter production of the plant cover. In *Symposium on the Methodology of Plant Eco-physiology,* edited by F. E. Eckardt; pp. 519–527. UNESCO, Montpellier, France.

Plantclimate Mapping: The Key to Conservation of Resources

MARSTON H. KIMBALL, *Agricultural Extension Service, University of California, Los Angeles, California*

DEWAYNE E. GILBERT, *Agricultural Extension Service, University of California, Davis, California*

PROTECTION OF AGRICULTURAL PRODUCTION is based upon climate adaptation of food crops and livestock and the continued agricultural use of land areas suitable for the production of food. Because of California's population explosion, resulting in urban encroachment into agricultural areas with its accompanying land requirements, farmland is being diverted at a rate exceeding 400 acres per day. Climatically these diverted land areas are capable of maintaining the state's agriculture comprised of more than 275 different farm products. Maintenance of food sources is dependent upon climate and, therefore, accurate and detailed climatic maps are needed, coupled with equally detailed and specific listings of agricultural, horticultural, and livestock crops adapted to the climates.

Most existing climatic maps show four to six climates, a few list eight or ten (Visher, 1954) and one shows 11 zones (Russell, 1926). These are based on isotherms and isohyets derived from U. S. Weather Bureau data. While these records are valuable for characterizing specific areas with temperature data, the paucity of stations prohibits construction of other than generalized maps.

California is not divisible into homogeneous climatic units on any geographical or topographical basis. Complexity arises from several factors: the 1,000 mile length oriented north-south for about 200 miles, then curving southeasterly; the ever-present and dominant influence of the Pacific Ocean, with its normal ocean breeze from the northwest striking some places hard and flowing parallel to the coast ranges for the balance; the inclusion of large areas of three deserts; and two mountain ranges parallel to the coast line and two east-west oriented mountain masses, one in the north and the other some 150 to 200 miles north of the Mexico-California border.

Inflow of marine air is buffered and in some places concentrated by the multi-ranged coastal mountains from 1,500 to 3,500 feet in elevation. Continental air masses are channeled north-south by a tremendous state-long mountain barrier from 4,500 to 12,000 and 14,000 feet—the Cascade, Sierra Nevada, San Gabriel, San Bernardino, and lesser ranges to the south. Wind patterns in valleys are greatly affected by the eddying and swirling of the winds caused by this continental high pressure system.

These and other complexities result in subtropical conditions north of the 40th parallel, and temperate zone conditions in the mountains south of the 33rd parallel. Within a mile of these areas, conditions can be reversed from subtropical to cool temperate and vice versa.

Statewide maps are needed which show the hundreds of climate zones and subzones grouped into regional and statewide climates. The great numbers of different climates result from elevation effects; direction, steepness, and length of slopes; exposure to or shelter from wind; proximity to or remoteness from the Pacific Ocean; latitude; and many other variables.

Needs for accurate knowledge of climates include:

1. The ability to make intelligent recommendations for growing crops in specific locations. This applies to all agricultural and livestock fields.
2. The relocation of farm production with minimum losses to individuals, the communities, and the state when urban development drives out agriculture.
3. An accurate determination of the potential agricultural economy of new irrigation developments which involves knowledge of adaptable crops, their yield, quality, and season of maturity, as a basis for justifying the expenditures.
4. The appraisal, assessment, and tax equalization for planning

land use that will include agricultural, industrial, and residential uses and simultaneously protect the basic potential food production.

Plants as Indicators of Temperature

A plan was developed using plants as indicators of climate (Kimball and Brooks, 1959). Plants are master integrators of climatic as well as other influences. There are hundreds of these indicators per acre and thousands per square mile, in contrast to the one weather station for each five hundred square miles of California. Exploratory surveys and mapping between 1955 and 1957 revealed that county staff members of the University of California, Agricultural Extension Service (County Farm Advisors or County Agents) knew the climates of local areas in relation to all crops grown in their counties. In fact Farm Advisors of major counties totaling over 60 percent of the state's agriculture and population requested lists of ornamentals for landscape use ". . . not one list, but *lists* for our different climates." Nurserymen knew distribution of species and varieties. Foresters knew the elevation and distribution of conifers and native woodland. Botanists and others were cognizant of distributional differences caused by climate. The latter group includes staffs of universities, state and junior colleges, private institutions, official agencies, agricultural commissioners, USDA representatives, and laymen.

Early in the project it was recognized that only general use could be made of native plants. By their nature they are tolerant of wide differences in the climate of their location and there are significant varieties among them, but they have not been subjected to phenological study and their behavior has not been "dated" for comparisons.

Because the physical climate and plant performance were so equally represented in the end product—detailed zones and subzones—the term *plantclimate* was adopted (Kimball and Brooks, 1959). (Plantclimate is defined as the condition wherein specific plants, groups or associations of plants and the physical climate are in complete harmony. Physical climate components of diurnal and seasonal temperature fluctuations are the controlling factors. Both plants and the physical climate will reflect each other. Detailed knowledge of one will make delineation of the other possible. Neither soil nor water is considered.)

County-by-County Mapping

A technique for making plantclimate maps was developed. Because the basic source of information was the Agricultural Extension county staff, each county was mapped separately. U. S. Geological Survey 15-minute quadrangle maps (scale: approximately one inch per mile) were used as a working base. It was planned to assemble the county maps first into logical regions and, finally, into the entire state.

The quadrangles were carefully aligned and secured as a maximum of three maps wide by four long. Whole counties were laid out in many instances, but some counties required multiple layouts—one needed nine such assemblages (Fig. 1). The maximum assembly covered an area four by seven feet. The quadrangles were covered with tracing paper and essential identifying features were traced: county boundary, principal highways, towns and cities, and very importantly, corners of all quadrangles and their map names. Townships, ranges, latitude, and longitude were noted on the final maps (Fig. 2).

Details of crop patterns were recorded in conference with county staff members. Care was exercised to confine reasons for crop location, limitation, and adaptation to temperature, with humidity and wind as supplemental factors. Soil, water, and topography were not considered in the distributional pattern. Only temperature and other atmospheric aspects of climate were used. The staff would locate a boundary between one district and another because of early or late frost, a significant decrease in prevailing wind, warm nights favoring one crop and depressing another, approximate limits of belts or bands called thermal zones of warm conditions on slopes, limits of altithermal effects, etc.

Extensive notes were often placed directly on the tissue tracing. Care was taken for adequate reference numbers to define later the areas under discussion (Fig. 3). Field trips were made with staff members. Other authorities added their knowledge. The result was a mass of data concerning crop history, crop performance, planting dates, blooming and fruit-setting dates, harvest dates, early districts,

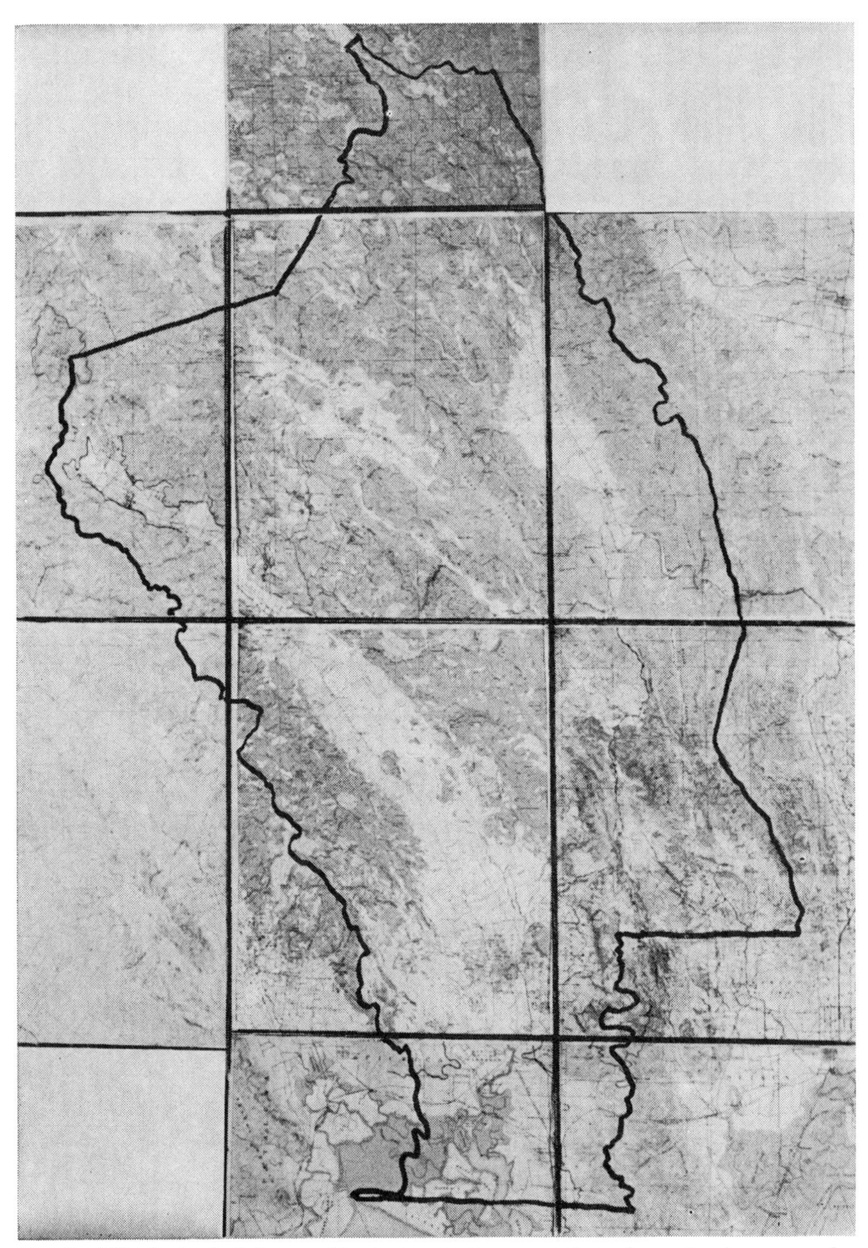

Fig. 1. U.S. Geological Survey 15-minute quads arranged to form the base map for Napa County, California.

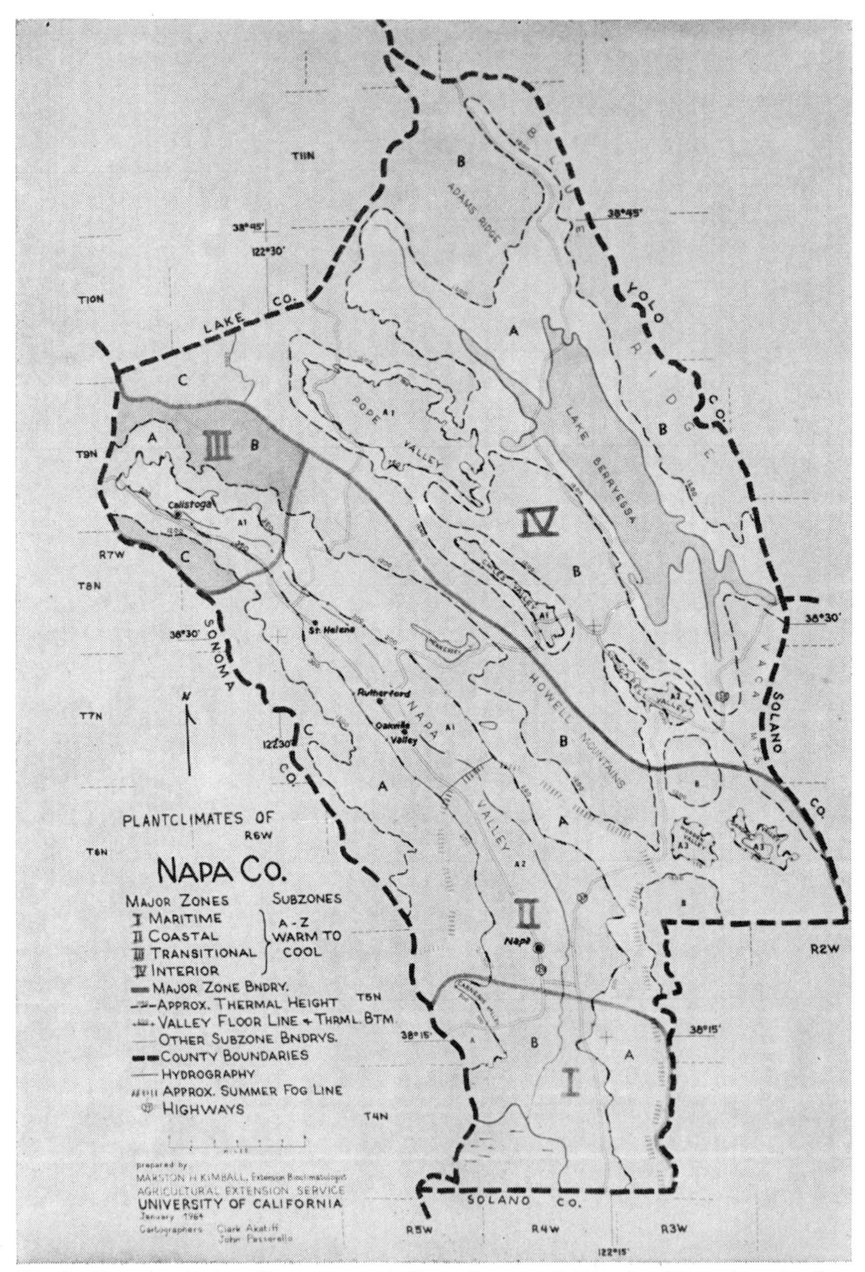

Fig. 2. Completed plantclimate map of Napa County, California, illustrating the four major climate zones.

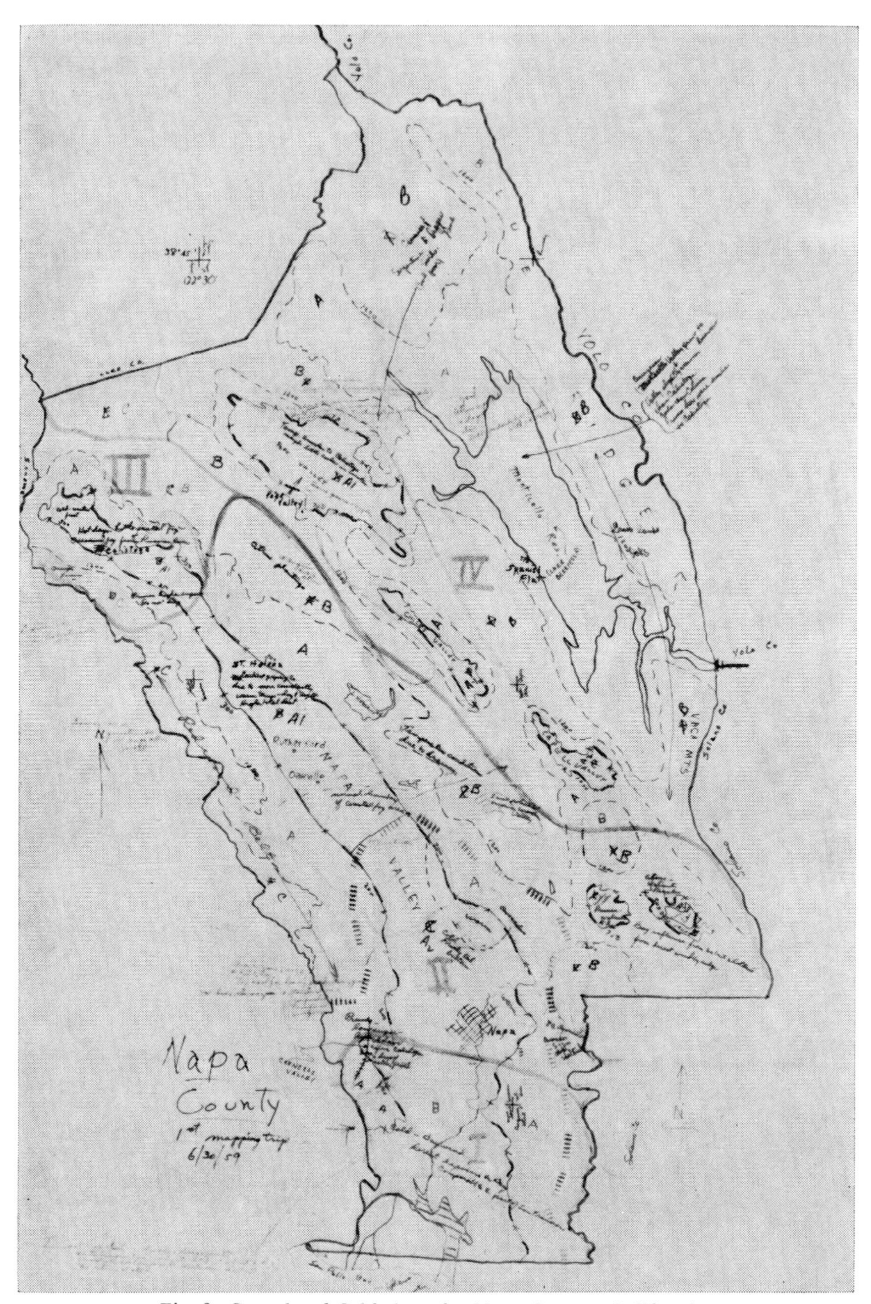

Fig. 3. Completed field sheet for Napa County, California.

late districts, warm spots, cool spots, quality differences, varietal variations, and other plant reactions to the climates of the county.

As the work progressed throughout the state it was found that subzone lines at a county border usually coincided with the same line established by the staff in the next county. This testified to the consistency and soundness of their observations and knowledge.

A total of 88 maps was required to complete state plantclimate delineations. Completed maps were colored to indicate different plantclimates, plantclimate zones, and subzones (shaded areas in Fig. 2). They were then reduced in scale to four inches per mile (1:250,000) for distribution to counties, to eight inches per mile (1:500,000) for assembly into a state map some eight and a half feet long, and by photographic reduction to one inch per 16 miles (1:1,000,000) for convenience of study (Kimball *et al.,* 1967b).

Major and Regional Plantclimates

It became evident there were four distinct major plantclimates oriented north and south in the state. In fact these plantclimates are more than statewide. All four major plantclimates are present in Napa County (Fig. 2). Within the major plantclimates are several regional subdivisions, the deserts of eastern California being an example (Fig. 4).

An explanation of the data shown in Figure 4 follows:

Nineteen subzones of regional plantclimate warm-arid to subtropical-temperate are located in the lower (south) half of the map (subzones A through E). Eleven are based solely on temperature. Eight are wind-modified (shaded area), but experience the same temperatures. Six subzones of regional plantclimate, the middle elevation desert, occupy the upper (north) half of the map (subzones 3 through 5).

Heavy north winds of sand-blowing velocity modify crop possibilities in the shaded area. This results in cabbage, cauliflower, and Brussels sprouts being confined to non-windy sections of subzones with alfalfa and vegetables not damaged by wind in the windy areas.

Significant plant and crop indicators are:

Subzone A—Warmest subtropical thermal zone. Poinsettia and lantana need no shelter; Guatamalan avocado, lime, and

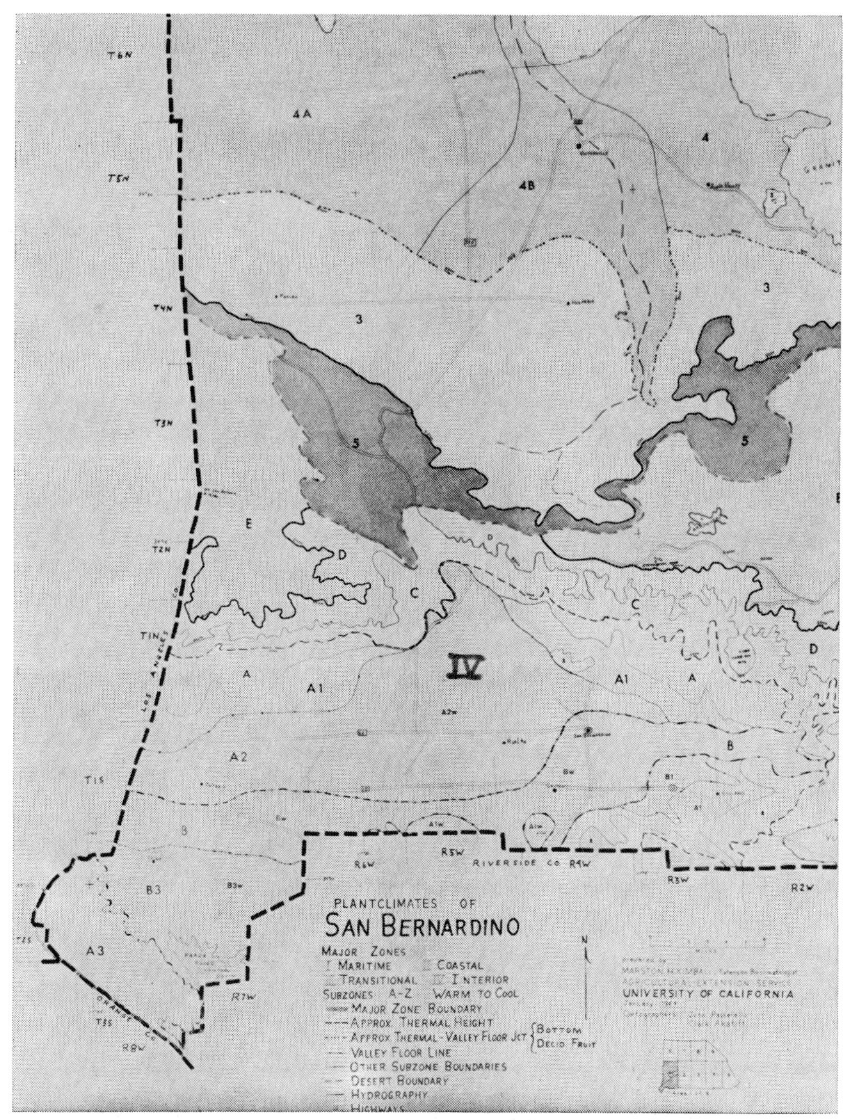

Fig. 4. Completed plantclimate map of the southwestern segment of San Bernardino County, California, showing desert and non-desert regions of the county.

lemons can be grown with possible frost damage once in 12 to 15 years. Warm winters occasionally supply insufficient chilling for best orange set. Almonds are about the only deciduous fruit or nut produced; it is too warm for lilacs.

Subzone A1—Standard avocados and lemons need occasional frost protection; oranges receive adequate chilling for normal set, but need no frost protection; lantana and poinsettia need mild shelter near buildings; almonds are satisfactory but apricots set poorly; winters are too warm for peaches and Placentia walnuts; grapes are occasionally damaged by spring frost; it is too warm for lilacs.

Subzone A2—Poinsettia and lantana need south exposures of buildings to avoid frost; common Eastern lilacs produce some straggly, small blooms if in winter shade (November to February) ; hardy avocados and lemons need frost protection regularly while oranges require occasional protection; Placentia walnut suffers mild dormosis regularly and the Eureka variety is unsatisfactory; low-chilling deciduous fruits perform suitably in many years, grapes are often spring-frosted.

Subzone A3—Conditions are similar to A2 and the cooler levels of A1, but there is some coastal influence resulting in Valencia rather than the navel oranges in A1 and mixed navel-Valencia orchards in A2; avocado and lemon require no heating; deciduous fruits suffer severe dormosis, as does lilac.

Subzone B—No lemons, avocados, or tender ornamentals can be grown except by covering for protection against frost; oranges are present with moderate heating on higher ground and regular heavy heating at lower levels; Placentia walnut and moderate-chilling peaches are satisfactory most years; Eureka walnut and high-chilling deciduous fruits often have serious dormosis; spring frost is often serious on grapes.

Subzone B3—Cold valley floor. No citrus fruits grown; tender subtropicals are usually frosted even in the shelter of south exposure; lilac has moderate bloom in winter shade, but not in the open; Placentia walnut, most peaches, plums, grapes, etc., are spring-frosted too regularly for economic success; Eureka walnuts are satisfactory; agriculture is non-dormant varieties of alfalfa and pasture, with 7 to 8 cuttings annually yielding 8 to 9 tons; vegetables; and dairy.

Subzone C—Upper limit of subtropical conditions at 3,250 feet on south slopes and 3,500 feet on southwest slopes. The altithermal transition to warm temperate climate of Subzone D is rapid. Low-chilling deciduous fruits in cooler canyon bottoms toward upper elevations are satisfactory most years. The upper boundary is the top of the rice-Bermuda grass association which is automatically included for the warmer subzones of A and B series.

Subzone C1—West and northwest slopes at the same elevations as Subzone C have sufficient winter chilling for J. H. Hale and Rio Oso Gem peaches, prunes, plums, sweet cherries, and Placentia and Eureka walnut in most years; chilling is not sufficiently high for apples; lilacs are only fair.

Subzone D—Warm summer—arid-temperate climate, from 3,250 to 5,000 feet. In most places above 4,000 feet, particularly on the north and northeast slopes, winter temperatures will satisfy dormancy of apples, lilacs, and similar plants. Wide diurnal fluctuations often result in spring frost. Adapted range grasses are intermediate and pubescent wheat grasses, orchard grass, tall fescue, Harding grass, and annual ryegrass. It is too cold for Smilo.

Subzone E—Moderate to cool summers—arid-temperate above 5,000 feet. Wide diurnal fluctuations make deciduous fruits hazardous. It is primarily grazing area with intermediate wheat and crested wheatgrass growing best. The range continues upward into coniferous forest with timberline at about 9,000 feet; it is subalpine above.

Subzone 3—Deciduous fruit thermal zone from 3,000 to 4,500 feet in arid-temperate desert. Spring frost is limited by air drainage. Irish potato, Labrusca grapes, and vegetables can be grown.

Subzone 4—Air-drained valley. Late apples grow, although midsummer heat often causes injury; dormant varieties of alfalfa produce 5 to 6 cuttings and yields of 6 to 7 tons; vegetables are also grown.

Subzone 4A—Flat desert floor. Spring frosts are too severe for deciduous fruits; alfalfa and vegetables are two weeks later than in Subzone 4.

Subzone 4B—Lower colder air basin. No fruit grows; alfalfa and vegetables are a week later than 4A.

Subzone 4C—Cold river channel concentrating air drainage. Crops are somewhat later.

Subzone 5—Altithermal cooling above 4,500 feet. Deciduous fruits and Irish potatoes are hazardous. Summer nights are cool and winters are cold. Coniferous forests range from about 5,000 feet to timberline at 9,000 feet; rain-shadow brings winter rains.

The four major plantclimates are:

I. *Maritime*—a continuous strip from Oregon to Mexico varying, with one exception, from a fraction of a mile to six or eight miles inland from the Pacific Ocean. The ocean influence is dominant all year with small diurnal and seasonal temperature changes. Topography varies from flat coastal plain or valley mouth to abrupt hill or mountain sides. Elevation at the inland boundary varies from a few feet to a maximum of 500 feet. The deepest penetration is the above exception—the mouth of the Sacramento River inland from San Francisco Bay—a much modified maritime condition.

II. *Coastal*—a continuous strip from Oregon to Mexico inland from maritime, extending inland from a few to 30 miles. Decreasing marine influence and wider diurnal and seasonal temperature fluctuations are characteristic. Diminishing coastal influence is present 85 percent of the time at the inland border. Topography consists of coastal plains, valleys, foothills, coast ranges to 2,000 or 2,500 feet, and occasionally to 3,500 or 4,000 feet where abrupt barriers occur.

III. *Transitional*—a discontinuous strip between coastal and interior plantclimates. Conditions can be similar to either for parts of a day, a day, a week, or longer, or the climate can be intermediate between the coastal and interior plantclimates. The area varies from four or five to 20 miles in width except for a 60-mile penetration into the foothills of the Sierra east of San Francisco Bay. The inland boundary is usually where the high mountain ranges act as positive barriers at elevations of 4,000 to 4,500 feet.

IV. *Interior*—a continuous area from north to south dominated about 85 percent of the time by continental air masses, except during major storm periods. Diurnal and seasonal temperature changes are increasingly wide with distance inland and with elevation. Topography varies, with low-elevation valleys, foothills, foothill and mountain valleys, high mountains, and deserts.

These major plantclimate boundaries, shown as a "line", must be considered somewhat flexible. The boundaries are as close as a fixed line can represent progressively changing conditions.

Plantclimate Zones and Subzones

There are three or more regional plantclimates within each major plantclimate. These regional plantclimates are, in turn, composed of zones and subzones, called micro- and miniplantclimate zones. The latter may be only a few square feet of doubly sheltered conditions within a microplantclimate, such as will exist within the shelter of a heavy windbreak surrounding a homesite or a square mile or so of markedly warmer or cooler conditions in a plantclimate subzone, never in a larger subdivision. Plant behavior within the boundaries of a subzone will be so uniform that it can be considered, for all practical purposes, a homoclimate. A plantclimate zone will encompass sufficient range to accommodate different kinds and varieties of deciduous fruits, for example, or most of the subtropical fruits. They may be hundreds of miles long and will contain many subzones. Figure 4 is the southwestern portion of San Bernardino County, all of which is in California's interior Plantclimate IV. Two regional plantclimates are represented: the temperate middle elevation desert to the north (Subzones 3, 4, 5) and subtropical semidesert to the south (Subzones A, B, C, D, E). The progressive sequence in both regions indicates a general cooling trend of overall conditions in winter and summer.

Within major and regional plantclimates there may be widely separated segments of the same plantclimate subzone. Separations may be a few to many miles. There may be one to several subzones of a different character between. Subzone variations within major plantclimates mav be so great as to result in small areas being practically identical to large or principal areas in adjoining plantclimates. Boundary lines are necessarily flexible. They indicate the approximate location of change, not a precise point. The boundary indicated between subzones in a gradually changing valley floor, for example, should be considered a "band" perhaps 10 to 20 miles wide. In rough hilly terrain boundaries indicating altithermal change should be interpreted as approximate, plus or minus two to three hundred feet or more from the indicated elevation. This is the inevitable result of differences in north, south, east, or west exposures, slope changes, shelter, etc.

Characterization with Physical Data

Plantclimate maps for the entire state were made without reference to physical temperature data. In this connection, plantclimate subzones are the most important units of this method of climate delineation for they most closely approximate a true homoclimate with only a degree or two of temperature variance. For their broadest uses it is necessary and desirable to characterize each subzone with the best physical data available. U. S. Weather Bureau records for the growing areas are the basic source. They can be supplemented in some locations with records from other sources.

Almost without exception, plants require higher day than night temperatures. Night temperature is more commonly the controlling growth factor. The photoperiod, or duration of daylight for photosynthesis, is probably second in importance (Kimball and Brooks, 1959). Mean or average temperatures are inadequate for studying and interpreting plant performances and responses because they do not reflect diurnal fluctuations; navel and Valencia orange production in California is an example. Except for desert the average annual temperature of all orange-producing areas is 62.4°F with a range from 61.7° to 63.5°F. Diurnal and seasonal changes account for the five- to seven-month range of harvest for navels and eight- to ten-month for Valencias, with navels predominant in the interior and Valencias almost exclusively at the coast. It is therefore necessary to consider night and day temperatures as individually functioning components of the daily temperature cycle (Went, 1957). Monthly mean minimum and monthly mean maximum temperatures as reported by the U. S. Weather Bureau can represent night temperature and day temperature, respectively, for plants growing in the field. They must be calculated to effective day and effective night values for comparison to well-regulated greenhouses or phytotrons (Kimball and Brooks, 1959).

A graphic projection of the year's temperature cycle can be constructed for any plantclimate subzone if temperature data are available. Ordinate and abscissa axes are established with degrees Fahrenheit at the same interval on each. The lowest temperature at the junction should be below those to be posted. Night temperature—the monthly mean minimum—is carried on the ordinate axis with day temperature on the abscissa. Extending the two components for any month will establish a point which represents that month's day-night temperature (After Went, 1957). Points are numbered (1) for January to (12) for December, and are connected in sequence. The resulting figure will extend upward from the low point of January and will angle to the right to the high temperatures of summer.

The graphic representation of the physical climate within the boundaries of the plantclimate subzone is termed as *climatograph* for easy reference.

When plantclimate subzones are characterized with day and night temperatures it is tantamount to characterizing all phenological events of the yearly growth cycle including total production and quality—all the factors of plant behavior responsible for delineation of the subzone.

Uses and Applications

Area Comparisons

General differences or similarities between zones and subzones can be immediately visualized by superimposing climatographs. Knowledge of these differences or similarities permits use of better management practices, such as more timely planting, wiser use of laborsaving devices, arrangements for harvest labor, and in long-range planning for diversification of cropping patterns.

Determining Specific Plant-Temperature Requirements

A technique was developed by which the optimum day-night temperature for any specific phenomenon or phenological event or for total quality-quantity production can be determined. The method is relatively simple if essential data are available. The requirements are:

1. The same variety of crop, or temperature-similar varieties,

must be grown in several different plantclimate subzones, resulting in different seasons for all phenological events. (Temperature-similar varieties will react alike to the same day-night temperature regime. This can be determined by observations in the field or greenhouse.)

2. Accurate phenological data for the events to be studied are necessary to date the events; examples are soil temperature at seeding, germination and emergence, growing period, flower bud initiation, fruit set, size development, etc. for annuals. Somewhat different events will be recorded for perennials.
3. Adequate temperature records for the growing area are necessary for construction of climatographs.

The technique of developing a *temperameter* can be illustrated with head lettuce, *Lactuca sativa* (Kimball *et al.,* 1967a). (Temperameter is a coined word, representing the figure produced by establishing a boundary, or parameter, on a day-night temperature chart enclosing the point of optimum temperature for 100 percent potential performance of a phenological event, or total crop production at top quality and permissible day-night temperature deviations for any acceptable percentage of performance (TEMPERature and parAMETER). Ninety percent temperameter is used in the example that follows.)

The same or similar varieties of head lettuce are grown in 12 plantclimates of California, four in Arizona, and one in Colorado. Conditions vary from below sea level in the hot, arid areas of subtropical desert subzones of the Imperial Valley to 400 foot elevation at Bakersfield, both in California's interior plantclimate, and from coastal plains near San Diego to San Francisco Bay in both maritime and coastal plantclimates; and at Brentwood, elevation 75 feet, in transitional plantclimate west of Sacramento. In Arizona, elevations range from about 100 feet near Yuma to 1,300 feet in the Salt River Valley, 2,600 feet at Aguilla, and 4,300 feet at Willcox. The San Luis Valley, near Alamosa, Colorado, is 7,530 feet above sea level. Head lettuce is being harvested 12 months of the year from one or more of these plantclimate subzones. From one to four U. S. Weather Bureau records are available for construction of climatographs in all subzones.

Dates of commercial harvest for each growing area are indicated

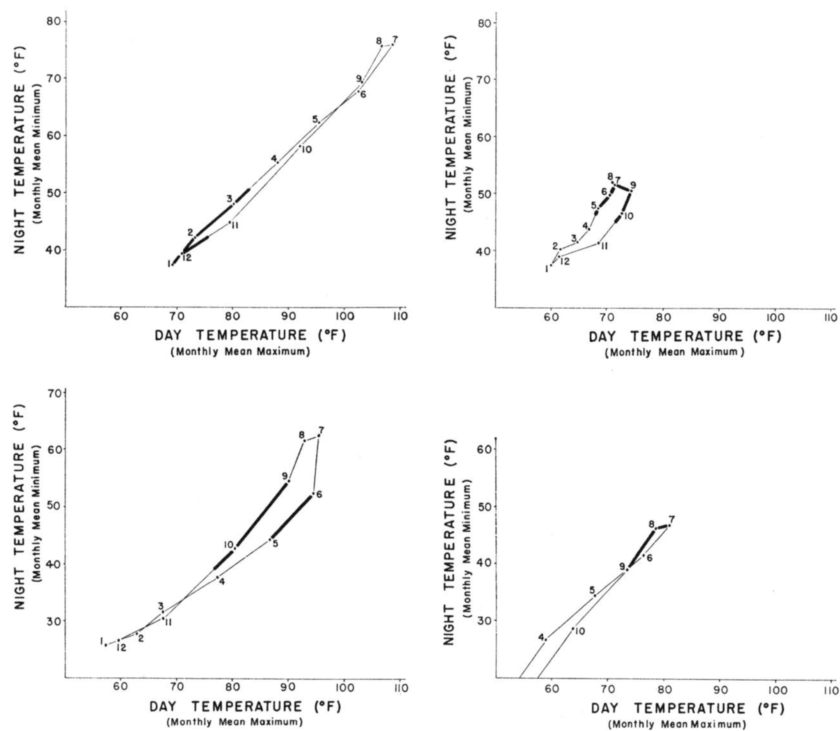

Fig. 5. Climatographs of four head lettuce-growing regions of California, Arizona, and Colorado. Numbers 1 through 12 indicate the long-term mean monthly temperatures (January through December). Heavy lines indicate harvest season. *Upper left:* Imperial Valley, California. Elevation: —50 to —150 feet. *Upper right:* Salinas – Watsonville, California. Elevation; 75 feet. *Lower left:* Willcox, Arizona. Elevation; 4,200 feet. *Lower right:* San Luis Valley, Colorado. Elevation: 7,530 feet.

on the respective climatographs by a section of heavy line. Figure 5 shows four typical climatographs: (1) Imperial Valley; (2) Salinas-Watsonville; (3) Willcox, Arizona, in a cool, arid, temperate, middle-elevation desert interior plantclimate; and (4) San Luis Valley, Colorado, cold-temperate, arid, high-elevation desert interior plantclimate. Harvest-season sections of all 17 climatographs were transferred to one day-night graph and the area of 90 percent quality-quantity production is enclosed by a dashed line. This was determined from Federal-State Market News reports and experienced observation (Fig. 6). The resulting oval-shaped figure is a graphic projection of the day-night temperature regime necessary to produce

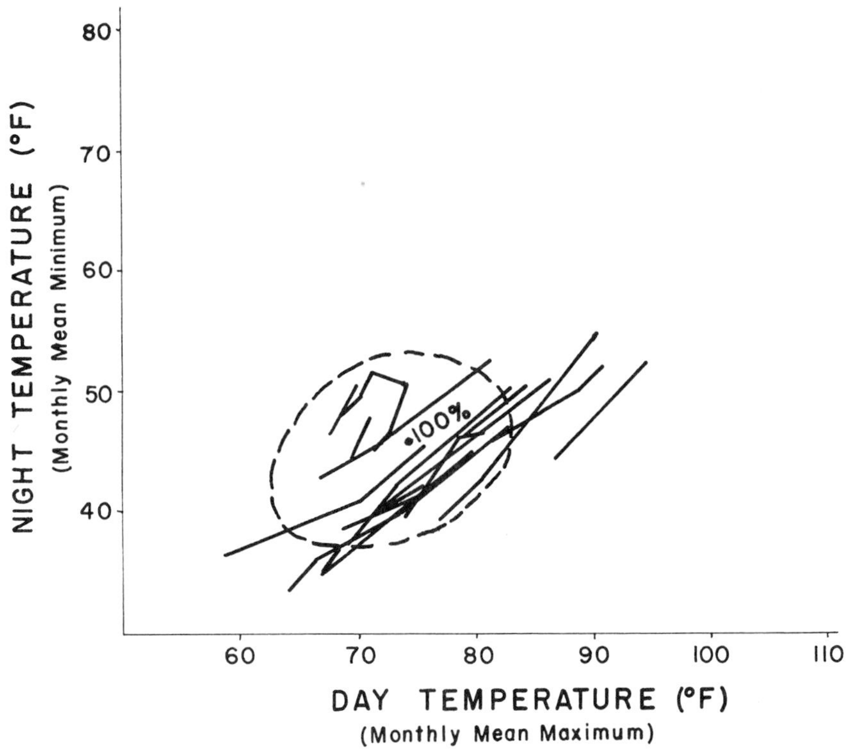

Fig. 6. Head lettuce temperameter (dashed line) established from the harvest periods (solid lines) of 15 lettuce-producing areas of California, Arizona, and Colorado. The 100% point represents day–night temperature conditions necessary for optimum quantity-quality production. The dashed line encloses the day–night temperature ranges for 90 percent of optimum quantity-quality production.

head lettuce at 90 percent of theoretical maximum quality and quantity. This figure is the "head lettuce temperameter". An 80 percent enclosure would probably include nearly all of the early and late harvest season during which marginal quality was shipped, usually because of seasonal price advantages.

Analysis of the temperameter reveals:

1. Range of day temperatures from the abscissa axis is 83° to 63°F with an average of 73°F established as optimum daytime field temperature, with a 10°F plus or minus range for 90 percent performance.
2. A range of night temperatures from 53° to 37°F with an aver-

age of 45°F is established as optimum nighttime field temperature with 8°F plus or minus for 90 percent performance.

3. Plotting the averages, 73° and 45°F, as a single point establishes the optimum daily temperature cycle for 100 percent quality–quantity production.

This range compares closely with a 75°–45°F recommendation (Knott, 1962). It is also in close agreement with the findings of geneticists testing new lettuce varieties in greenhouses. They hold as closely as possible to a 65° day and 53°F night, to permit comparison of new varieties of top-quality head lettuce with established varieties when grown in a greenhouse (J. E. Welch, personal communication). The optimum field range of 73° and 45°F from the daily sinusoidal curve of field temperatures converts to 66°–52°F for the square curve which results from plotting the abrupt temperature changes from day to night conditions, and vice versa, of a controlled-temperature growth chamber (Kimball *et al.*, 1967a).

Thus temperature relationships to all phenological events, to maturity of the crop, to total yield, and quality can be studied in detail. Specific day-night temperatures needed by plants for optimum growth can be determined. Permissible temperature deviations from optimum conditions evaluated in terms of percentage performance can likewise be determined. Hence a tool has been developed by which the following determinations can be made: (1) specific temperature requirements for any phase in the development of plants and crops; (2) areas (plantclimate subzones) in which necessary temperatures exist; and (3) temperature deviations from the optimum—a limited range of day and night temperatures—in which the plant will tolerate and perform at any specified percentage of theoretical 100 percent.

Crop Prospecting

Usefulness of temperameters is illustrated by Figure 7. The left portion is the climatograph for Eureka, California. Following the disastrous flood of December, 1964, the possible use of head lettuce as a high-income crop to assist in economic recovery was questioned. The climatograph is entirely outside the head lettuce temperameter, and a negative recommendation was made. Inquiry relative to growing head lettuce in an area of the western Mojave Desert in which

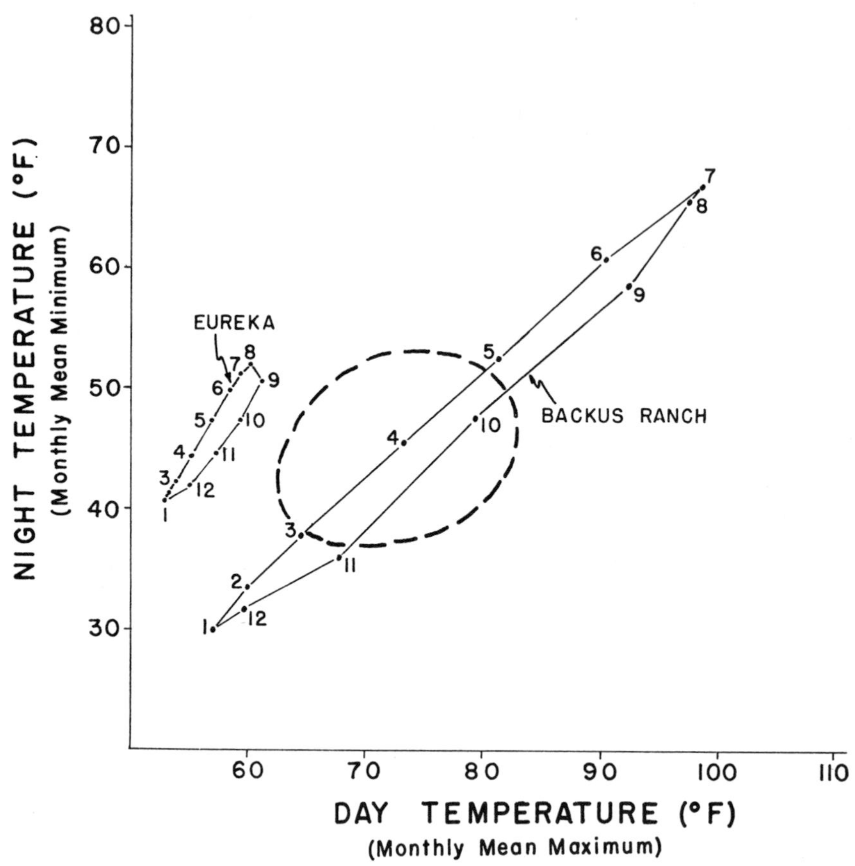

Fig. 7. Head lettuce temperameter and climatographs of two prospective producing locations. The figure shows agreement between head lettuce temperature requirements and conditions existing at Backus Ranch in the Mojave Desert near Rosamond, California; and disagreement between temperature requirements and conditions at Eureka, on the north coast of California.

the crop was unknown revealed the possibility of two crops a year. A fall crop appeared certain—two ten-day spaced trials produced 400 and 625 cartons respectively, with 325 cartons needed to repay costs. Rapid rise in spring temperatures, indicated by distance between temperature points for April, May, and June, and the steepness of the climatograph caused by rapid increase in night temperatures indicated probable low quality. Spring trials are under way.

Using the same general technique for a perennial species, a negative recommendation was made, on the certainty of poor quality, for Valencia oranges in a cool coastal, almost maritime, plantclimate. From ten to fifteen miles inland, in the warmer section of the same coastal plantclimate, the recommendations were favorable for the crop.

Extensive use of this new method of determining precise temperature requirements of plants and crops is limited by lack of adequate phenological data from different producing areas (plantclimate subzones). Prospecting in undeveloped areas is often handicapped by lack of temperature records. Temperature extrapolation techniques are being used to alleviate this shortcoming.

Where records are available and where specific climatic requirements can be enumerated, the plantclimate maps provide the key to site location for specialty crop production.

Ornamental Horticultural Surveys

Botanists, foresters, Farm Advisors, and others have surveyed the ornamental plants of California's low-elevation desert in the Colorado Desert (Mathias *et al.,* 1955), and of California's middle-elevation desert in the western part of the Mojave Desert (Mathias *et al.,* 1967). Plantclimate maps, with zone and subzone characterization, have permitted establishing the bases for ornamental plant distribution. Similarly, knowledge of specific areas has permitted possibilities of species selection heretofore unknown.

Nurserymen and other plantsmen have classified extensive lists of ornamentals according to preliminary plantclimate zones established in 1956 (Kimball *et al.,* 1956a, b). These have resulted in development of commercial enterprises as well as home landscape improvement.

Establishment of Plant Associations

Significant plant associations have been developed, permitting an immediate and assured interchange of plants or crops between disconnected plantclimate subzones or allowing conditional introduction into plantclimates that appear sufficiently similar from study of plant association lists or comparison of climatographs. Two associations have been discovered: successful rice growing with dominance of Bermuda grass for lawns, and deciduous fruits with the Irish potato. Successful rice production requires warm night temperatures in late summer. At the same warm night temperatures Bermuda grass will thrive while bluegrass vigor will be depressed (Youngner *et al.,* 1962), resulting in Bermuda grass dominance under normal management in home lawns within five years. Altithermal limits for Irish potatoes are valley floors below slopes of cool to cold temperate thermal belts. The relative freedom from spring frost in the thermal belts permits fruit-set of the high-chilling varieties of deciduous fruits found at such elevations.

Pest and Disease Distribution

The geographical areas (plantclimate zones and subzones) favorable or unfavorable for pests and diseases can be delineated. Investigation reveals a high correlation between zone and subzone delineation and infestations of citrus insects (Ebeling, 1959) and mildew on lettuce (Schnathorst *et al.,* 1962).

Crop Distribution

Crop distribution maps depicting primary and secondary centers for rice, Irish potatoes, grapes, citrus, and deciduous fruit have been prepared. Turfgrass species distribution maps are currently in use (Youngner *et al.,* 1962).

Animal and Avian Behavior

Analysis of plantclimate zones and subzones can be correlated with environmental factors known to influence animal and avian behavior. Of vital importance are the temperature relationships with periods of infertility, poor conception, embryonic death losses, rates of gain, and lowered rates of ovulation (Bond and Kelly, 1960; Dutt, 1960). As an example, the hot night environment of the Imperial Valley (low-elevation desert, interior plantclimate) is responsible for the five- to six-month breeding period required to get 80 to 90 percent of the ewes with lambs. This is in contrast to 2½ to 3 months for the interior plantclimate regions and one month or less in north coastal and mountain plantclimates.

Agricultural Stabilization

Losses of agricultural production caused by urban encroachment can be related to plantclimate subzones, permitting assessment of loss and indicating the climates needed for replacement acreage. Crop, species, and variety temperameters can be determined for ornamental and agricultural plants and crops (and probably animals, insects, and diseases) for the purpose of:

1. Locating developed areas into which displaced agriculture can be moved quickly and with assurance of successful reestablishment, thus conserving personal, community, and state resources, and the assessed values.
2. Revealing new crops capable of successful introduction into established or devastated areas to improve or rejuvenate the local economy.
3. Determining with reasonable certainty crops adaptable to, and the potential economy of, proposed new developments such as reclamation projects, irrigation districts, and private developments.

The development of climate information for potentials, limitations, and defined geographic limits has been used as a factor in land classification for appraisal, assessment, taxation, and as a basis for loans by financial institutions (Keith, 1966; Kimball, 1961). An example of the latter is that of a bank with large agricultural interests. It invested an estimated $10,000 and three years of investigation to build a "climatic" map showing limited areas where grapes could be marketed early in the season. The map became the basis for agricultural loans.

Land-Use Planning

National, state, county, city, or local land-use planners can determine and correlate food-producing potentials of any area, new or old (assuming good soil and water), with ultimate need, and the essentiality of sacrificing it to urban, metropolitan, and industrial uses. Conservation of resources for the future may dictate limiting high-quality agricultural land to food production and locating the urban complex on areas climatically favorable but lacking the climate-soil-water trinity. This trinity is the nation's greatest asset. It is expendable. It is not replaceable.

Resource planners, particularly in hilly locations, can combine detailed plantclimate maps with equally detailed soil and water maps to correlate soil fertility, permeability for irrigation and for handling drainage from septic tanks, and location of warm and cool micro-plantclimate subzones. They can then prepare appropriate plant lists as an aid to individuals and the community, and thus make the best use of resources and hopefully avoid a subdivision slum in years to come. This is now being done in some soil conservation districts.

Comprehensive County Studies

The maps have provided a working base for intensified studies of climate, soils, water, and crops on a county basis, a cooperative project involving the Agricultural Extension Service, University of California, and the United States Weather Bureau of the Environmental Science Services Administration. Santa Barbara, Mariposa, and Kern County reports have been completed and 30 more are in process (Gilbert and Peterson, 1966; Goodall, 1965; Luvisi *et al.*, 1967).

Other Uses

Plantclimate studies of California (Kimball and Brooks, 1959) are being used for teaching botany, ecology, ornamental horticulture, plant distribution, climatic requirements, etc., and by researchers in many fields from land-use planning to investigations of grass tetany. They are also used as an aid to industry in locating areas of favorable climate for manufacturing sites where water is available and housing for employes presents no climatic problem. The details of California's many climates, their role in the basic economy, and their potential uses are major factors in the future well-being of the population (Stone, 1965).

Conclusions

A knowledge of climate and its effects is exceedingly valuable for the evaluation and inventory of the limited and expendable basic natural resource of any area, state, or the nation. Climate, soil, and water are the essential trinity for food production and prosperity. Soil can be manipulated, modified within limits, improved, fertilized, even transported. Water can be impounded, transported, stored underground, and later pumped for irrigation. Cloud seeding is the only modification of "overhead" weather that man has devised.

Irrigation, of course, is man's way of overcoming nature's deficiencies in precipitation, and in this sense the ancient process is man's greatest modifier of total climate. But aside from this and puny efforts with shelters, plastic covers, and heaters, thus to gain or lose a few degrees of heat or cold, climate is where you find it. It cannot be transported. It cannot be stored. It cannot be used alone. But of the three—climate, soil, and water—climate is the controlling factor. When soil is buried under concrete and water is polluted or squandered, a beneficent climate becomes useless. All three are basic to human life.

REFERENCES

Bond, T. E., and C. F. Kelly, 1960. *Environment of Animals,* edited by A. Stefferud; pp. 231–242. U.S. Dept. Agriculture. U.S. Government Printing Office, Washington, D.C.

Dutt, R. H., 1960. Factors of temperature and light in reproduction. *J. Dairy Sci., 43* (suppl.) : 123–144.

Ebeling, Walter, 1959. *Subtropical Fruit Pests.* Agricultural Publications, Univ. California, Berkeley, California.

Goodall, G. E. (editor), 1965. *The Climate of Santa Barbara County, Plantclimate Map and Climatological Data.* Agr. Ext. Serv. Unnumbered Publication, Santa Barbara, California.

Gilbert, D. E., and G. D. Peterson, Jr. (editors), 1966. *Climate and Plantclimate Map of Mariposa County.* Agr. Ext. Serv. Unnumbered Publication, Mariposa, California.

Keith, J. H., 1966. *Property Tax Assessment Practices.* Highland Publishing Company, Monterey Park, California.

Kimball, M. H., 1961. Climate and values. In *Proceedings of the Fifty-Ninth Annual Conference of County Assessors of California and State Board of Equalization,* edited by J. H. Keith; pp. 51–61. State Board of Equalization, Sacramento, California.

Kimball, M. H., and F. A. Brooks, 1959. Plantclimates of California. *Calif. Agr., 13(5):* 7–12.

Kimball, M. H., M. E. Mathias, and V. T. Stoutemeyer, 1956a. *Plant Materials for Northern California Climatic Zones.* Unpublished paper presented at the Northern California Nursery Institute, Berkeley, California.

Kimball, M. H., M. E. Mathias, and V. T. Stoutemeyer, 1956b. *Plant Materials for Southern California Climatic Zones.* Unpublished paper presented at the Southern California Nursery Institute, Los Angeles, California.

Kimball, M. H., W. L. Sims, and J. E. Welch, 1967a. Plantclimate analysis for lettuce. *Calif. Agr., 21(4):* 2–4.

Kimball, M. H., F. A. Brooks, and D. E. Gilbert, 1967b. California's plantclimates. *Calif. Agr.* (In press)

Knott, J. E., 1962. *Handbook for Vegetable Growers.* John Wiley and Sons, New York.

Luvisi, D. A., D. E. Gilbert, and G. D. Peterson, Jr. (editors), 1967. *Kern County's Climates, Soils, Waters, Crops.* Agr. Ext. Serv. Unnumbered Publication, Bakersfield, California.

Mathias, M. E., W. Metcalf, M. H. Kimball, R. S. Ayers, C. L. Hemstreet, and D. D. Halsey, 1955. Ornamentals for low-elevation desert areas of Southern California. *Calif. Agr. Exp. Sta. Bull., 750.*

Mathias, M. E., W. Metcalf, M. H. Kimball, C. L. Hemstreet, D. E. Gilbert, and W. B. Davis, 1967. Ornamentals for the middle elevation desert section of California. *Calif. Agr. Exp. Sta.* (In press)

Russell, R. J., 1926. Climates of California. In *University of California Publications in Geography, 2(4):* 73–84. Univ. California Press, Berkeley, California.

Schnathorst, W. C., H. B. Schultz, and R. Bardin, 1962. Distribution of lettuce mildews as related to environment. *Calif. Agr., 16(12):* 6–7.

Stone, A. (editor), 1965. *California Information Almanac.* California Information Almanac and California Year Book. Lakewood, California.

Visher, S. S., 1954. *Climatic Atlas of the United States.* Harvard Univ. Press, Cambridge, Massachusetts.

Went, F. W., 1957. *Experimental Control of Plant Growth.* Chronica Botanica Co., Waltham, Massachusetts.

Youngner, V. B., J. H. Madison, M. H. Kimball, and W. B. Davis, 1962. Climatic zones for turfgrass in California. *Calif. Agr., 16(7):* 2–4.

Potential Evapotranspiration and Plant Distribution in Western States with Emphasis on California[1]

JACK MAJOR, *Botany Department, University of California, Davis, California*

AN OBVIOUSLY CLOSE RELATIONSHIP exists between climate and the growth and occurrence of plants. But the specifics of this relationship, particularly the functional, quantitative connections between vegetational properties and climatic parameters, are not at all obvious, and are neglected in recent ecological literature.

Early plant geographers used climatic data effectively to help explain plant distribution. Christ (1879) and Schimper (1898), for instance, quoted climatic data to characterize the habitats of different plant formations. Eyre (1963) has warned, however, ". . . there is always a danger of misunderstanding when exact values of temperature and precipitation are mentioned in the same context as biotic distributions. The reader may be tempted to assume that the latter are determined by the former. Systematic treatment of climate is limited here to an appendix in which some mean monthly precipitation and temperature figures are tabulated for two or three stations within the area occupied by each vegetation type. It will be found that these emphasize the climatic diversity of the terrain occupied by many plant formations rather than the reverse." Still, ". . . the overall world pattern [of vegetation] is very obviously

[1] The author of this contribution was out of the continental United States and was unable to approve the final proofs. *Robert H. Shaw, Editor*

controlled by climatic factors" (Eyre, 1963). The hope expressed in the title of Schimper's classical treatise (1898), *Plant Geography on a Physiological Basis,* has not been fulfilled so far as climate goes, partly because plant distribution and growth are functions of many factors, and not of climate alone. Although we may seek functional relationships between plant properties and climatic parameters, the relationships can not be profitably expressed as causal (Dahl, 1951; Faegri, 1960; Major, 1958, 1961).

It is not usually possible, for example, to answer the question, "Which of the environmental factors, climate, soil parent material, fire, etc. is most important in determining plant distributions?" Consideration of even a simple, but general, formulation of the relationship of plants to environment (Major, 1951) shows this. The equation relating properties of vegetation as dependent variables to independently defined site factors is totally differentiated. An integration shows dependence of a difference in a vegetational property on three parameters:

1. The existence of a change in the independent variable. If climate does not vary between two areas, differences between the vegetations of these two areas cannot necessarily be ascribed to climate.

2. The value of the partial effect on the change in the independent variable property of vegetation. The partial effect of a 10 mm difference in precipitation is much greater on vegetation yield at a mean July precipitation of 30 mm than at a mean July precipitation of 500 mm.

3. The limits of variation, or integration, of the independent variable.

It follows that no universal correlation between vegetation and climate can be found, and also that it is difficult even to rank the relative importance of a climatic difference in relation to differences in other site factors. No general climatic classification which corresponds to vegetation types should be expected.

Climate may be, however, the overriding factor in some ecosystems, and ecologists ascribe to climate major importance in differentiating the kinds of vegetation on earth. An interesting question, then, is which of the vegetation units described for California possess, in fact, unique climatic parameters?

Purpose

One purpose of this paper is to suggest what kinds of native Californian vegetation may actually be conditioned by a regional climate. Another is to suggest what kinds are conditioned by a locally operative climate, edaphic conditions, a particular biota, or groundwater, or are successional states to some other kind of vegetation. Another purpose is to apply to the types of California vegetation that seem to be climatically determined a rational system of climatic description which is pertinent to the physiological responses of plants. Climates will be illustrated, and the relationships between types of vegetation and climates will be examined.

Potential Evapotranspiration

The operationally defined climatic parameters used here describe water balances of ecosystems; heat available to the ecosystem is also measured as evaporable water equivalent.

Potential evapotranspiration has been defined as the water lost to the atmosphere from a short, complete plant cover which is actively growing and is fully supplied with water. It represents optimum conditions for plant growth as far as soil water is concerned. "Fully supplied" does not mean an excess of soil water, but that the amount of soil water lies in the range between permanent wilting point and field capacity—nearer to field capacity. Aeration is adequate. Potential evapotranspiration is also a heat index. It is an exponential function of temperature. It is expressed as depth in mm of water loss. By means of known values of the heat of evaporation of water (almost 600 cal/g), the water depth lost by evapotranspiration per month can be converted into heat units per unit area per unit time (100 mm/month $= 10 \times 0.600 = 6$ kcal/cm^2 per month), and vice versa.

Few experimental determinations of potential evapotranspiration are available. There is a great deal of interest in its determination in arid regions, but in such areas the only plants fully supplied with water occur in oases. In these oases much of the incoming radiant energy is used to heat, and therefore dry, the air, and the advective heat from surrounding dry areas increases markedly the water use by plants. Every irrigated plot in a dry region is an oasis, as is every standard evaporation pan exposing a free water surface. Thus Swinbank (1965) said, "I would suggest . . . that the concept of potential evapotranspiration is a useless one, in that it cannot be defined and cannot be measured . . . ." His strictures, however, apply only to ecosystems where heat comes in from beyond the horizontal boundaries of the system. Where advection of heat is not possible, or the amount very small, as in most humid climates and at least theoretically for all zonal vegetation, potential evapotranspiration must be less than the water-loss equivalent of the net radiation received (Major, 1963a). Actual evaporation then is always equal to or less than potential evaporation.

Various methods of estimating potential evapotranspiration are available. The best known are the formulas of Thornthwaite (1948), which requires fewest data, and Penman (1956), which is usually considered more accurate. Holdridge (1962) has suggested that potential evapotranspiration is equal to the mean biotemperature (above freezing) times 58.93.

In this paper we have used Thornthwaite's empirical correlation of mean monthly temperature with potential evapotranspiration to estimate the latter. His method of calculating a water balance for a specific ecosystem was reviewed from an ecological standpoint by Major (1963a).

Given potential evapotranspiration and total water income to the ecosystem by months, one can calculate the water balance through the hydrological year by a bookkeeping process (Thornthwaite *et al.*, 1957). We have assumed income to be the monthly average precipitation, and 100 mm to be soil storage of available water, with impaired availability as it is used (unequal availability). Under an equal availability hypothesis no water deficit occurs until the 100 mm of available water stored in the soil is used; under the hypothesis of availability being proportional to the amount present, any use of soil water produces some deficit. The first hypothesis results in a sharp peak in water use, and a sharp drop when water is not plentiful; the second results in more gradual changes.

I have recalculated Mather's (1964) yearly water balance figures for various climatic stations in the United States, using 100 mm of available water storage in the soil instead of the 300 mm he assumed.

As an example of soil water storage we can consider a completely fine-grained solum having no rocks. If the permanent wilting point (PWP) is 10 percent by weight, field capacity (FC) is 30 percent, and bulk density (BD) is 1.25 g/cm^3, available water content by volume will be 25 percent and a depth of 100 mm of available water will be contained in 40 cm of fully root-exploited soil. If the soil is 50 percent impervious gravel, 100 mm of available water will be contained in 80 cm of soil. If the soil is light-textured, with PWP of 5 percent and FC of 15 percent, then the volume percentage of water will be 12.5 with the same BD, and the corresponding rooting depth will be 80 cm with no gravel and 160 cm with 50 percent gravel. If the soil has natural structure, untrampled and unplowed, its BD will be nearer 1.00 than 1.25 g/cm^3; in such a case water by volume will be decreased 25 percent from that of the original example, with a corresponding increase in necessary soil depth. For 300 mm of available soil water storage, the depths of soil fully exploited by roots must be tripled. In most plant communities, such great soil depth as 1.2 to more than 4.8 m is not available. An average figure for the available water content of soils in the United States is about 90 mm, according to Russell and Hurlbut (1959).

The three parameters that characterize the interaction of water demand (potential evapotranspiration, PE) and supply (precipitation) are actual evapotranspiration (AE), water deficit (D), and water surplus (S). They can be used to characterize climates. Actual evapotranspiration can be used as a measure of dryland vascular plant productivity (Major, 1963a), since net photosynthesis is impossible without concomitant water loss from leaves under field conditions. Arkley (1963) has shown how this relationship can be tested. Bierhuizen and Slatyer (1965) discussed variations associated with transpiration and photosynthesis. For example, when CO_2 no longer limits photosynthesis, the relationship breaks down; but, ". . . as a first approximation, variability in the ratio between transpiration and apparent photosynthesis from region to region is due largely to variability in Δ e" (the difference in water vapor pressure between leaf and air). Net photosynthesis occurs when CO_2 diffuses into the leaf and is fixed; but if the stomata are open so that CO_2 can diffuse inwards, water vapor can diffuse outwards. Both gases diffuse in a direction determined by their gradients in partial pressures, and under most field conditions the gradient for CO_2 is towards the leaf and for water vapor away from the leaf.

Estimated water surplus, when it shows up as runoff from the watershed, provides a check on all the calculations connected with the water balance. If, however, all the water yield from the basin does not flow past a gauge or if pervious strata dip and conduct groundwater into the watershed from outside its boundaries, the check will not work.

Differences between maritime and continental climates are important. Our measure of continentality is the range in mean monthly temperatures decreased by the normal increase in range between summer and winter temperatures with latitude over the open oceans (Khromov, 1957), expressed by $K = A–5.4 \sin$ latitude.

Climate is regarded in terms of availability of water and a heat factor, with both determined wholly or partially by potential evapotranspiration. We will correlate vegetation and climate on these terms. Arkley and Ulrich (1962) have published maps of potential and actual evapotranspiration in California.

Another way of showing the water balance has been used by Walter (1955, 1960) following a suggestion of Gaussen (1954). Valuable data have been published using this system (Walter and Leith, 1960). Gaussen suggested that potential evapotranspiration in mm is equal to about two times the monthly temperature in °C. If precipitation and temperature are plotted by months on scales of 2:1 (2 mm = 1°C), areas below the temperature line and between it and the precipitation line will show drought, and areas above the temperature line and below the precipitation line will show an excess of water. Unfortunately, this relationship is inexact, and no provision is made for soil storage of water and its subsequent use by plants. The climatic diagrams in this paper show mean monthly temperature figures on the scale suggested by Gaussen and Walter.

Using the four climatic parameters suggested by Thornthwaite (1948), namely indexes of humidity and aridity and their seasonal variations, Daubenmire (1956) found that the climatic classification was too elaborate to fit the vegetation of eastern Washington and adjacent Idaho. This paper uses no climatic classification; instead, it uses the numbers expressing the water balance, that is, absolute values in mm of water potentially lost by the ecosystem (PE), actually lost (AE), difference between actual and potential losses (D), and difference between water supplied and that used (S). The climatic diagrams in this paper reflect Daubenmire's suggestion (1956) that "Nothing short of a method showing simultaneous month-to-month trends in moisture and heat relations can be expected to prove adequate." The yearly sums of AE, D, and S are also summations from monthly water balances.

Kinds of Far Western Vegetation

This paper considers vegetation rather than individual plants. Native plants are studied to avoid problems attending the history of plant introductions. Because there are some 6,000 species of vascular plants in California (Munz and Keck, 1959), and because detailed information on plant distribution and detailed studies of the relationships of the 6,000 plants to any element of climate are lacking, it is impossible to go from the particular to the general by way of autecology. Ecologists have found, too, that vegetation units are better indicators of habitat than are individual plants.

Association of several species, each with a different tolerance for a given ecological factor, narrows the tolerance of the plant community, since competition usually narrows the tolerance range of each species. Because plants occur in nature as competitors in particular ecosystems, their habitat indicator value must be relative to the plants with which they are associated. These differences between physiological and ecological tolerances have been discussed by Ellenberg (1953, 1956, 1963), Knapp (1954), and Walter (1960).

The major kinds of vegetation in California are limited in number, reasonably familiar, and fairly well agreed upon. There are three recent classifications–Munz and Keck (1959), Knapp (1957, 1965), and Küchler (1964). In Tables 1–7 specific climatic stations are arranged under kinds of vegetation whose names are taken primarily from Munz and Keck (1959), with additions from Major (1963b).

It is well known that vegetation types are determined not only by climate but also by other factors of their environment. We shall focus on the regional vegetation, determined primarily by climate. This zonal vegetation is contrasted with those specialist types the presence of which within one climatic region is correlated with differences in such non-regional factors as soil parent material, slope steepness and exposure, presence of groundwater or snow accumulation, etc.

At the end of the chapter are a number of figures and tables that provide detailed data for the climatic findings pertaining to evapotranspiration and plant distribution in some of the Western States. Figure 1 shows the key to all subsequent illustrations in this chapter. Stations listed in the tables are located in California, unless indicated otherwise.

Correlations Between Climates and Vegetation

Coastal Vegetation

The coastal vegetation of California is clearly different from that inland. It belongs to two different floristic provinces, the northwest coastal and the Californian; these provinces intergrade and interfinger.

The coastal maritime climates are characterized by a great similarity of PE (heat) both absolutely and in variation between summer and winter (Table 1). The amount is some 650 mm of water a year, and seasonal variation is small.

The climate at Pt. Reyes (Fig. 2) is extreme in the latter regard, with only 3.8°C between lowest and highest monthly average temperatures—only 0.5°C more than the normal seasonal difference over the open ocean, according to Khromov (1957). The stretch of the California coast from Monterey north to Del Norte County is so maritime that it has a negative continentality value on Conrad's (1946) index, which was adjusted to give 0.0 percent for the Lofoten Islands off the northern coast of Norway and 100 percent for Verkhoyansk near the Northern Hemisphere's cold pole in eastern Siberia. The difference between minimum and maximum monthly PE is only 31 mm of water at Pt. Reyes, and only 55 mm of water use is possible in May, the period most favorable for plant growth. Crescent City (Fig. 3) has a much more favorable climate for plants than exists farther south. It has a maximum of 76 mm of water use in June, and a minimum of 25 mm in August. If 300 mm of soil water were available at Crescent City instead of the assumed 100 mm, AE would be increased from 538 mm to 601 mm.

The climate of northern coastal California with mesic vegetation is characterized by more precipitation in general, but particularly by having AE of more than 400 mm a year. The climate of the sitka spruce community (Fig. 3) has significantly less D and greater S than the others. Its climate is similar to that from coastal Oregon to the Kenai Peninsula in Alaska. The mesic areas of the northern California coast (Eureka, Ft. Bragg, and Crescent City) all have much higher AE in both the months of lowest and highest AE than do the more southern, sclerophyll areas. The soil recharge is never complete at San Diego but all the other coastal stations listed have some S.

Both the north coastal mixed coniferous and the redwood forest areas (Fig. 4) have maritime climates. Their high AE of more than 450 mm of water a year is rather equably distributed, with more than 25 mm AE in the coldest months and more than 10 mm in the driest months in the redwoods. Farther north the water use in the driest month is more than 30 mm. And at Forks, on the Olympic Peninsula of Washington, AE (calculated plant growth) is more than 600 mm of water use a year with a low figure of less than 20 mm a month in winter but 80 mm as a low in the driest summer month. The very heavy precipitation at Forks, mainly in winter, almost obliterates summer drought, partly by extending the period of soil storage of available water. Average precipitation, however, drops to only 1/8 of its maximum winter value in the driest summer month so there is atmospheric drought—the summer need for water is 96 mm in August when average precipitation is only 57 mm, for a D of 39 mm.

Central Valley Vegetation

Moving inland, the habitat of the now almost vanished bunch-grass vegetation which once covered so much of lowland California is characterized by a continental climate. It has a very short period favorable to plant growth in spring with about 60 mm evapotranspiration a month, followed by a sharp drop to zero water use in late summer as the soil dries. There is a lower fall peak of activity (green, aboveground growth) as the winter rains commence (Table

2). Some plant growth continues even during the low temperatures of winter, but at a rate only about ⅓ that of the coastal climates. For a more extended discussion of this climate, including its variability, see Major and Pyott (1966).

Fresno is probably too dry to represent such bunchgrass vegetation, and the southern San Joaquin Valley (Middlewater) certainly is too dry (Twisselmann, 1956). It is in this extra-hot, arid climate that the introduced annual grass, *Schismus arabicus,* has naturalized and spread spectacularly in the last 30 years or so (Twisselmann, 1956) just as *Avena fatua, A. barbata, Bromus rigidus, B. mollis,* and *Hordeum leporinum* have replaced *Stipa pulchra* northward. (Nomenclature and taxonomy follow Munz and Keck (1959) except where authors are named.) The present wide variety of annual vegetation which has replaced the original *Stipa pulchra* bunchgrass is unrecognized in any classification. The place of the drier-site *Stipa cernua* in California's bunchgrass vegetation is unclear.

The vegetation classified as chaparral contains many different kinds of plant cover. They differ in composition, location, climates, soil parent materials, relief, successional position, and probably history. Their climates range from those of coastal San Diego and Mt. Tamalpais (Table 1) to Ash Mountain (Table 2). Within this range are the climates of foothill woodland vegetation.

We specifically exclude clearly secondary, montane brushfields resulting from logging and burning of forests—Küchler's montane chaparral (1964).

We can be specific about one kind of chaparral, the *Arctostaphylos myrtifolia* heath near Ione. Its climate is figured in Gankin and Major (1964). The Ione area is more maritime than Ash Mountain at least, but not more so than San Diego or many other coastal sites which have even *Adenostema fasciculatum* chaparral. The specialist Ione vegetation is edaphically determined.

We have compiled enough data on the climates of the foothill woodland vegetation to make averages meaningful (Table 2). We bracket this vegetation type in central California between the climates of Rocklin and Auburn (Figs. 5 and 6). The altitudinal range between Rocklin and Auburn is 322 m. Foothill woodland vegetation occurs on shallow or rocky soils at the lower elevations and is replaced by ponderosa pine at the higher elevations on north slopes and in draws with cold air drainage. Rocklin and Auburn are evidently only local limits. They are far surpassed climatically by the differences between the hot, dry continental climate of the San Joaquin Experimental Range and the cooler, wetter coastal climate of Mt. Hamilton.

Valley oak climates are less continental (Fig. 7) than those of the foothill woodland and the alluvial soils supporting valley oak are deeper, but, perhaps paradoxically, less chemically weathered in general. Climatic differences between valley oak and foothill woodland are small, bearing out Thompson's (1961) characterization of much valley oak vegetation as riverine and confined to the deep, silty, but not clayey, soils of broad levee areas bordering the major streams.

The northern oak woodland needs better definition. Its climate may be somewhat less continental than that of the foothill woodland. The northern oak woodland intergrades with both the mixed evergreen forest (Fig. 8) and foothill woodland, the latter having both greater water deficit and less precipitation. The climate of Cloverdale in the northern oak woodland is diagrammed in Major (1963a). The Douglas fir forest has the same climate as the mixed evergreen forest.

In the region with zonal Douglas fir forest or northern oak woodland, soils with low available water content, such as gravels, or soils on warmer sites on south slopes have the northern oak woodland vegetation.

Sierran Vegetation

The Sierra Nevada with its marked topographic contrasts from the low western base in foothill woodland at a few hundred meters elevation to alpine vegetation above about 3,000 to 3,400 m (from north to south) shows correspondence between vegetation types and climate (Table 3).

From the climate of foothill woodland (Fig. 5) to that of ponderosa pine vegetation (Fig. 6) AE increases as precipitation increases with altitude, and demand for water decreases with decreasing temperature. Increased AE is principally related to high values in July–September. However, in the drier and warmer climate of the southern Sierra Nevada (Yosemite region) actual evapotranspiration is low (< 350 mm/yr).

As actual evapotranspiration decreases with increasing altitude and cooler temperatures, and soil leaching becomes more than 1,000 mm a year, the mixed coniferous forest of the Sierra Nevada results.

East of the Sierra crest *Pinus jeffreyi* dominates but *Pinus ponderosa* also occurs, and both are associated with *Artemisia tridentata* and *Purshia tridentata* and, to the north, with *Juniperus occidentalis*. Precipitation is more than 470 mm a year as compared with over 840 mm in west-slope ponderosa pine areas, and in the continental climates of the east slope AE decreases to less than 250–300 mm a year. Even where precipitation differs by a factor of two (Woodfords versus Twin Lakes), vegetation is still similar—and so is AE. At Bend, Oregon, on the border between the ponderosa pine and *Juniperus occidentalis* types, with only a third the precipitation of Twin Lakes, AE is not greatly different (Fig. 17). The difference in precipitation shows in S.

Climatically east- and west-slope ponderosa pine forests have very little in common. Associated plants also differ. Dominance of the ubiquist *Pinus ponderosa* is a poor criterion for classification of vegetation.

Sequoiadendron gigantea may not be climatically limited. Its climate lies within the range of variation of the Sierran mixed coniferous forest. Figure 9, the Giant Forest in Sequoia National Park, and the numbers of Table 3 may adequately describe its climate. However, Gleason and Cronquist (1964) mention that cold winters with no snow will kill planted specimens. Its native habitat is noted for great snow depths which prevent soil freezing.

In the red fir forest climate of higher elevations at Soda Springs (Fig. 10) PE is less than 500 mm a year, and AE is less than 280 mm a year. The last figure is about equal to that in the east side ponderosa pine forests.

The subalpine forest climate (Fig. 11) is still cooler, with PE less than 470 mm a year as shown for Ellery Lake, but AE may be greater than 300 mm a year at Crater Lake or 430 mm at Paradise, near timberline on Mt. Rainier in Washington. In this subalpine climate the driest summer period is shifted from August in the red fir climate to a low point in AE in September. At the higher elevations a summer thunderstorm peak in precipitation becomes evident in the monthly averages. At the northern stations, summer drought progressively vanishes as total precipitation increases. For example, at Mt. Rainier the summer low precipitation month with 44 mm has less than a tenth the maximum precipitation month. The maximum monthly demand for water is consistently about 100 mm in this climate.

To approximate the Sierran alpine climate I have projected that of Ellery Lake upward to timberline (Fig. 12) and then to the top of the nearby Dana Plateau (Fig. 13), 540 m above timberline. A lapse rate of −0.6°C/100 m was used for temperature and an annual rate of +100 mm/100 m for precipitation. The additional precipitation was allocated to the various months in proportion to their contribution to total precipitation at Ellery Lake.

This increase of precipitation with altitude is an approximate mean for the transect over the railroad grade at Donner Pass between Sacramento and Reno, Nevada. On the west slope 14 stations show an increase of about 131 mm/100 m of annual mean precipitation with altitude, while on the east slope the rate is about 57 mm/100 m for 9 stations. (Davis, Sacramento, Rocklin, Auburn, Colfax, Lake Spaulding, Blue Canyon, Soda Springs, Donner Memorial State Park, Truckee, and Reno form an altitudinal sequence of climates over the Sierra Nevada at latitude 39°N along Interstate Highway 80 and the Southern Pacific Railroad.)

The period of positive mean air temperatures shortens from some six months at Ellery Lake (eight months at Gem and Crater Lakes) with PE of about 400 mm, to about 370 mm in six months at timberline (3,230 m), and to 270 mm in four months at 3,770 m on the Dana Plateau in the alpine belt. Calculated AE increases from Ellery Lake to timberline and then decreases only slightly to the top of the Dana Plateau. In the alpine belt of the arid White Mountains (Fig. 14), although PE corresponds to that calculated for the Dana Plateau, AE is only 180 mm instead of 225 mm. At high altitudes available soil water is only 70 to 90 percent depleted during summer instead of the 95 to 100 percent depletion of lower elevations.

Northern Great Basin Vegetation

We find some striking climatic differences between vegetation types in the northern Great Basin vegetation (Table 4). Significantly, this is the only vegetation of the area that has been studied comparatively (Billings, 1949).

The climate of shadscale stations (Fig. 15) has zero S. Therefore AE is equal to precipitation, and on the average there is no soil leaching. Soil storage of available water is from 18 mm at Mina, Nevada, to 53 mm at Lahontan Dam, Nevada. In other words, on the average the water storage capacity of the soil is utilized by only half or less. In comparison with the climate of the sagebrush vegetation type, the climate supporting shadscale vegetation has less water available to plants and, corresponding to usually lower elevations, higher temperatures. Both factors mean that more of the incident radiation is available to heat the air, and PE is greater than 550 mm a year. Continentality is also greater than in the sagebrush.

There is, of course, a transition between the shadscale and sagebrush (Fig. 16) climates. Normally, however, some S characterizes the latter. AE is almost twice the shadscale figure of 110–135 mm a year.

These figures are not quite borne out by climatic data from the eastern area of the shadscale vegetation (Table 5). Still, even Thompson Springs in eastern Utah, where *Atriplex corrugata* S. Wats. is the characteristic species rather than the usual *A. confertifolia,* has estimated AE only slightly greater than 200 mm a year whereas even the driest sagebrush areas have AE greater than 230 mm. These eastern shadscale areas are also developed over Mancos shale, a clayey, saline, marine deposit on which *Artemisia tridentata* grows poorly if at all. Thompson Springs lies in a region of maximum (late) summer precipitation; 50 percent more precipitation comes in the three months of August–October than if precipitation were evenly distributed throughout the year.

The period with monthly average temperatures above freezing is ten months long (December and January being excepted), but at many of the climatic stations just east of the Sierra Nevada, at higher altitudes and to the east in Wyoming (Table 5) this period shortens to seven or even six months (Dubois Experiment Station, Idaho).

There is a good deal more constancy in the AE figures for either the shadscale or the sagebrush vegetation types (Table 5) than in the figures for precipitation, PE, length of growing season, etc.

We should note, with reference to Table 5, that the climates of Dubois, Idaho, and Kemmerer, Wyoming, are close to the climates of the drier-site shadscale vegetation. The Utah stations along the Wasatch Mountain front are close to *Quercus gambellii* Nutt. brush. Logan borders on *Agropyron spicatum* bunchgrass steppe. At Evanston only one particular relief is required to support *Amelanchier alnifolia* on north slopes and areas of snow accumulation. The Dubois Experiment Station in Idaho is in an area with much *Purshia tridentata* and here the sagebrush is *A. tripartita* Rydb. Both Pinedale and Jackson, Wyoming, have *Pinus contorta* Dougl. ex Loud. ssp. *latifolia* (Engelm.) Critchf. on north slopes or where groundwater is high in draws accompanied by cold air drainage or accumulation. Finally the southern Utah stations have monthly summer rainfalls which exceed those of the winter months.

Daubenmire has not only studied carefully the vegetation of eastern Washington and adjacent Idaho but has also discussed the climatic relationships of this vegetation (1942, 1952, 1956). Some of the climatic stations he lists for particular vegetation types are assembled in Table 6. His is an area of considerable climatic diversity, and even the normal Pacific Coast pattern of dominantly winter precipitation, which extends east through the northern Great Basin, breaks down in some cases. Spring or early summer precipitation peaks occur in all *Agropyron spicatum* climatic stations. In the sagebrush, Lind has a late summer maximum of precipitation, and all four of the sagebrush climatic stations show the same spring-early summer peak as the *Agropyron spicatum* grassland although amounts are generally only half as much. Again, in the ponderosa pine climate all stations have this same spring peak, except Leavenworth in the eastern foothills of the Cascades, which is normal. Even the easternmost station, Kooskia, Idaho, has its maximum monthly precipitation in spring.

Daubenmire's *Pinus ponderosa* vegetation borders the *Artemisia* zone except at Kooskia. The climate of this forest differs from that of the northern sagebrush steppe in having more precipitation, as one might expect. PE values do not differ much and in fact overlap in some cases. AE in the forest is greater, D less, and S much higher. Again, there are overlaps in all but S.

Daubenmire's ponderosa pine is similar to the northeastern ponderosa pine forests of California, except for Kooskia, Idaho. All the stations east of the northern Cascades, however, are more continental than those east of the Sierra Nevada or southern Cascades.

The climate of Daubenmire's *Agropyron spicatum* grassland seems to provide a longer growing season than the generally lower-lying sagebrush and a less variable growing season month by month in terms of actual water use.

Daubenmire's sagebrush (Table 6), that east of the Sierra Nevada (Table 4), and that still farther east (Table 5) show little correspondence in climates, but they are still differentiated by some features from the climates of other vegetation types. Remarkably, the *Agropyretalia spicati* climatic station chosen for northern California corresponds fairly well to the climate of Daubenmire's similar vegetation.

Pinyon-juniper vegetation is probably zonally controlled. It certainly often occurs in moister environments than the lower-lying sagebrush. Billings (1954) has suggested it occupies a warm belt above the valleys of the Great Basin. It also is more common on rocky sites which are naturally on mountain slopes rather than in valley bottoms, and it invades sagebrush or even meadows (*Elymetalia cinerei*) following overgrazing.

We bracket the northern juniper woodland between its mesic limit at Bend, Oregon (Fig. 17), with *Pinus ponderosa* and Redmond, Oregon (Fig. 18), where it is common (Driscoll, 1964).

Finally, the *Pinus aristata* type can be characterized climatically by the White Mountains subalpine station (Fig. 19). Although precipitation is half that in even the driest of Sierran-Cascade subalpine forests, AE is only some 50 mm a year, or a sixth, less. The big difference is S of less than two-thirds of the lower Sierran values. As the AE figures indicate, sagebrush can fit into even this environment, and it does. The curves of monthly AE are similar for the sagebrush vegetation of the lowlands and for that in this arid subalpine forest type.

Southern Desert Vegetation

Although a wide variety of vegetation is present in this hot and arid region, average climates are not strikingly different (Table 7), but all reflect the extreme heat and drought. Evidently *Larrea divaricata* dominates lowland zonal vegetation throughout the area—including both the Colorado Desert and most of the Mojave (Fig. 20). Major (1963a) has furnished a climatic diagram for Blythe in the Colorado Desert. AE is strictly equal to precipitation; no S occurs in the creosote bush vegetation. Surpluses do occur in the higher altitude and wetter Joshua tree vegetation.

Alkali sink vegetation is not well defined, but probably the climate of the *Atriplex polycarpa* type in the southwestern San Joaquin Valley differs from the creosote bush climate only in its slightly cooler temperatures.

It is difficult to obtain any climatic data in California on sites with *Coleogyne ramosissima* as zonal vegetation. According to Küchler (1964), Bluff, Utah, lies in this type of vegetation. PE is considerably less than in the creosote bush type. At least two months have mean temperatures below freezing. Probably the extreme continentality of the Utah sites does not hold for *Coleogyne* vegetation in California.

The Joshua tree forest climate (Fig. 21) has no months with average freezing temperatures and has at least double the AE of most creosote bush climates. In the Joshua tree climate, monthly precipitation and heat curves are so exactly out of phase that a small S results, although the dominant feature of the climate is its aridity.

Conclusion

There is no one-to-one correspondence between climates and vegetation types in the Western States. Climates of the habitats of particular kinds of vegetation have been described by means of physiologically pertinent climatic parameters.

The lack of correlation between climates and vegetation may be related to defects in classifying both the climate and the vegetation. The classification of climate is the best we have, however, being based on the logical interpretation from the data of plant physiology that plant growth is related to available soil water and heat. The classification of vegetation is, I believe, the subject of a general consensus based on field observations. But even if we confine our discussion to those environmental factors closely associated with climate—water and heat—our chosen climatic parameters cannot be fully adequate, because the factors of the environment interact to produce a result not easily predictable from the factors taken alone. The climate we have discussed is regional climate, not local climate (Major, 1951). Levels of available soil moisture and heat are clearly influenced by local climates, including groundwater levels and snow drifting as well as soil types (albedo, texture, structure, porosity, infiltration rate, depth, and nutrient status). The Thornthwaite system of describing climates allows scope for soil differences. Nash (1963) has shown how different the calculated water balance is on different slopes and exposures.

It might be thought desirable to use such factors as moisture, temperature, etc. which act directly on plants (Walter, 1960), but these have not been operationally useful parameters. A functional approach which seeks correlations, not causation, may be more fruitful.

Of the 29 broad vegetation types suggested by Munz and Keck (1959) as making up California's vegetation, at least a third occur in the same regional climate as another quite different type. These are, then, not primarily climatically determined. Of the types added by Knapp (1957, 1965) probably less than half are climatically determined. All these climatic types are probably distinct classes in the European terminology, or formations in a physiognomic sense.

REFERENCES

Arkley, R. J., 1963. Relationships between plant growth and transpiration. *Hilgardia, 34(13)*: 559–584.

Arkley, R. J., and R. Ulrich, 1962. The use of calculated actual and potential evapotranspiration for estimating potential plant growth. *Hilgardia, 32(1)*: 443–469.

Bierhuizen, J. F., and R. O. Slatyer, 1965. Effect of atmospheric concentrations of water vapour and CO_2 in determining transpiration-photosynthesis relationships of cotton leaves. *Agr. Meteorol., 2*: 259–270.

Billings, W. D., 1949. The shadscale vegetation zone of Nevada and eastern California in relation to climate and soils. *Am. Midland Naturalist, 42(1)*: 87–109.

Billings, W. D., 1954. Temperature inversions in the pinyon-juniper zone of a Nevada mountain range. *Butler Univ. Botan. Studies, 11*: 112–118.

Christ, H., 1879. *Das Pflanzenleben der Schweiz.* Schulthess, Zürich.

Conrad, V., 1946. Usual formulas of continentality and their limits of validity. *Am. Geophys. Union Trans., 27(5)*: 663–664.

Dahl, E., 1951. On the relations between summer temperature and distribution of alpine vascular plants in the lowlands of Fennoscandia. *Oikos, 3:* 22–52.

Daubenmire, R., 1942. An ecological study of the vegetation of southeastern Washington and adjacent Idaho. *Ecol. Monographs, 12(1):* 53–79.

Daubenmire, R., 1952. Forest vegetation of northern Idaho and adjacent Washington, and its bearing on concepts of vegetation classification. *Ecol. Monographs, 22:* 301–330.

Daubenmire, R., 1956. Climate as a determinant of vegetation distribution in eastern Washington and northern Idaho. *Ecol. Monographs, 26:* 131–154.

Driscoll, R. S., 1964. Vegetation-soil units in the central Oregon juniper zone. *Pacific Northwestern Forest and Range Exp. Sta., U.S. Forest Serv. Res. Paper PNW-19.*

Ellenberg, H., 1953. Physiologisches und Okologisches Verhalten derselben Pflanzenarten. *Ber. Deut. Botan. Ges., 65(10):* 350–361.

Ellenberg, H., 1956. Grundlagen der Vegetationsgliederung. I. Aufgaben und Methoden der Vegetationskunde. In *Einführung in die Phytologie,* edited by H. Walter; Bd. 4, Teil 1. Ulmer, Stuttgart, Germany.

Ellenberg, H., 1963. Vegetation Mitteleuropas mit den Alpen, in kausaler, dynamischer und historischer Sicht. In *Einführung in die Phytologie,* edited by H. Walter; Bd. 4, Teil 2. Ulmer, Stuttgart, Germany.

Eyre, S. R., 1963. *Vegetation and Soils, a World Picture;* pp. v–11. Edw. Arnold, London.

Faegri, K., 1960. *Coast Plants. Vol. 1. Maps of Distribution of Norwegian Vascular Plants,* edited by K. Faegri, O. Gjaerevoll, J. Lid, and R. Nordhagen; p. 22. Oslo Univ. Press, Oslo. Cf. 1965. *Ecology, 46(1/2):* 217–218.

Gankin, R., and J. Major, 1964. *Arctostaphylos myrtifolia,* its biology and relationship to the problem of endemism. *Ecology, 45(4):* 792–808.

Gaussen, H., 1954. Théories et classification des climats et microclimats. *Congr. Intern. Botan., 8e, Paris, Sect. 7 et 3:* 125–130.

Gleason, H. A., and A. Cronquist, 1964. *The Natural Geography of Plants.* Columbia Univ. Press, New York.

Holdridge, L. R., 1962. The determination of atmospheric water movements. *Ecology, 43:* 1–9.

Khromov, S. P., 1957. [On the question of continentality of climate]. *Izv. Vses. Geogr. Obshch., 89:* 221–225.

Knapp, R., 1954. *Experimentelle Soziologie der höheren Pflanzen.* Ulmer, Stuttgart, Germany. Cf. 1956. *Ecology, 37(3):* 623–624.

Knapp, R., 1957. Ueber die Gliederung der Vegetation von Nordamerika, höhere Vegetations-Einheiten. *Geobotan. Mitt. Univ. Köln,* Heft 4.

Knapp, R., 1965. *Die Vegetation von Nord- und Mittelamerika.* Fischer, Stuttgart, Germany.

Küchler, A. W., 1964. Potential natural vegetation of the coterminous U.S. *Am. Geograph. Soc. Spec. Publ., 36:* 1–37.

Major, J., 1951. A functional, factorial approach to plant ecology. *Ecology, 32:* 392–412.
Major, J., 1958. Plant ecology as a branch of botany. *Ecology, 39(2):* 352–363.
Major, J., 1961. Use in plant ecology of causation, physiology, and a definition of vegetation. *Ecology, 42(1):* 167–169.
Major, J., 1963a. A climatic index to vascular plant activity. *Ecology, 44(3):* 485–498.
Major, J., 1963b. Vegetation mapping in California. In *Bericht über das Internationale Symposion für Vegetationskartierung vom 23.–26. 3. 1959, in Stolzenau/Weser,* edited by R. Tüxen; pp. 195–218. Cramer, Weinheim, Germany.
Major, J., and W. T. Pyott, 1966. Buried, viable seeds in two California bunchgrass sites and their bearing on the definition of a flora. *Vegetatio, 13(5):* 253–282.
Mather, J. R., 1964. Average climatic water balance data of the continents. Part VII. United States. *Drexel Inst. Tech., Publ. in Climatology, 17(3):* 415–615.
Munz, P. A., and D. D. Keck, 1959. *A California Flora.* Univ. California Press, Berkeley, California.
Nash, A. J., 1963. A method for evaluating the effects of topography on the soil water balance. *Forest Sci., 9(4):* 413–422.
Penman, H. L., 1956. Estimating evaporation. *Am. Geophys. Union Trans., 37:* 43–50.
Russell, M. B., and L. W. Hurlbut, 1959. The agricultural water supply. *Advan. Agron., 11:* 6–19.
Schimper, A. F. W., 1898. *Pflanzengeographie auf Physiologischer Grundlage.* Gustav Fischer, Jena, Germany.
Swinbank, W. C., 1965. Discussion of G. Stanhill, The concept of potential evapotranspiration in arid zone agriculture. *Arid Zone Research, 25:* 109–117.
Thompson, K., 1961. Riparian forests of the Sacramento Valley, California. *Ann. Assoc. Am. Geograph., 51(3):* 294–315.
Thornthwaite, C. W., 1948. An approach toward a rational classification of climate. *Geograph. Rev., 38:* 55–94.
Thornthwaite, C. W., J. R. Mather, and D. B. Carter, 1957. Instructions and tables for computing potential evapotranspiration and the water balance. *Drexel Inst. Tech., Publ. in Climatology, 10(3):* 183–311.
Twisselmann, E. C., 1956. Flora of the Temblor Range. *Wasmann J. Biol., 14(2):* 161–300.
Walter, H., 1955. Klimagramme als Mittel zur Beurteilung der Klimaverhältnisse für ökologische, vegetationskundliche und landwirtschaftliche Zwecke. *Ber. Deut. Botan. Ges., 68:* 331–344.
Walter, H., 1960. Standortslehre. Grundlagen der Pflanzenverbreitung. In *Einführung in die Phytologie, 2nd ed.,* edited by H. Walter; Bd. 3, Teil 1. Ulmer, Stuttgart, Germany.
Walter, H., and H. Lieth, 1960–1964. *Klimadiagramm Weltatlas.* Fischer, Jena, Germany.

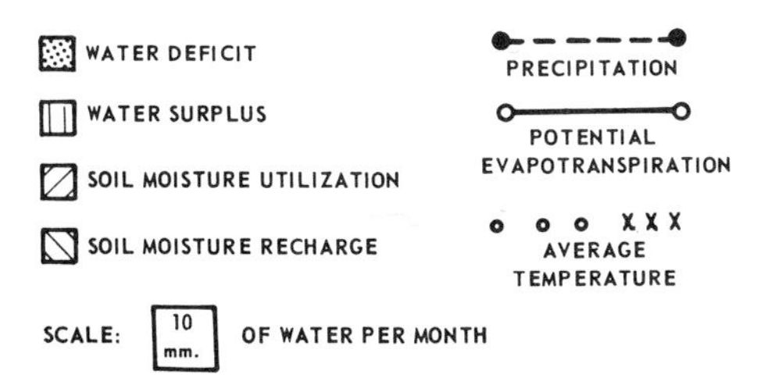

Fig. 1. Key to illustrations in this chapter.

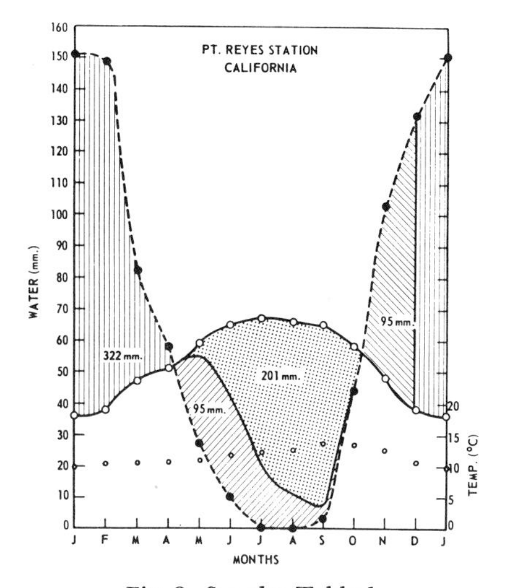

Fig. 2. See also Table 1.

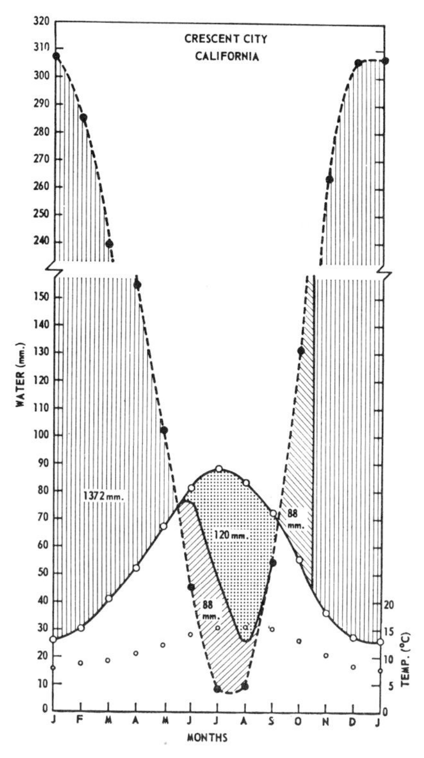

Fig. 3. See also Table 1.

Table 1. Coastal vegetation and its climates.

Vegetation type	Station	Lat. (°N)	Long. (°W)	Alt. (m)	Ppt. (mm)	Av. Temp. (°C)	PE (mm)	AE (mm)	Def. (mm)	Surplus (mm)	K
Coastal strand	Pt. Reyes Station	38°	123°	9	759	11.5	638	437	201	322	0.5
North coastal scrub	Eureka	40°08′	123°10′	13	918	11.3	645	460	185	458	2.0
Coastal prairie	Berkeley	37°52′	122°15′	91	616	14.0	693	384	309	232	4.9
Closed cone pine	Ft. Bragg	39°27′	123°48′	23	965	11.7	649	462	187	503	1.6
	Del Monte	36°36′	121°52′	12	376	13.9	706	338	368	38	3.5
Sitka spruce	Crescent City	41°45′	124°12′	11	1910	11.7	658	538	120	1372	3.9
Douglas fir	Los Gatos					(See Table 2)					
North coastal conifer	Port Orford, Oregon	42°45′	124°30′	20	1712	11.2	645	553	92	1159	3.5
	Forks, Washington	47°57′	124°22′	107	2997	9.5	624	604	20	2393	7.9
Redwood	Scotia	40°29′	124°06′	42	1223	12.8	686	459	227	764	4.3
	Branscomb	39°40′	123°38′	610	2091	11.8	673	483	190	1608	9.5
North coastal live oak	San Francisco	37°47′	122°25′	16	551	13.7	702	388	314	163	3.2
	Mt. Tamalpais	37°54′	122°34′	305	701	12.8	695	353	342	348	10.7
Coastal sagebrush	Pismo Beach	35°08′	120°38′	24	423	14.3	708	387	321	36	2.4
Chaparral	San Diego	32°44′	117°10′	6	262	15.9	785	262	522	0	5.0

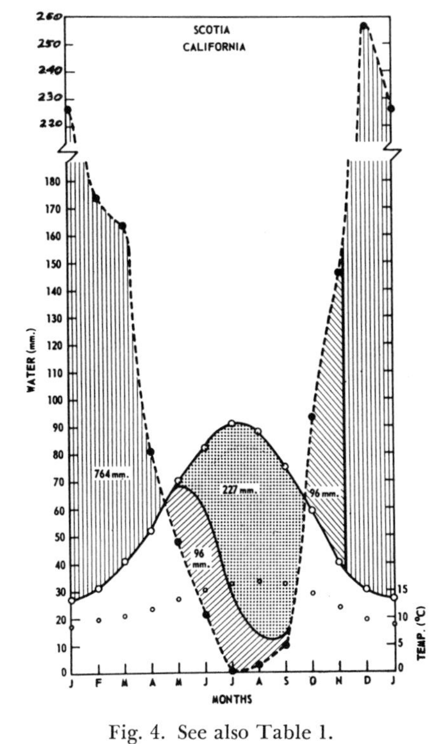

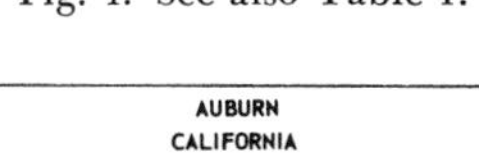
Fig. 4. See also Table 1.

Fig. 5. See also Table 2.

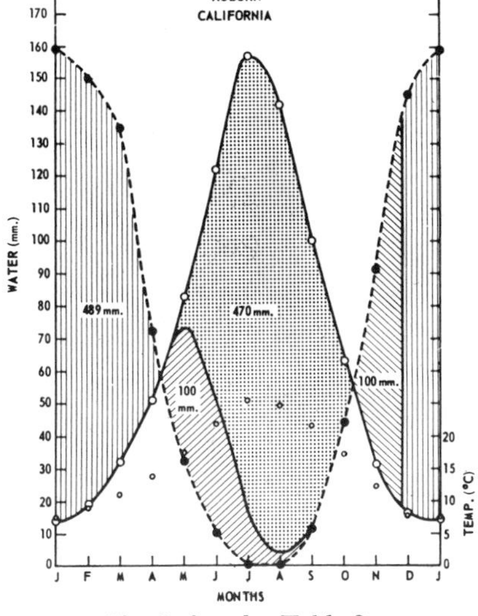

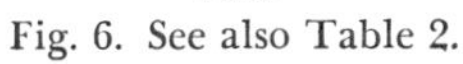
Fig. 6. See also Table 2.

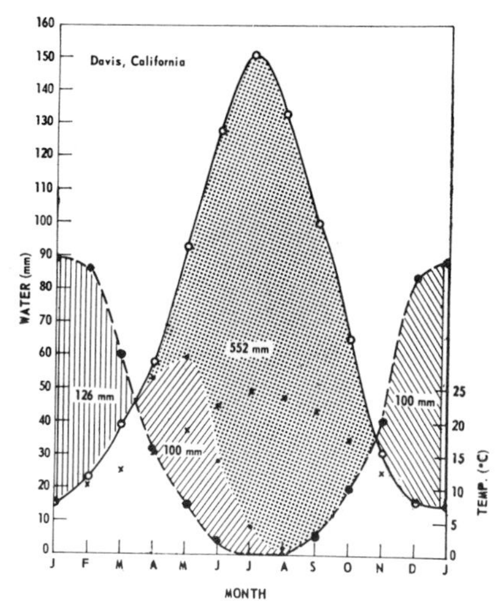

Fig. 7. See also Table 2.

Table 2. Central Valley vegetation and its climates.

Vegetation type	Station	Lat. (°N)	Long. (°W)	Alt. (m)	Ppt. (mm)	Av. Temp. (°C)	PE (mm)	AE (mm)	Def. (mm)	Surplus (mm)	K
Valley grassland	Putah Creek	38°30′	122°03′	56	484	16.3	876	304	572	180	14.6
	Fresno	36°46′	119°43′	101	236	16.8	905	236	669	0	16.9
Atriplex polycarpa	Middlewater	35°30′	119°49′	245	129	17.9	973	129	844	0	18.5
Chaparral	Ash Mtn.	36°29′	118°50′	530	696	17.5	974	375	617	339	17.6
Arctostaphylos myrtifolia	Ione	38°23′	120°57′	88	533	16.1	826	336	490	197	14.4
Foothill woodland	Rocklin	38°48′	121°15′	73	569	16.2	855	324	531	245	14.6
	Auburn	38°54′	121°04′	395	849	15.7	830	360	470	489	14.4
	Redding	40°35′	122°24′	173	948	17.2	919	405	514	543	16.9
	Mt. Hamilton	37°20′	121°39′	1310	744	11.5	672	315	357	429	13.5
	Sonora	37°59′	120°23′	556	847	15.4	825	367	458	480	15.3
	San Joaquin Exp. Sta.	37°05′	119°44′	450	513	15.7	874	282	592	231	17.7
	Average				737	15.3	830	342	487	402	15.2
Valley oak	Davis	38°33′	121°45′	15	426	16.3	852	300	552	126	13.2
	Woodland	38°41′	121°46′	19	444	16.7	873	305	568	139	14.2
	Sacramento	38°55′	121°30′	8	416	16.1	846	305	541	111	13.4
	Average				429	16.4	857	303	554	125	13.6
Northern oak woodland	Ukiah	39°09′	123°12′	198	908	14.3	754	368	386	540	11.7
	Cloverdale	38°49′	123°01′	104	1014	15.4	824	414	410	600	10.2
	Hat Creek	40°56′	121°33′	919	467	10.9	685	308	377	159	16.4
Mixed evergreen forest	Los Gatos	37°14′	121°58′	152	777	14.6	743	369	374	408	8.2
Southern oak woodland	Pasadena	34°09′	118°03′	264	506	16.8	883	368	515	138	8.4
	Palomar Mtn.	33°21′	116°51′	1696	647	13.1	722	294	428	353	13.9

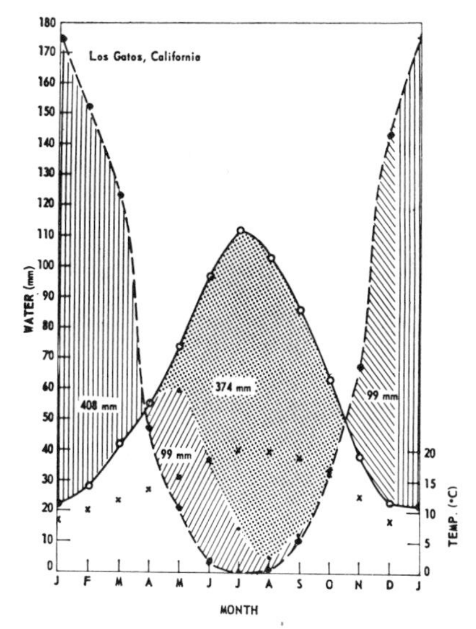

Fig. 8. See also Table 2.

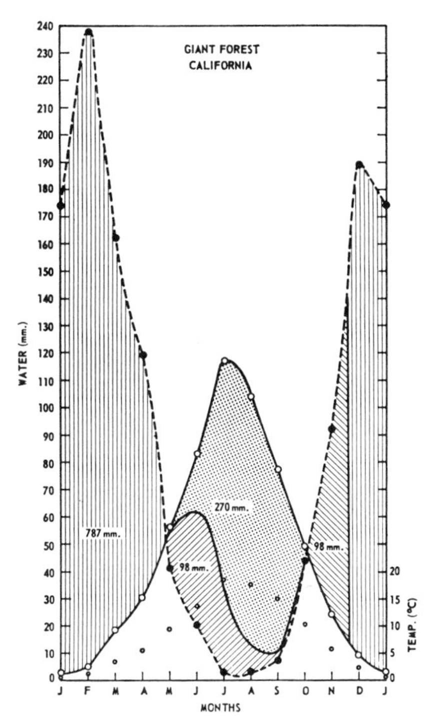

Fig. 9. See also Table 3.

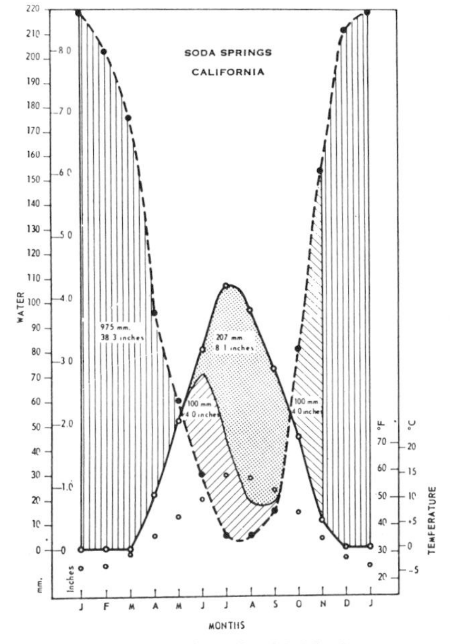

Fig. 10. See also Table 3.

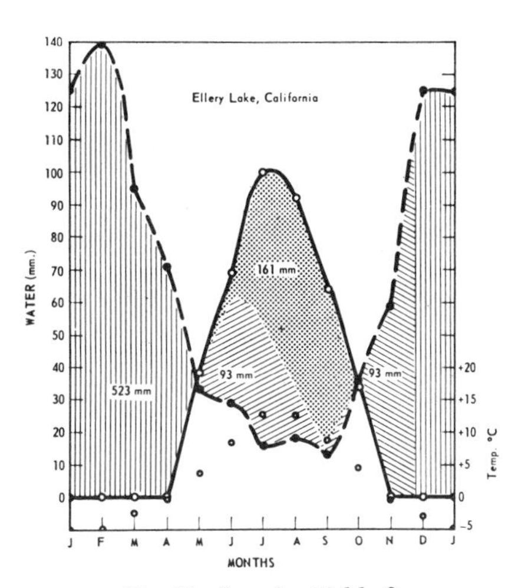

Fig. 11. See also Table 3.

Table 3. Sierran vegetation and its climates.

Vegetation type	Station	Lat. (°N)	Long. (°W)	Alt. (m)	Ppt. (mm)	Av. Temp. (°C)	PE (mm)	AE (mm)	Def. (mm)	Surplus (mm)	K
Ponderosa Pine	Auburn	38°54′	121°04′	395	849	15.7	830	360	470	489	14.4
	Placerville	38°44′	120°49′	586	1056	13.1	715	379	336	677	15.0
	Colfax	39°06′	120°58′	736	1179	14.7	793	394	399	785	15.0
	Nevada City	39°16′	121°02′	790	1325	12.0	688	393	295	932	12.4
	Mt. Shasta City	41°19′	122°19′	1080	897	9.6	628	354	274	543	15.6
	Average				1056	13.0	730	375	355	685	14.5
Mixed conifer forest	Yosemite	37°45′	119°35′	1214	839	11.8	659	355	304	484	16.4
	Hetch Hetchy	37°57′	119°47′	1230	887	11.9	685	362	323	525	16.2
	Lake Eleanor	37°57′	119°53′	1423	1082	11.4	657	343	314	739	15.8
	Lake Spaulding	38°19′	120°38′	1571	1693	8.8	602	376	226	1317	13.0
	Blue Canyon	39°16′	120°43′	1610	1382	10.1	620	353	267	1029	14.3
	Average				1177	10.8	645	358	287	819	15.1
East side ponderosa pine	Donner Mem. St. Park	39°19′	120°14′	1809	1022	5.5	488	283	205	739	15.6
	Tahoe City	39°10′	120°09′	1900	754	5.8	501	244	257	510	15.4
	Truckee	39°20′	120°11′	1822	702	6.5	530	233	297	469	17.4
	Woodfords	38°47′	119°49′	1730	510	9.4	621	258	363	252	17.1
	Twin Lakes	38°42′	120°03′	2420	1058	4.2	452	277	175	781	15.1
	Susanville	40°22′	120°34′	1220	483	9.9	639	262	377	196	18.5
	Hat Creek	40°56′	121°33′	919	467	10.9	685	308	377	159	16.4
	Bend, Oregon	44°04′	121°19′	1098	332	7.9	580	266	314	66	14.8
	Average				666	8.4	562	266	296	396	16.3

Table 3 (continued)

Vegetation type	Station	Lat. (°N)	Long. (°W)	Alt. (m)	Ppt. (mm)	Av. Temp. (°C)	PE (mm)	AE (mm)	Def. (mm)	Surplus (mm)	K
Big tree	Giant Forest	36°34′	118°46′	1940	1092	8.6	575	305	270	787	14.5
Red fir	Huntington Lake	37°13′	119°14′	2140	775	6.5	509	262	247	513	14.1
	Soda Springs	39°19′	120°23′	2060	1256	4.8	488	281	207	975	15.2
Subalpine forest	Crater Lake, Oregon	42°54′	122°08′	1974	1369	4.0	431	322	109	1047	13.1
	Paradise, Mt. Rainier, Washington	46°47′	121°44′	1690	2963	3.6	453	436	17	2527	11.5
	Gem Lake	37°45′	119°08′	2780	623	5.2	479	248	231	375	15.1
	Ellery Lake	37°56′	119°14′	2930	760	2.2	397	236	161	523	14.4
Alpine	Do., timberline	38°	119°	3230	994	+0.8	367	250	117	744	14.4
	Do., Dana Plateau	38°	119°	3770	1534	−2.4	272	226	46	1308	14.4
	White Mts. Alpine	37°55′	118°15′	3800	368	−2.4	274	180	94	188	13.8

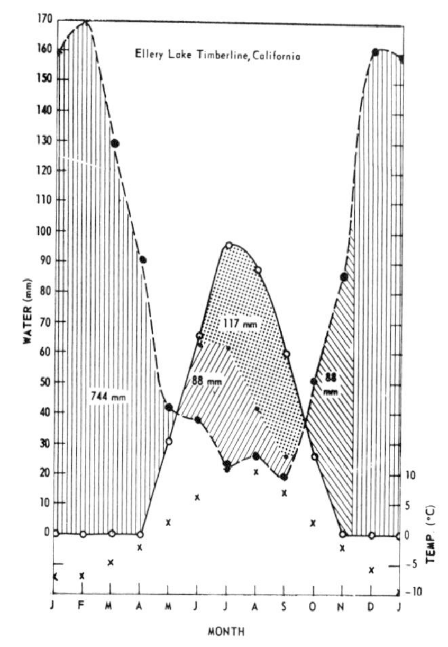

Fig. 12. See also Table 3.

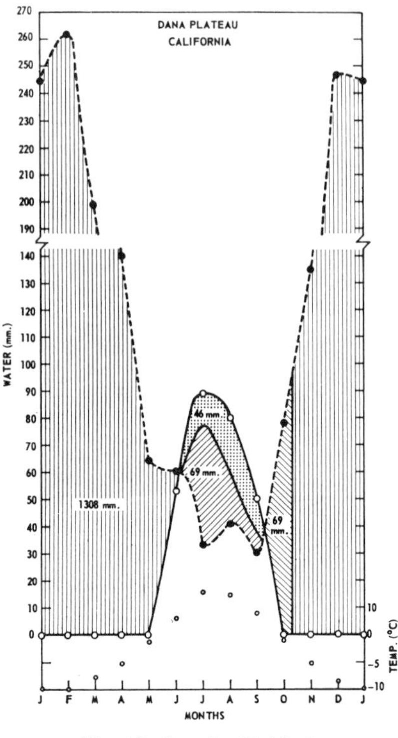

Fig. 13. See also Table 3.

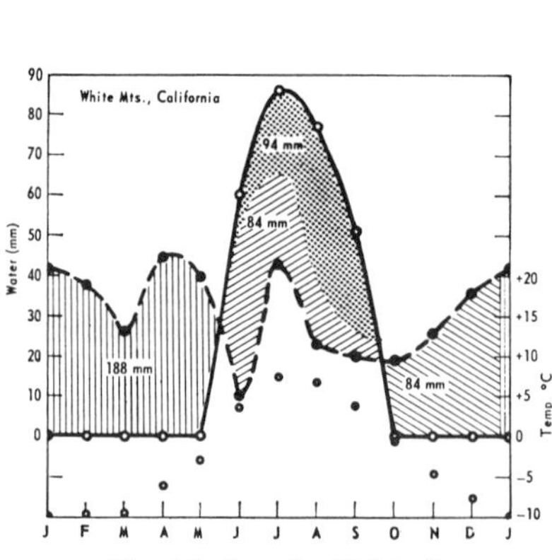

Fig. 14. See also Table 3.

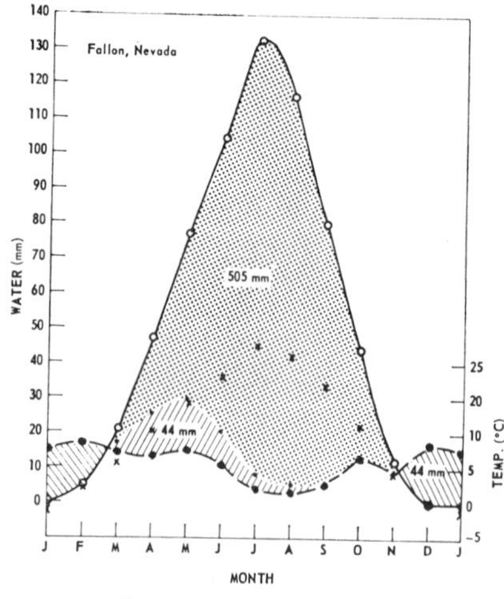

Fig. 15. See also Table 4.

Table 4. Northern Great Basin vegetation and its climates.

Vegetation type	Station	Lat. (°N)	Long. (°W)	Alt. (m)	Ppt. (mm)	Av. Temp. (°C)	PE (mm)	AE (mm)	Def. (mm)	Surplus (mm)	K
Shadscale	Lahontan, Nevada	39°28′	119°04′	1280	112	12.1	551	112	439	0	22.2
	Fallon, Nevada	39°27′	118°47′	1210	136	10.3	641	136	505	0	20.2
	Mina, Nevada	38°23′	118°06′	1326	98	12.0	728	98	630	0	22.5
	Lovelock, Nevada	40°12′	118°28′	1212	103	10.3	679	103	576	0	21.8
	Yerington, Nevada	38°59′	119°10′	1332	123	10.1	647	123	524	0	19.1
	Average				114	11.0	649	114	535	0	21.2
Sagebrush	Bridgeport Dam	38°19′	119°13′	1960	267	6.4	530	198	332	69	19.5
	Reno Airport, Nevada	39°30′	119°47′	1340	178	9.7	632	178	454	0	17.9
	Carson City, Nevada	39°10′	119°46′	1426	283	9.8	625	217	408	66	17.1
	Minden, Nevada	38°57′	119°46′	1432	250	9.9	634	218	416	32	17.6
	Winnemucca, Nevada	40°58′	117°44′	1309	217	9.1	617	217	400	0	19.8
	Elko, Nevada	40°50′	115°47′	1549	246	7.8	590	230	360	16	22.1
	Average				240	8.8	604	210	395	30	19.0
Elymetalia cinerei	Wells, Nevada	41°07′	114°58′	1718	246	7.2	574	212	362	34	22.8
Agropyretalia spicati	Yreka	41°43′	122°38′	800	441	11.0	664	275	389	166	17.7
Pinyon-juniper	Austin, Nevada	39°30′	117°04′	2021	300	8.4	585	269	316	31	20.0
Northern juniper woodland	Alturas	41°29′	120°32′	1330	321	8.2	575	260	315	61	18.0
	Redmond, Oregon	44°18′	121°10′	906	216	9.0	610	216	394	0	15.2
	Bend, Oregon	44°04′	121°19′	1098	332	7.9	580	266	314	66	14.8
Pinus aristata	White Mts. subalpine	37°30′	118°10′	3100	308	1.8	354	192	162	116	15.7

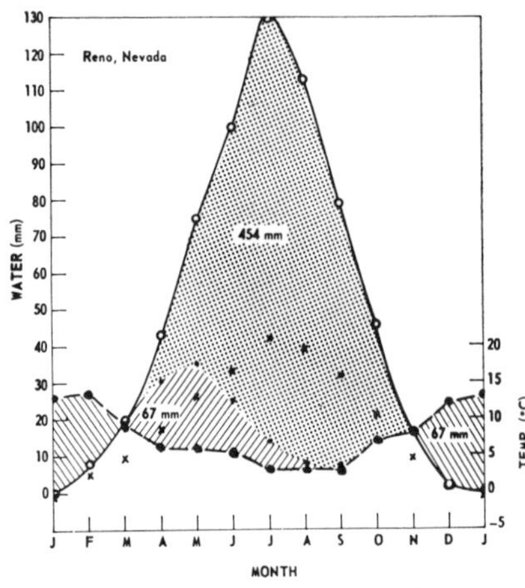

Fig. 16. See also Table 4.

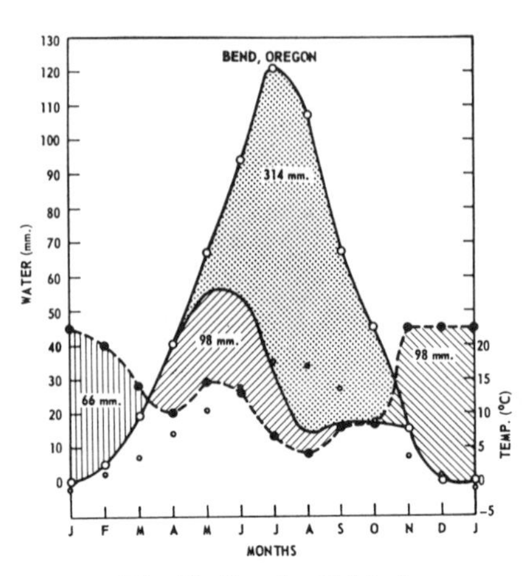

Fig. 17. See also Table 4.

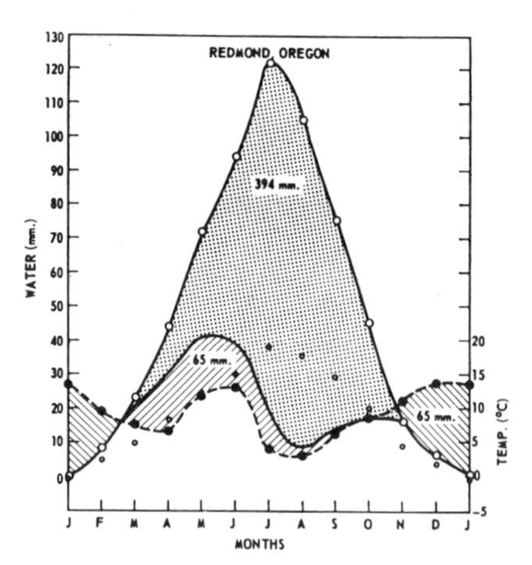

Fig. 18. See also Table 4.

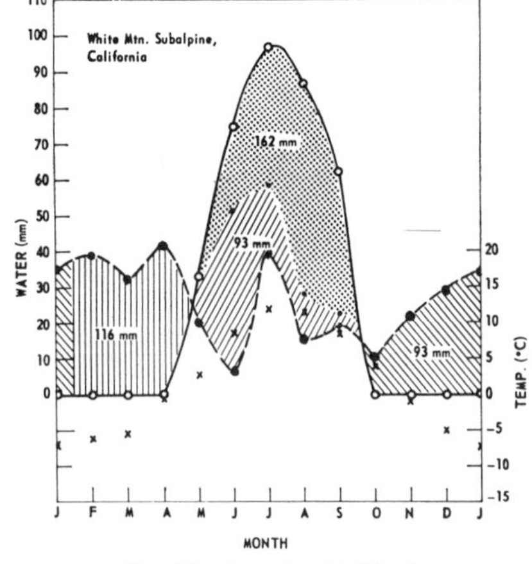

Fig. 19. See also Table 4.

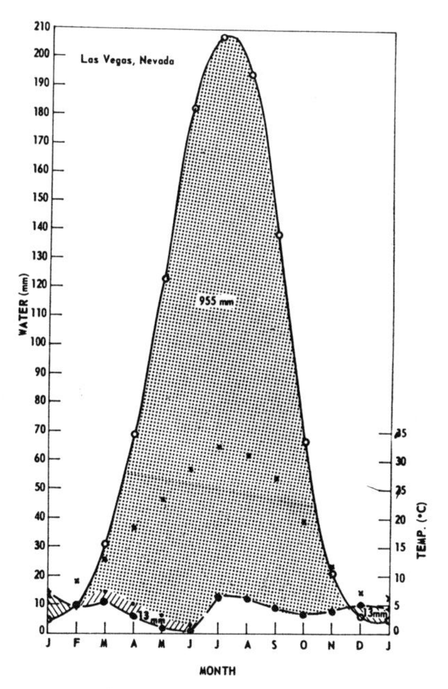

Fig. 20. See also Table 7.

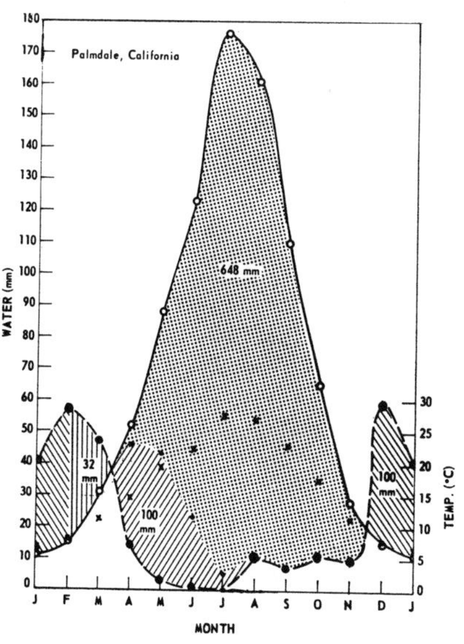

Fig. 21. See also Table 7.

Table 5. Northern desert shrub vegetation in the eastern part of its range and its climates.

Vegetation type	Station	Lat. (°N)	Long. (°W)	Alt. (m)	Ppt. (mm)	Av. Temp. (°C)	PE (mm)	AE (mm)	Def. (mm)	Surplus (mm)	K
Shadscale	Wendover, Utah	40°44′	114°02′	1291	120	11.3	744	120	624	0	25.6
	Green River, Utah	39°00′	110°09′	1246	157	11.4	743	157	586	0	27.6
	Thompsons, Utah	38°59′	109°43′	1570	212	11.6	732	212	520	0	25.4
	Rangeley, Colorado	40°05′	108°40′	1539	255	6.7	595	255	340	0	26.8
	Grand Junction, Colorado	39°07′	108°32′	1478	215	11.3	740	215	525	0	25.6
	Average				192	10.5	711	192	519	0	26.2
Sagebrush	Dubois, Wyoming	43°33′	109°37′	2108	230	4.7	474	230	244	0	18.2
	Kemmerer, Wyoming	41°48′	110°32′	2120	240	4.3	505	240	265	0	22.3
	Provo, Utah	40°13′	111°42′	1356	387	9.6	640	325	315	62	22.0
	Salt Lake City, Utah	40°46′	111°58′	1286	393	10.5	706	326	380	67	24.1
	Ogden, Utah	41°15′	111°56′	1341	407	10.2	663	323	340	84	22.6
	Logan, Utah	41°44′	111°49′	1456	414	9.3	631	336	295	78	24.0
	Evanston, Wyoming	41°16′	110°57′	2091	362	4.1	490	297	193	65	21.7
	Dubois, Idaho	44°15′	112°12′	1665	282	6.1	385	243	142	39	24.9
	Pinedale, Wyoming	42°52′	109°51′	2186	283	2.0	456	269	187	14	23.9
	Jackson, Wyoming	43°28′	110°46′	1903	442	3.3	481	331	150	111	22.3
	Fillmore, Utah	38°59′	112°19′	1600	368	11.3	693	326	367	42	23.2
	LaSal, Utah	38°19′	109°15′	2065	305	7.7	572	305	267	0	21.2
	Monticello, Utah	37°52′	109°20′	2154	461	8.2	569	360	209	101	20.7
	Average				373	7.0	571	313	259	66	22.4

Table 6. Some xeric vegetation of eastern Washington and adjacent Idaho and its climates (See Daubenmire, 1956).

Vegetation type	Station	Lat. (°N)	Long. (°W)	Alt. (m)	Ppt. (mm)	Av. Temp. (°C)	PE (mm)	AE (mm)	Def. (mm)	Surplus (mm)	K
Sagebrush	Prosser, Washington	46°15′	119°45′	259	187	10.6	697	187	510	0	18.9
	Ephrata, Washington	47°19′	119°33′	389	196	11.2	737	196	541	0	24.2
	Davenport, Washington	47°39′	118°09′	747	323	7.9	600	266	334	57	20.0
	Lind, Washington	47°00′	118°35′	492	372	9.9	679	359	320	13	20.5
	Average				270	9.9	678	252	426	17	20.9
Agropyron spicatum	Pomeroy, Washington	46°28′	117°35′	579	443	10.1	670	322	348	121	17.3
	Lewistown, Idaho	46°23′	117°01′	431	338	11.1	687	338	349	0	20.8
	Walla Walla, Washington	46°02′	118°20′	289	410	11.6	748	339	409	71	19.0
	Riggins, Idaho	45°25′	116°19′	513	385	12.6	674	370	304	15	19.7
	Average				394	11.3	695	342	352	52	19.2
Pinus ponderosa	Kooskia, Idaho	46°09′	115°59′	384	597	10.6	673	431	242	166	19.1
	Spokane, Washington	47°37′	117°31′	718	410	8.7	625	285	340	125	19.0
	Leavenworth, Washington	47°36′	120°39′	354	494	8.8	639	253	386	241	21.0
	Average				500	9.4	646	323	323	177	19.7

Table 7. Southern hot desert vegetation and its climates.

Vegetation type	Station	Lat. (°N)	Long. (°W)	Alt. (m)	Ppt. (mm)	Av. Temp. (°C)	PE (mm)	AE (mm)	Def. (mm)	Surplus (mm)	K
Creosote bush	Barstow	34°54′	117°02′	196	104	17.7	933	104	829	0	18.1
	Indio	33°43′	116°14′	6	78	22.9	1275	78	1191	0	19.9
	Las Vegas, Nevada	36°05′	115°10′	658	102	18.9	1057	102	955	0	22.8
	Blythe	33°37′	114°36′	81	101	21.4	1168	101	1067	0	18.7
	Imperial	32°51′	115°34′	−6	93	22.4	1201	93	1108	0	18.1
	Average				96	20.7	1127	96	1030	0	19.5
Alkali sink	Middlewater	35°30′	119°49′	245	129	17.9	973	129	844	0	18.5
	Cow Creek	36°32′	116°53′	−14	53	24.9	1381	53	1328	0	24.0
Joshua tree forest	Palmdale	34°34′	118°07′	810	259	16.3	875	227	648	32	17.7
Coleogynetalia	Bluff, Utah	37°17′	109°35′	1317	183	13.1	776	183	593	0	24.8

Orange Fruit Maturity and Net Heat Accumulations

J. E. NEWMAN, *Department of Agronomy, Purdue University, Lafayette, Indiana*

W. C. COOPER, *Crops Research Division, Agricultural Research Service, U. S. Department of Agriculture, Orlando, Florida*

W. REUTHER, *Department of Horticultural Science, University of California, Riverside, California*

G. A. CAHOON, *Ohio Agricultural Research and Development Center, Wooster, Ohio*

A. PEYNADO, *Crops Research Division, Agricultural Research Service, U. S. Department of Agriculture, Weslaco, Texas*

RELATING OBSERVED RESPONSES of plants to some measured expression of climate is not new. In fact, relating the growth, development, and maturity of various agricultural crops to observed seasonal climatic changes dates back to the earliest records of ancient civilizations. In a modern scientific sense, however, the thermal constant concept (Reaumur, 1735) could certainly be regarded as a milestone.

If one reads any reasonable portion of the existing literature on the general subject of plant-climate indexes, one wonders why no approach has gained wide application. This problem was discussed by Wang in his 1960 study when he wrote, "In spite of the many intensive investigations conducted over two centuries, the heat-unit system (meaning degree-hour or degree-day accumulations) has been subjected to serious criticisms." In 1952, Thornthwaite pointed out one of the big flaws in the degree-hour approach, the difficulty of establishing correct values for the threshold temperatures, that is, the proper base and ceiling temperature values. A second point equally important in most literature is the fact that the basic measurement in almost all indexes is merely air temperature and not a true heat measurement. This is generally the case for the heat-unit system approach. Technically, this term, heat-unit, meaning a temperature-time unit accumulation, is a misnomer. The same is true for most photothermal units and the various remainder index methods, as well as the several exponential indexing systems based on the Van't Hoff principle.

In recent years, several workers have raised the question of whether more meaningful plant-climate indexes can be developed from the more basic radiational measurements rather than the conventional temperature measurements. Gates came to grips with some of the basic concepts of this question in his 1962 treatise, *The Energy Exchanges in the Biosphere*. It was Gates's treatment of the basic radiational energy exchanges within a given plant leaf environment that inspired the senior author to apply some of the procedures reported in this study.

The central objective of this study was to understand some of the possible climatic causes of the wide variations within and between seasons in the flowering, growth, and maturity patterns of citrus fruits observed among the various citrus-growing regions in the United States. Within the continental limits there exists a wide variety of subtropical climates, ranging from completely arid deserts to humid rain forests. Several of the world's most widely grown citrus varieties are produced throughout the gamut of these subtropical climates. In the peninsula of Florida, citrus production takes place under humid climates with an annual rainfall of 50 to 60 inches. By contrast, the arid areas of Arizona and southern California produce citrus under irrigation where the mean annual rainfall is less than five inches. There are many gradations between these extremes, such as the mediterranean types of the coastal and valley regions of California and the steppe climate of the lower Rio Grande Valley in Texas. All these areas fall within the general classification of subtropical and can produce citrus. Yet there are some striking differences when they are considered in detail.

The effects of climate on the growth and maturity of citrus fruits among these various geographic regions of production has been understood in a gross way by horticulturists, growers, and commercial interests for some time. On the other hand, the specific mechanisms of just how the various aspects of climate influence the production and quality of fruit, as well as the adaptation of varieties and species, are largely beyond scientific understanding. For example, the excellent table quality of the grapefruit in the lower Rio Grande Valley of Texas and the Indian River section of Florida is generally recognized. The highest quality of navel oranges grow mostly in the valleys and deserts of California and Arizona, while the Temple orange reaches its peak fruit quality in Florida. Such dominant adaptation patterns of species as well as varieties used in commercial production justified an extensive investigation of just how climate affects the growth, maturity, and quality of citrus fruit.

Methods and Procedures

A five-year study concerning the effect of climate on the growth and maturity of the citrus crop was initiated in the spring of 1960. Data were collected at selected locations within all major geographic areas of continental United States where citrus is grown commercially. To reduce the complexity of the study, data collecting was limited to that of the sweet orange (*Citrus sinensis* L.). For the sake of genetic uniformity, data collecting was further restricted to the Valencia variety. The Valencia orange is grown extensively in all major citrus-producing areas. Its use enabled the investigators to eliminate variety and species variations from consideration of those of an environmental nature.

Both detailed phenological and climatic data were logged routinely. Numerous measurements were made during the first days of each biweekly period during the phenological crop-year, to assess the state of the trees as well as the growth and maturity of the fruit. Concurrently, biweekly climatic data were collected on the four major atmospheric energy-transfer parameters of radiant energy, wind, humidity, and sensible temperature. In addition, routine observations were made on soil moisture, soil temperature, and rainfall.

These data were subjected to a massive time and space analysis. The first step in the analysis was that of data reduction. Since the phenological measurements were taken biweekly, all climatic data were reduced to biweekly values as well.

Data collecting began on March 1, 1960. Figure 1 illustrates the

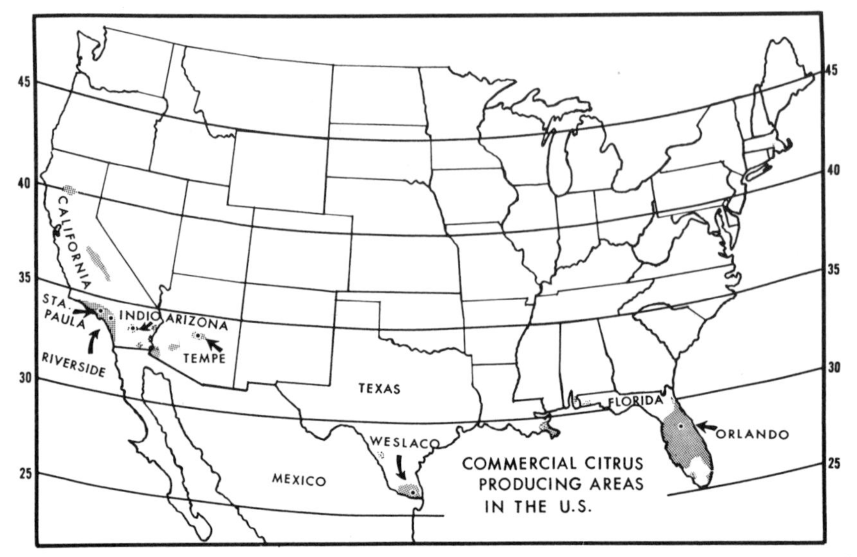

Fig. 1. Data collection locations within six major citrus-producing areas in the United States.

geographic sampling points. The climatic and phenological data representing the humid subtropical climates of the Florida peninsula were collected near Orlando. Data representing the steppe subtropical climate of the lower Rio Grande Valley in Texas were collected near Weslaco. The low subtropical desert production areas of southern California and Arizona are represented by Indio. Data representing the continentally modified mediterranean climates found in the valleys of California are represented by Riverside. Mediterranean climates of the coastal areas in California are represented by Santa Paula.

Since the mean blooming date in all geographic regions commonly falls within a 60-day period following March 1 each year, this date was chosen for the beginning of both the phenological and climatic year. The first biweekly period covered March 1 to March 15, extending through 26 such 14-day periods, with the last ending February 27, thus completing a phenological crop-year.

The first date reporting observed bloom in each phenological year at each location was used as the beginning blooming date; the ending date was the time that petal fall was complete. The mean of these two dates was used as the official mid-bloom date.

Measurements of fruit growth were obtained biweekly beginning with the fruit at three centimeters in diameter, that is, about the size of golf balls. A special hand tool consisting of a wooden handle attached to a steel measuring tape calibrated in centimeters was designed for this purpose. The tape was looped snugly around the fruit at the point of greatest circumference. Twenty-four fruits were measured in each orchard sampled. From such measurements fruit growth in volume was computed by a method developed by Taylor and Furr in 1937. The resulting values were plotted against biweekly dates. The dates of 25, 50, 75, and 100 cm^3 volume were interpolated from graphs of fruit volume growth against time.

Sampling for fruit analysis began on November 1, 1964, in Florida and Texas and continued until June 1, 1965, at Santa Paula, California. The fruit samples were obtained by picking one to three fruits from each of several trees. All fruits were obtained from trees at a height of from five to seven feet, uniformly distributed in the four quadrants of the canopy. This procedure was repeated for each of several orchards within each of six major citrus-producing areas of the United States. These orchards were selected to represent the climatic and cultural conditions of the key orchard in which the climatic observations were taken in each particular geographic area.

The sample trees in each orchard were identified with tapes so that subsequent monthly sampling could be taken from the same trees in each orchard. These trees were all of the Valencia variety, budded on sweet or sour orange rootstock, and were between thirty and thirty-five years old.

The samples sent to the Citrus Research Center, University of California, Riverside, and the Weslaco and Orlando laboratories were analyzed for diameter size, rind thickness, color of rind and flesh, percentage of juice by weight, percentage of total soluble solids, percentage of citric acid, and percentage of ascorbic acid. Percentage of total soluble solids was read directly from a refractometer. Citric acid was titrated against a NaOH (sodium hydroxide) base. Harding *et al.* (1940) offer a more complete discussion of these methods and procedures. Fruits were arbitrarily considered mature when the percentage of total soluble solids and the percentage of total acids in the juice reached a 9 to 1 ratio.

The climatic data were obtained from spot microclimate stations designed by Foxboro. These instrument packages were exposed some seven feet above the soil surface within well-maintained mature Valencia orange orchards. Well-packed bare ground was maintained at the exposure site. The sensing elements included sensible air temperature, wet-bulb temperature, wind, and radiant black-globe temperatures. Data were recorded continuously.

Estimated daily radiant energy available was derived from bi-hourly black-globe temperatures minus sensible air temperatures as recorded by the spot climate stations. The following equations were used to calculate radiant energy levels.

$$MRT, °F = [(t_g + 460)^4 + 1.028 \sqrt{V} (t_g - t_a)]^{1/4} - 460, \quad (1)$$

where MRT = mean radiant temperature,

t_g = black-globe temperature in °F,

V = wind in feet per minute,

t_a = temperature of air in °F,

and $$MRT, °F = (MRT, °C + 273)^4 \times \sigma, \quad (2)$$

and $$(MRT, °C + 273)^4 \times \sigma = \text{cal/cm}^2 \text{ per min}, \quad (3)$$

where $\sigma = 0.817 \times 10^{-10}$ cal /cm^2 per min/°K^4.

For a detailed account of the mathematical derivation of these mean radiant temperature calculations for equations (1), (2), and (3) the reader may refer to the 1955 findings of Bond and Kelly. (K = Kelvin, or absolute temperature scale.)

From equations (1), (2), and (3) a radiant heat flux to and from the black globe was determined for each bi-hourly period. The resulting radiant heat values in calories (cal) per cm^2 per minute were multiplied by the appropriate number of minutes resulting in an estimated number of calories for each bi-hourly period. All bi-hourly values for each day were added to give an estimated total cal per cm^2 per day.

The degree-hour accumulations were derived from bi-hourly readings of sensible temperatures as recorded by the spot climate stations.

Daily values were computed from the 12 bi-hourly values of sensible temperature by the following equation:

$$DH = (T_s > 55 < 95 \times 2) + \Sigma^n{}_i, \quad (4)$$

where DH = degree-hours,

T_s = sensible temperature,

i = bi-hourly readings of T_s,

n = number of bi-hourly readings in each 24 hours recording above 55°F and below 95° F.

From equations (1), (2), and (3) heat indexes in cal per cm² per day were computed for the various recorded phenological periods of growth and maturity of the fruit. From equation (4) degree-hour accumulation indexes were computed for the same periods. These computations were repeated for all geographic crop-years involved in this study. These index values were subjected to an analysis of variance. Several standard statistical expressions were computed from these analyses, which included the standard errors (S.E.) and coefficients of variation (C.V.) reported in Tables 1, 2, 3, 4, 5, and 6.

Table 1. The degree-hour accumulation between 55° and 95°F for each major phenological growth period as well as the resulting total for each crop-year from 1961 through 1965, for Valencia orange fruit growth and maturity at Santa Paula, California.

Phenological year	Bloom to 25 cm³ (hours)	25 cm³ to 100 cm³ (hours)	100 cm³ to 9-1 ratio (hours)	Bloom to 9-1 ratio (hours)
1961–62	19,516	25,428	19,660	64,604
1962–63	19,897	20,898	14,674	55,469
1963–64	20,047	20,886	18,990	59,923
1964–65	20,515	18,377	21,366	60,258
S.E.	207	1,469	1,424	1,866
C.V.%	2	14	15	6

Table 2. The net heat accumulation in calories per square centimeter per minute above the mean radiant temperature of 50°F for each major phenological growth period as well as the resulting total for each crop-year from 1961 through 1965, for Valencia orange fruit growth and maturity at Santa Paula, California.

Phenological year	Bloom to 25 cm^3 (cal)	25 cm^3 to 100 cm^3 (cal)	100 cm^3 to 9-1 ratio (cal)	Bloom to 9-1 ratio (cal)
1961–62	22,233	24,351	29,403	75,987
1962–63	24,010	26,807	20,502	71,319
1963–64	23,122	21,149	32,720	76,991
1964–65	23,270	19,686	26,611	69,567
S.E.	366	1,600	2,590	1,793
C.V.%	3	14	19	5

Table 3. The degree-hour accumulation between 55° and 95°F for each major phenological growth period as well as the resulting total for each of five geographic locations of commercial Valencia orange production in the United States during the 1964–1965 crop-year.

Location	Bloom to 25 cm^3 (hours)	25 cm^3 to 100 cm^3 (hours)	100 cm^3 to 9-1 ratio (hours)	Bloom to 9-1 ratio (hours)
Orlando, Fla.	23,284	51,259	45,966	120,509
Weslaco, Tex.	33,022	63,162	46,756	142,940
Indio, Calif.	22,259	75,431	25,060	120,750
Riverside, Calif.	32,888	30,089	10,389	73,366
Santa Paula, Calif.	20,515	18,377	21,366	60,258
S.E.	1,214	4,681	3,192	7,015
C.V.%	23	49	53	34

Table 4. The net heat accumulation in calories per square centimeter per minute above the mean radiant temperature of 50°F for each major phenological growth period as well as the resulting total for each of five geographic locations of commercial Valencia orange production in the United States during the 1964–1965 crop-year.

Location	Bloom to 25 cm³ (cal)	25 cm³ to 100 cm³ (cal)	100 cm³ to 9-1 ratio (cal)	Bloom to 9-1 ratio (cal)
Orlando, Fla.	14,065	26,270	32,397	72,732
Weslaco, Tex.	17,245	28,036	23,835	69,116
Indio, Calif.	17,838	37,457	22,395	77,690
Riverside, Calif.	24,534	25,132	19,225	68,891
Santa Paula, Calif.	23,270	19,686	26,611	69,567
S.E.	1,961	2,893	2,222	1,673
C.V.%	23	24	20	5

Table 5. The net heat accumulation in calories per square centimeter per minute above the mean radiant temperature of 50°F for each major phenological growth period as well as the resulting total for each of four geographic locations of commercial Valencia orange production in the United States during the 1963–1964 crop-year.

Location	Bloom to 25 cm³ (cal)	25 cm³ to 100 cm³ (cal)	100 cm³ to 9-1 ratio (cal)	Bloom to 9-1 ratio (cal)
Weslaco, Tex.	17,366	17,802	31,120	66,288
Indio, Calif.	23,342	35,935	19,768	79,045
Riverside, Calif.	21,507	30,889	19,802	72,198
Santa Paula, Calif.	23,123	21,148	32,720	76,991
S.E.	1,385	4,209	3,520	2,835
C.V.%	13	32	27	8

Table 6. The net heat accumulation in calories per square centimeter per minute above the mean radiant temperature of 50°F for each major phenological growth period as well as the resulting total for each of three geographic locations of commercial Valencia orange production in the United States during the 1962–1963 crop-year.

Location	Bloom to 25 cm^3 (cal)	25 cm^3 to 100 cm^3 (cal)	100 cm^3 to 9-1 ratio (cal)	Bloom to 9-1 ratio (cal)
Orlando, Fla.	16,227	19,083	35,181	70,491
Indio, Calif.	18,393	33,079	23,399	74,871
Santa Paula, Calif.	24,010	26,807	20,502	71,319
S.E.	2,319	4,048	4,489	1,343
C.V.%	21	27	29	3

Discussion

The meteorological purpose of a sensible air temperature measurement is to record the temperature of the atmospheric gases. To accomplish this purpose the measurement must be properly shielded from solar and terrestrial radiation. Yet, plant and soil surfaces under natural conditions are always exposed in varying degrees to these same heat loads. The fact that soil and plant surfaces exposed to these radiant heat loads can and do deviate considerably from the heat levels as indicated by sensible air temperatures has long been understood. Just how much these changes in net heat loads affect crops remains largely unanswered.

In his 1963 and 1964 work Gates discussed leaf and air temperature departures on a theoretical basis. He postulated that reradiation of a living leaf can be approximated by the following:

$$R_1 = \epsilon \, \sigma \, (t_a + \Delta t)^4, \tag{5}$$

where R_1 = radiant flux,

ϵ = emissivity of the leaf,

σ = blackbody function,

t_a = air temperature,

Δt = air temperature minus leaf temperature.

Further, Gates postulated that energy transfer by free convection in still air for a broad flat leaf can be approximated by the following:

$$C = h_c\,(\Delta t/L)\,, \tag{6}$$

where C = heat transfer by convection,

h_c = heat transfer coefficient,

L = diameter of a leaf.

A graphic solution of equations (5) and (6) is provided in Figure 2 for a leaf having approximately the same dimensions as those of a Valencia orange. For a more detailed discussion of the mathematical and physical basis for Figure 2, the reader is referred to Gates's 1963 and 1964 studies.

As diagramed in Figure 2, a living leaf could superheat or supercool from its environmental sensible temperature depending upon its gain or loss of heat by radiation and convection. Therefore, in still air a leaf would either superheat or supercool depending upon

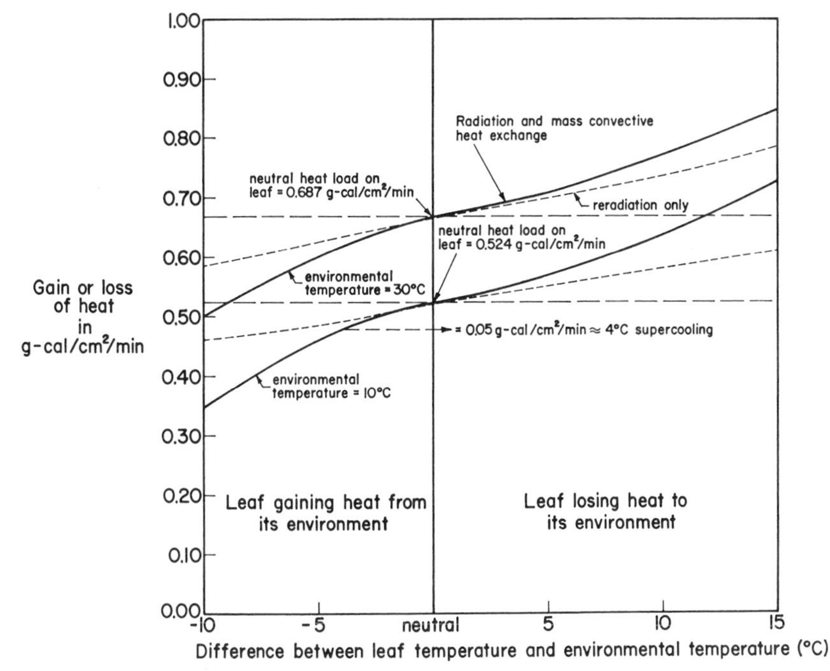

Fig. 2. Radiant and convective energy exchange between a living leaf and its environment.

the magnitude of the radiant flux and the direction of heat transfer. During the daylight hours the radiant flux is normally positive. In fact, the total positive radiant heat load can exceed 2.0 cal/cm^2 per minute under a full solar and terrestrial sky radiation load during warm summer days. It should be remembered, however, that such excessive heat loads are dissipated primarily by wind and transpiration. Therefore, climatic conditions that will allow excessive heating of more than 1° or 2°C above sensible air temperatures do not normally exist for more than a few tenths of a second at a time. When the flux of radiant exchange becomes negative with respect to soil and vegetative surfaces, calm conditions often exist in out-of-door environments. Such conditions occur in the absence of any direct or diffused solar radiation, that is, a few minutes before sunset to a few minutes after sunrise. In other words, climatic conditions that will allow supercooling, as graphed in Figure 2, may persist for hours during the negative radiant exchange period of the diurnal cycle. In fact, supercooling of 3° to 5°C often occurs. For example, a negative flux of 0.10 cal/cm^2 per minute (see Fig. 2) could produce nearly 5°C of supercooling under calm conditions.

The authors have hypothesized that supercooling during the negative radiant exchange period of the diurnal cycle is an important climatic consideration in determining the length of the flowering-to-maturation cycle of Valencia orange fruit. Therefore, it was postulated that the total summation of net heat loads in cal per unit area per unit time should give a more accurate prediction of orange fruit growth and maturity cycles than the summation of sensible temperatures.

To satisfy the question of proper base and ceiling air temperature for degree-hour accumulations, several combinations of base and ceiling temperatures were used in the total analysis. The base temperatures were varied from 40° to 65°F at 5° intervals. Likewise, ceiling temperatures were varied from 85° to 105°F. The combination of a 55°F base temperature and a 95°F ceiling temperature gave the smallest statistical errors during the four crop-years studied at Santa Paula, California.

A similar analysis was performed in search of the proper base and ceiling radiant temperatures as computed by equations (1), (2), and (3). The base radiant temperature was varied from 40° to 65° on the Fahrenheit scale at 5° intervals. The ceiling radiant temperature was varied from 85° to 125°F at 10° intervals. No change in accuracy for statistical measurements could be associated with change of ceiling radiant temperatures. Perhaps this is to be expected in view of the heat exchange potential of wind flow and transpiration normally occurring during the day. On the other hand, there were changes in the accuracy of various statistical expressions for the different radiant base temperatures. After much study of several statistical measurements consisting of total variance, standard deviations, standard errors, and coefficients of variation, the 50°F base radiant temperature was selected as the base temperature for computing the values reported in Tables 1 through 6. In many sets of data, however, a radiant temperature base of 45°F gave equally accurate statistical estimates.

Since the various statistical measurements were not consistent in estimating a base radiant temperature relationship, it was decided to subject the resulting standard errors to additional study. The results of this effort are reported in Figures 3, 4, and 5. In these figures the pooled values for all standard errors resulting from the net heat accumulations at all locations for all fruit growth and development periods in each crop-year were plotted as the dependent variable in relation to varying base radiant temperatures.

In Figure 3, the minimum value of x is 8.86°C (47.95°F) for the equation of least squares fit. This value is believed to be the best mathematical estimate of the correct base radiant temperature for accumulating net heat for all data collected during the 1963 crop-year. Similarly in 1964, as related in Figure 4, the minimum value for x is 7.43°C (45.37°F). The minimum value for x in the 1965 crop-year, as related in Figure 5, is 7.56°C (46.61°F). The grand mean estimate of minimum base radiant temperature necessary for Valencia orange fruit growth and development for all three crop-years for all locations and for all fruit growth and development periods studied is 7.95°C (46.31°F) or a minimum net flux of 0.509 cal per cm^2 per minute.

According to a 1958 study by Bain, Valencia orange fruit growth, development, and maturity, throughout the phenological crop-year, conveniently fall into three stages. Stage 1 is the cell-division stage beginning with fruit-set and extending through the period of cell

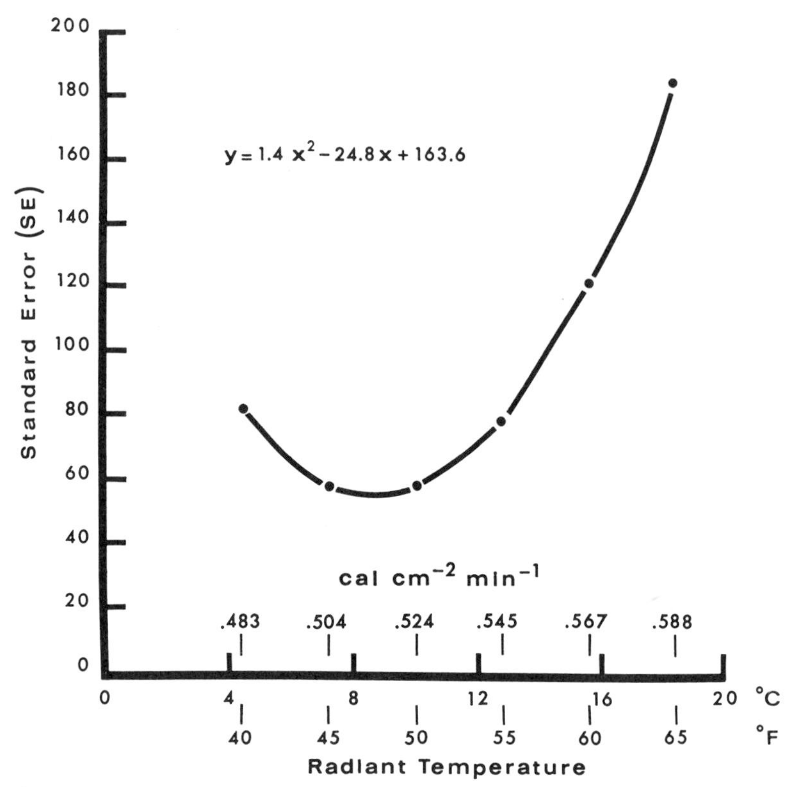

Fig. 3. Night radiant energy levels as related to Valencia orange fruit growth and development for crop-year 1963.

division for all fruit tissues except the outermost cell layers of the developing fruit. Stage 2 is the period of rapid cell enlargement, thus rapid fruit growth. However, cell division is normally absent within the fruit proper. Stage 3 is the maturation and ripening period in which the fruit continues to increase in size and weight at a much reduced rate, but increases in juices and total soluble solids rapidly.

As illustrated by the Scora and Newman (1966) study, Valencia orange fruit in the lower Rio Grande Valley reaches the 9 to 1 total solids-to-acid ratio around December 1 each year, or about eight to nine months after mid-bloom date. At Orlando, Florida, this same degree of maturity is attained about eight weeks later, or in late January, about 10 to 11 months after mid-bloom date. In the low

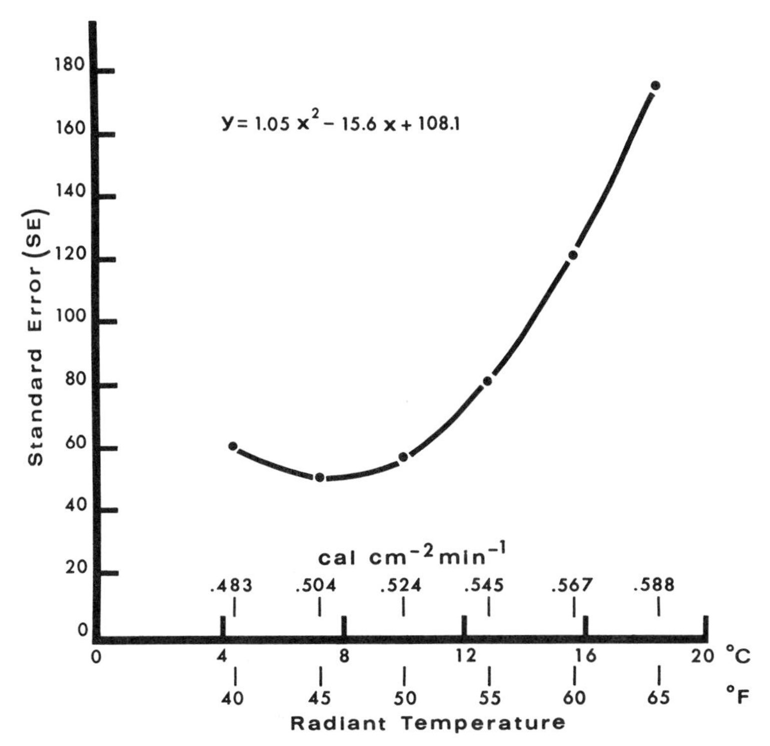

Fig. 4. Night radiant energy levels as related to Valencia orange fruit growth and development for crop-year 1964.

desert, near Indio, California, the Valencia crop reaches the 9 to 1 ratio in mid-February or about nine to ten months after mid-bloom date. At Riverside, California, fruit reaches a 9 to 1 ratio near mid-April, some 11 to 12 months after the mid-bloom date. Near Santa Paula, Valencia oranges normally require 14 to 15 months to reach commercial harvest maturity.

Following these general definitions the authors partitioned the fruit development cycle into the following divisions: mid-bloom date to 25 cm^3; 25 cm^3 to 100 cm^3; 100 cm^3 to a 9 to 1 ratio; and from bloom through 9 to 1 ratio. At this 9 to 1 ratio of total soluble solids to total acids in the juice the fruit arbitrarily was considered mature, since this is associated with acceptable market maturity according to Harding *et al.* (1940). Time periods in days for the stages of Valencia orange fruit growth, maturation, and for bloom to maturity are reported in Tables 7 through 10. Results of degree-

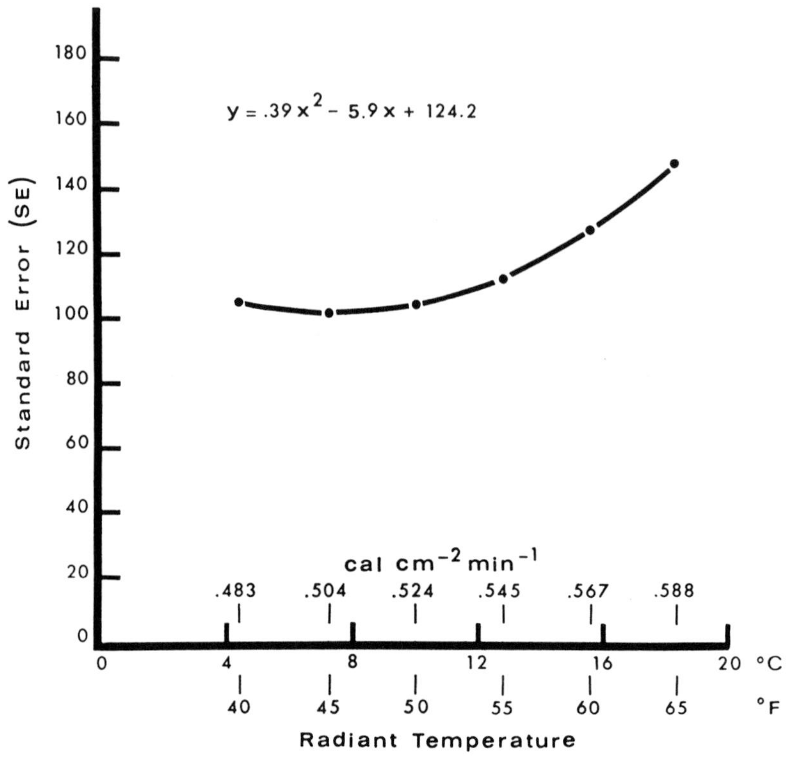

Fig. 5. Night radiant energy levels as related to Valencia orange fruit growth and development for crop-year 1965.

hour accumulations and net heat accumulations are reported in Tables 1 through 6 for the time periods in days reported in Tables 7 through 10.

Results

In Tables 1 and 2 a comparison is made between degree-hour accumulations and net heat accumulations in Santa Paula, California. The figures in Table 1 represent degree-hour sums for each reported time period in days above the temperature base of 55°F and below a temperature ceiling of 95°F as computed by equation (4). The figures in Table 2 represent a net heat accumulation, using a mean radiant temperature base of 50°F, or a net heat flux of 0.5240 cal/cm² per minute, accumulated over each time period in days as computed from black-globe data by equations (1), (2),

Table 7. Time in days for the degree-hour and net heat accumulations associated with the various phenological periods during four crop-years at Santa Paula, California, 1961–1965.

Pheno-logical year	Begin-ning date	Ending date	Bloom to 25 cm³ (days)	25 cm³ to 100 cm³ (days)	100 cm³ to 9-1 ratio (days)	Bloom to 9-1 ratio (days)
1961–62	5/7/61	7/20/62	114	143	182	439
1962–63	5/3/62	6/20/63	118	164	131	413
1963–64	5/18/63	5/28/64	97	97	181	375
1964–65	5/18/64	7/23/65	96	98	237	431

Table 8. Time in days for the degree-hour and net heat accumulations associated with phenological periods of growth and development during the crop-year, 1964–1965, at five geographical locations of commercial Valencia orange production in the United States.

Location	Beginning date	Ending date	Bloom to 25 cm³ (days)	25 cm³ to 100 cm³ (days)	100 cm³ to 9-1 ratio (days)	Bloom to 9-1 ratio (days)
Orlando, Fla.	3/27/64	2/2/65	60	93	159	312
Weslaco, Tex.	3/16/64	11/18/64	67	91	89	247
Indio, Calif.	4/27/64	2/6/65	55	103	127	285
Riverside, Calif.	5/18/64	4/13/65	91	116	123	330
Santa Paula, Calif.	5/18/64	7/23/65	96	98	237	431

Table 9. Time in days for the net heat accumulations associated with phenological periods of growth and development during the crop-year, 1963–1964, at four geographic locations of commercial Valencia orange production in the United States.

Location	Beginning date	Ending date	Bloom to 25 cm³ (days)	25 cm³ to 100 cm³ (days)	100 cm³ to 9-1 ratio (days)	Bloom to 9-1 ratio (days)
Weslaco, Tex.	3/30/63	11/22/63	64	60	113	237
Indio, Calif.	3/30/63	1/24/64	79	86	135	300
Riverside, Calif.	5/18/63	4/16/64	81	128	124	333
Santa Paula, Calif.	5/18/63	5/28/64	97	97	181	375

Table 10. Time in days for the net heat accumulations associated with phenological periods of growth and development during the crop-year, 1962–1963, at three geographic locations of commercial Valencia orange production in the United States.

Location	Beginning date	Ending date	Bloom to 25 cm^3 (days)	25 cm^3 to 100 cm^3 (days)	100 cm^3 to 9-1 ratio (days)	Bloom to 9-1 ratio (days)
Orlando, Fla.	4/12/62	2/5/63	65	59	175	299
Indio, Calif.	4/26/62	2/2/63	66	104	112	282
Santa Paula, Calif.	5/3/62	6/20/63	118	164	131	413

and (3). Note the similarity in the statistical measurements (S.E. and C.V.) for the two sets of data reported in Tables 1 and 2. Further, remember that the figures in Tables 1 and 2 are for the same location over a four-crop-year period.

Here one can see what has been reported in the literature many times—that degree-hour accumulations are of some value as an index of climate for predicting seasonal variations in the rate of growth, development, and maturity of agricultural crops in a given place. Further, the net heat accumulation in Table 3 does not demonstrate any superiority to that of degree-hour accumulations as an index of climate on the growth, development, and maturity of Valencia oranges at the same geographic location.

A similar comparison is made in Tables 3 and 4 for five different geographic locations during the same crop-year. Here it is evident that degree-hour accumulations in Table 3 are not as closely associated with Valencia orange fruit growth or maturity as the net heat accumulations in Table 4. However, it is evident also that net heat accumulation is more closely related to the time required to reach maturity, that is, days from bloom to 9 to 1 ratio, than for the shorter periods of fruit growth as measured by volume increments. The same comparisons were made in Table 5 for crop-year 1963–1964 at four locations and in Table 6 for crop-year 1962–1963 at three locations, with similar results. In 1963–1964 in a comparison of Weslaco, Texas, Indio, Riverside, and Santa Paula, California, the net heat accumulation in cal/cm^2 is 73,635 for the total bloom-to-maturity period. The S.E. was 2,835 with a C.V. of 8 percent. In the 1962–1963 comparisons of Orlando, Florida, Indio, and Santa Paula, California, the mean value for net heat accumulation is 72,227 for the bloom-to-maturity period with a S.E. of 1,343 and a C.V. of only 3 percent. In contrast, total degree-hour accumulations for the same locations over the same crop-years produced C.V. of 49 percent in 1963–1964 and 51 percent in 1962–1963.

A grand mean for net heat accumulations required from bloom to maturity for the total phenological crop-years for all geographic locations for all crop-years studied is 72,730 with a mean S.E. of 1,911, and a mean C.V. of 5 percent. This suggests that, on the average, Valencia orange fruit should reach a 9 to 1 maturity index as defined in this study upon the accumulation of 72,730 cal/cm^2 of net radiant heat above the base radiant heat load of 0.524 cal/cm^2 per minute. In contrast, degree-hour accumulations for the same pooled locations and total crop-years failed to give meaningful results.

The relationship of both the net heat accumulations and the degree-hour accumulations gave poor predictions for the various substages of growth of orange fruit. The mean S.E. for the heat-unit accumulations for mid-bloom to 25 cm^3, 25 to 100 cm^3, and 100 cm^3 to 9 to 1 ratio, for all locations and all crop-years studied is 2,634 with a mean C.V. of 21 percent. Similar degree-hour comparisons were meaningless, having C.V. ranging from 40 to 60 percent.

One possible factor contributing to the poor relationships of these net heat flux statistics for most of these subperiods of fruit growth and development is that of inherent error in phenological observations and measurements used to derive the proper time period for each stage studied. There could be errors of several days in the mid-bloom date for the particular samples of fruits that were measured to obtain the rate of growth. Likewise, similar errors may have occurred in the sampling of orange fruit for determining the 9 to 1 maturity date. Further, these inherent errors could be compounded in relationship to mid-bloom date, the fruit sample measured, and the fruit samples obtained for the maturity date determinations. Such errors probably contribute in a major way to the increased statistical variability in the shorter phenological periods. It also suggests that change in fruit volume may not be a good index of progress toward maturity.

Conclusions

The results reported in this study present strong evidence that net radiant heat loads on vegetative surfaces in cal per unit area per unit time are a more sensitive climatic index of orange fruit maturity cycles than sensible air temperatures. Also, it is very likely that other crops respond similarly to the net heat loads of their environments. Here the authors have particular reference to widely varying reports of chilling requirements in degree-hours for several deciduous fruit crops. Perhaps a chilling requirement could be more accurately expressed in terms of an accumulated deficit below a base net heat flux.

Second, this study suggests that a direct measurement of net radiant heat levels is a more meaningful parameter to observe as a climatic index of plant responses than sensible air temperature.

Last, soil temperatures should not be ignored in similar investigations in the future. This is particularly true for perennial crop response studies covering a complete annual growing cycle, since changes in soil temperature may control plant responses during certain time periods.

Authors' Note: Paper No. 1780, University of California, Citrus Research Center and Agricultural Experiment Station, Riverside, California. This study was supported in part by USDA Contract 6878-34.

The authors are grateful to Earl S. Morton, Laboratory Technician, Department of Horticultural Sciences, University of California, Riverside, for his diligent efforts in collection and analysis of the orange fruit phenological data. In addition, gratitude is expressed to Dr. Morris J. Garber, Associate Biometrician, University of California.

REFERENCES

Bain, J. M., 1958. Morphological, anatomical, and physiological changes in the developing fruit of the Valencia orange. *Australian J. Botany, 6:* 1–25.

Bond, T. E., and C. E. Kelly, 1955. The globe thermometer in agricultural research. *Agr. Eng., 36:* 251–254.

Gates, D. M., 1962. *Energy Exchange in the Biosphere.* Harper & Row, New York.

Gates, D. M., 1963. The energy environment in which we live. *Am. Scientist, 51:* 327–348.

Gates, D. M., 1964. Leaf temperature and transpiration. *Agron. J., 56:* 273–277.

Harding, P. L., J. R. Winton, and D. F. Fisher, 1940. Seasonal changes in Florida oranges. *U.S. Dept. Agr. Tech. Bull., No. 753.*

Reaumur, R. A. F., 1735. Thermometric observations made at Paris during the year 1735, compared to those made below the equator on the Isle of Mauritius, in Algiers and on a few of our American islands. *Paris Memoirs, Academy of Science,* p. 545.

Scora, R. W., and J. E. Newman, 1966. A phenological study of the essential oils of the peel of Valencia oranges. *Agr. Meteorol., 4:* 11–26.

Taylor, C. A., and J. R. Furr, 1937. Use of soil-moisture and fruit-growth records for checking irrigation practices in citrus orchards. *U.S. Dept. Agr. Circ., 426.*

Thornthwaite, C. W., 1952. *Temperature Relations to Time of Maturity of Vegetable Crops.* Presented at the 78th annual meetings of the New Jersey State Horticultural Society. Johns Hopkins Univ., Baltimore, Maryland. (Mimeograph)

Wang, J. Y., 1960. A critique of the heat-unit approach to plant response studies. *Ecology, 41:* 785–790.

Ground Level Climate in Relation to Forecasting Plant Diseases

JACK R. WALLIN, *Crops Protection Research Branch, Agricultural Research Service, U.S. Department of Agriculture, Iowa State University, Ames, Iowa*

A DIFFERENCE BETWEEN ground level climate and general climate was suspected and recognized in Germany by a Würzburg botanist, Gregor Kraus, who published *Boden und Klima auf Kleinstem Raum* in 1911. Because of this book he became known as the father of microclimatology. Individual papers on the relation of plant zone climate to the climate above are cited in excellent reviews (Geiger, 1950; Mattsson, 1961; Molga, 1958; Van Eimern, 1964a; Ventskevich, 1958; Vitkevich, 1960). The great volume of data indicates that climatic conditions in the two climatic zones are often very different.

We are concerned with the ground level or plant zone climate because most economic plants grow on the ground and their enemies are subject to the atmospheric components or variables immediately surrounding them. As soon as plants emerge from the soil, they influence the climate near the ground. A plant pathogen can attack a susceptible plant successfully only if the climate is favorable to the pathogen.

This discussion will relate to the influence of ground level climate on the growth and development of certain plant parasites, and to the degree to which climatic data are used in predicting and controlling plant disease outbreaks.

Ground Level Climate and Plant Disease Epiphytotics

Each plant pathogen has specific temperature-moisture requirements. Relating these requirements to the epiphytotics caused by these pathogens is the first step toward forecasting. Duration of temperature-moisture values is of critical importance because, if they are optimum for the pathogen growing in a large community of susceptible host plants in the field, the pathogen will produce an epiphytotic. For example, a water film on plant part surfaces is essential to the infection processes of many foliar plant pathogenic fungi (Hart, 1926; Yarwood, 1939). Because this condition occurs in the plant climate, it can be recorded there best. The numerous individual research papers dealing with plant zone climate and plant disease development may be found in a number of excellent reviews on weather and plant disease and plant disease forecasting (Miller, 1959; Miller and O'Brien, 1952, 1957; Waggoner, 1960; Yarwood, 1939). We shall cite some examples to illustrate the point.

Climate and powdery mildew on lettuce were studied in the Salinas Valley of California by Schnathorst (1957). He reported that favorable periods for germination of conidia (95–99 percent relative humidity at 25°C) were two hours longer in plant cover than records in the standard instrument shelter indicated. Meteorological data recorded in the standard instrument shelter above the lettuce seemed adequate, however, in depicting periods favoring the powdery mildew fungus.

Flax rust incidence increases at the onset of flowering because of changes in the plant climate which shifts toward optimum temperature-relative humidity values for the pathogen as plant cover increases (Schrodter and Hoffmann, 1961). Optimum conditions occur with greater frequency as the season advances and as the plant canopy increases.

Climatic conditions influencing the sugar beet leaf-spot fungus, *Cercospora beticola,* were studied by Pool and McKay (1916), who found that relative humidities are higher among sugar beet plants than at five feet above. They recommended that only records collected among sugar beet plants should be considered in correlating climatic conditions with conidial production and infection by *Cercospora.*

Temperatures are higher in sugar beets thinned to 20 inches (checked) than in beets thinned to 12 inches (drilled) in the row in Iowa, according to Vestal and Bell (1931). Relative humidity is three to ten percent higher in the drilled than in the checked plantings. More *Cercospora* leaf spot develops in the drilled plantings where the foliage canopy is heavier.

Microclimatic studies as a prerequisite for the organization of a *Cercospora* warning service were suggested in Lower Bavaria, Germany (Mischke, 1960). Temperature and relative humidity data, obtained in sugar beet cover, indicates that *Cercospora beticola* develops rapidly if the relative humidity exceeds 95 percent for at least eight hours, or if beet leaves are wet for a minimum of ten hours daily for a three- to four-day period, whenever the minimum temperature in the stand remains above 10°C. Coincidentally, five percent of the leaves in the study had ten lesions per leaf.

The explosive development of peanut leaf spot caused by two other *Cercospora* species was related to temperature and relative humidity in the peanut foliage by Jensen and Boyle (1965). They concluded that rains are probably helpful in dispersing spores and in inducing periods of leaf wetness favorable for spore germination and penetration. Relative humidity, however, seems to be a better measure of all the moisture factors that affect the onset and duration of leaf wetness.

Cereal rust infection and the peculiarities of the microclimatic zones in cereal plantings were explored by Roussakov in Russia (1924). He pointed out that the meteorological element among plants was a neglected facet of agricultural meteorology. He discussed the results of other investigations dealing with the influence of plant cover on the distribution of temperatures and moisture in the lower layers of the air.

The incidence and spread of white pine blister rust have been related to temperature, light, and humidity recorded in tree-crown covers (Van Arsdel *et al.*, 1956, 1961). The extent of blister rust decreases as the canopy increases. Rust incidence seems to correlate with periods of saturated air and high daytime relative humidities. Cool, wet periods favorable for development of rust were recorded by hygrothermographs located at various sites among the trees. These periods were not indicated by data taken at the nearest Weather Bureau station (Van Arsdel, 1961).

Epiphytotics of apple scab caused by *Venturia inaequalis* have been related to climatic conditions actually prevailing in and among trees in the orchards. Keitt and Jones (1926) recorded temperature, humidity, and rainfall in their experimental orchards. They determined the minimum number of hours of leaf wetness essential for infection. Mills (1944) determined criteria of air temperature and duration of leaf wetness favorable to infection and subsequent development of the apple scab fungus. He published a table for assessing infection. Later, Mills and LaPlante (1954) described the Mills Period as a period of leaf wetness and air temperature that results in light infection by ascospores of the apple scab fungus. In 1955, ascospore infections in apple orchards in England were related to the occurrence and duration of periods of leaf wetness (Hirst *et al.*, 1955). Data were taken in the orchards. Preece and Smith (1961) found, from weather data taken among apple trees during apple scab development, that the occurrence of the main meteorological conditions favoring spring infection can be determined at standard weather stations by observation of periods of high humidity after rain. In more than 200 observations of dew and rain measurements of apple trees in Germany, the trees were dry only four percent of the nights (Van Eimern, 1964b); measurements were made at 1.4 meters above the soil. Van Eimern found that, for apple scab prediction, the duration of apple leaf wetness could be interpreted from the duration of 85 percent or more relative humidity measured two meters high in a shelter. He observed that the amount of rain had no influence on the duration of leaf wetness. In addition, he observed that when rain ended before 6:00 P.M., the leaves dried within two to four hours. When rain ended between 6:00 P.M. and 8:00 A.M., apple leaves remained wet until about 10:00 A.M.

The elevation of the tea plantations in Indonesia influences the total ground level climate and hence the blister blight disease (*Exobasidium vexans*) of tea, according to De Weille (1960). Blister blight is common in the plantations at higher elevations where the temperature is lower, the relative humidity is higher, and there are more interruptions of direct sunshine than at lower elevations. Sunshine acts directly to curb the fungus on leaf blades as well as to affect high relative humidities in the crop cover. De Weille proposed a blister blight forecasting system by which fungicides are either applied or not applied depending on sun valuation rates in the tea plantation. The rates are based upon sunshine duration recorded by a Jordan sunshine autograph.

Plant zone temperatures in rice paddies were related to epiphytotics of rice blast, *Piricularia oryzae* (Green, 1958; Green and Van Arsdel, 1956). Night temperatures of more than 22°C in the paddy are required for spread. Night temperatures in flooded fields of short rice plants are high enough to produce epiphytotics, whereas temperatures in fields of unflooded rice or taller plants are not (Green, 1958). Planting rice on April 1 or earlier allows the crop to escape the warmer temperatures and, thus, the blast.

Dew deposition is the limiting factor in the distribution of downy mildew of cucurbits in Israel (Duvdevani *et al.,* 1946). Dew observations were taken at 5, 15, 50, and 100 cm above the soil level. Infection with the downy mildew fungus was increased by 304 successive nights of moderate dew and nightly temperature minima of 18°C or above at a height of 15 cm.

Data on dew taken in potato and tomato plots in the Negev region of Israel were related to early blight epiphytotics (Rotem and Reichert, 1964). Dew on the plant foliage is the principal moisture factor which causes early blight epiphytotics in the areas of low rainfall and low humidity. Dew forms despite air values of relative humidity far below the saturation point.

Investigations of ground level climate and plant disease development have been more numerous with potato blight than any other disease in phytopathological history. When our USDA plant disease forecasting program was initiated, Dutch and English "rules" for predicting late blight epiphytotics were in existence (Beaumont, 1947; Van Everdingen, 1926, 1927; Wiltshire, 1931). These rules were based upon experience with those plant zone climatic factors which produce late blight epiphytotics.

Ground level climate was considered in relation to late blight epiphytotics by the Dutch in 1926 (Van Everdingen, 1926–1927). Data on dew duration and temperature were taken in potato fields and related to the development of potato late blight. Late blight epiphytology in England in 1931 (Wiltshire, 1931) dealt with relating dew and temperature observations taken in potato cover to the spread of the late blight fungus. The importance of ground level or foliage climate in the epiphytology of potato late blight was stressed by Thomas (1946), who stated that possibly favorable moisture conditions among the leaves may not be detected in standard meteorological observations. Relative humidity differences between the plant and the five-foot level were great. Later, Hirst and Stedman (1956) found that temperature and relative humidity measured in the potato crop were more reliable in depicting blight outbreaks than measurements made above the crop. Late in the season, high humidity persists close to wet soil protected by dense foilage. These conditions are unlikely to be detected by instruments placed four feet above ground.

Dew and temperature data at the 40 cm level in potato cover were related to late blight development by Post and Richel (1951) in Holland.

Temperature and moisture conditions in plant cover were related to potato late blight outbreaks in Norway by Forsund and Flaatten (1959). They, too, related the general climatic conditions that favor late blight development.

Temperature and relative humidity in the upper third of plants were measured by Johannes (1953) and related to late blight development. Late blight, he reported, developed if the temperature was 10°–20°C and if relative humidity was greater than 90 percent for at least 33 hours. Two such periods were necessary for a late blight outbreak. Ullrich (1962) found that dew was the most important moisture factor causing the late blight epiphytotic in Germany in 1961. He found that a three-hour period of leaf wetness at 12°–13°C was sufficient for the germination of sporangia of *Phytophthora infestans* (Ullrich, 1957).

Relative humidity, dew, and temperature were measured at a height of 30 cm and were related to the development of *Phytophthora infestans* in furrow and overhead irrigated plots in Israel (Rotem *et al.,* 1962). The disease developed profusely under overhead irrigation, but was virtually absent from plots under furrow irrigation.

Temperature-relative humidity requirements for the regeneration and development of the late blight fungus were determined much earlier by Melhus (1915) and Crosier (1934).

In our ground level climate investigations, we wanted to record those meteorological requirements for sporulation, spore germination, subsequent infection, and development in the host. Hygrothermographs were placed 12 inches above the soil in plots inoculated with the late blight fungus. After some experience in recording temperature-relative humidity epochs in the inoculated plots, we wanted to know how closely the relative humidity period approximated the dew or leaf wetness period and how closely sheltered air temperatures in the crop approximated the crop plant temperatures.

Psychrometric readings, leaf and stem temperatures, and dew duration data were taken to determine the accuracy with which hygrothermographs in plant cover depicted these phenomena. The psychrometric, temperature, and humidity readings were taken at various levels in crop cover (Waggoner, 1950; Wallin and Shaw, 1953; Wallin and Waggoner, 1950). Differences as great as 11 percent in relative humidity were noted between the one- and five-foot levels in tomato cover.

Temperature readings in tomato cover (Waggoner and Shaw, 1952) revealed that instrument shelter and plant temperature differences were slight during cloudy days or at night; under clear skies, upper unshaded leaflets were about 7°C warmer during the day and only 3°C cooler at night than instrument shelter air temperatures; and on a clear day and night, temperatures of lower, sheltered leaflets were equal to those in the shelters. In later potato leaf temperature measurements we found a temperature difference of 8°C between upper and lower leaflets; a maximum temperature difference of 9°C between upper leaflets and the instrument shelter was recorded; and the maximum difference between lower leaflet and instrument shelter temperatures was 11°C although differences of this magnitude usually lasted less than an hour. These data provided a reference for interpreting hygrothermograph data and actual crop temperatures. The shelter temperatures generally represented temperatures of the shaded and lower leaves where the late blight fungus seems to develop first.

How accurately does the hygrothermograph depict the dew or wet leaf period in potato cover? Dew data taken over a period of years (Wallin, 1963) revealed that, in general, the dew period was about an hour longer than the period of 90 percent or more relative humidity. Extremes of dew periods 3.5 and 5.5 hours longer than the humidity periods were noted, but they were the exceptions. Dew was on the foliage, for example, at 10:40 P.M. one night, but the relative humidity did not reach 90 percent until 1:00 A.M. The reverse time lag between humidity reaching 90 percent and dew deposition was not noted. The hygrothermograph, then, in spite of its shortcomings, seems to be practical for estimating duration of dew periods—a critical factor for activity by the late blight fungus.

Forecasting Plant Diseases

We have shown the importance of identifying the variables of the ground or plant level climate that foster the development of plant diseases. The employment of ground or plant level climatic data in forecasting plant disease epiphytotics will be illustrated through the four classic examples of apple scab, downy mildew of grape, downy mildew of lima bean, and potato late blight.

Apple Scab

A report by Post *et al.* (1963) reviewed the forecasting and warning services employed in Europe and the United States. These services advise the growers of the time of ripening of the ascospores in the orchards, the date when discharge was observed, and the occurrence of infection periods. These advisories are not mandatory directives for the grower to apply fungicides. The infection periods are based on Mills's criteria for ascospore infection of leaves; the criteria are the duration of leaf wetness and the coincident temperatures in the orchard. Infection can be assessed from a table proposed by Mills (1944). The fruit growers then take whatever control measures they deem necessary. Dew recorders are employed in several European countries to record duration of leaf wetness in the orchards (Post *et al.,* 1963).

Downy Mildew of Grape

Forecasting and mildew warnings have received considerable attention since the 1920's and 1930's in Italy, France, Germany, Spain, and Russia (Miller, 1959; Miller and O'Brien, 1952), but the extent to which ground level or plant zone climatic measurements were used in the development of these techniques is not too clear.

Dew, a phenomenon definitely associated with the plant zone climate, is considered an important factor in mildew epidemics in

France where mildew forecasting was based on the interrelation of disease development and meteorological factors (I.R.A., 1933). In Italy, for example, Corneli (1932) stated that condensed moisture or dew is the predominant factor leading to an attack of downy mildew of grape. He used Lambrecht's polymeter to estimate the dew point temperature in Perugia. If the dew point was higher than 12°C, the lowest temperature at which spore germination occurs, an outbreak of vine mildew might be expected. He concluded that the safest procedure in forecasting vine mildew is to note changes in temperature and relative humidity by using a thermometer and psychrometer, and to observe directly the conditions leading to condensation of moisture.

Downy Mildew of Lima Bean

Ground level climate investigations have infiltrated the downy mildew forecasting program for lima beans (Hyre, 1960). Hyre related temperature, relative humidity, and dew data obtained in lima bean cover to the incidence and increase of severity of the disease. He found that air temperatures exceeding 29°C immediately after an infection period (ten hours or more of wet foliage at favorable temperatures) tended to prevent the successful establishment of the fungus in lima bean foliage. This was corroborated in a later study in controlled-environment chambers (Hyre, 1964). Hyre preferred to use rainfall and temperature data from the U. S. Weather Bureau for predicting lima bean mildew (Hyre *et al.*, 1962). The incidence of disease was predicted after eight consecutive days when the five-day mean temperature was less than 26°C and concurrent ten-day cumulated rainfall was 1.20 inches or more, provided that the current weather forecast called for continued mildew-favorable weather.

Potato Late Blight

Perhaps more attention will be given to potato late blight disease because we have devoted considerable time to interpreting its development from meteorological data taken in the plant zone.

We have related sporulation, spore germination with subsequent infection, and the development in the host to temperature and relative humidity data recorded by hygrothermographs in louvered shelters at the 12-inch level in potato or tomato plots inoculated with the blight fungus. Meteorological data were recorded in the plots as the fungus developed on and consumed the plants.

Having established the efficiency of the sheltered hygrothermograph in depicting the ground level plant zone, we utilized the laboratory results of Melhus (1915) and Crosier (1934), as well as the field results of the Dutch and English, in developing criteria for forecasting the rise and fall of the blight fungus. First, temperature-relative humidity data were related to the initiation and further development of the fungus in inoculated plots where we knew the pathogen to be present. Sporulation, secondary infection processes, and lesion development in these plots were documented as they occurred. The duration of the temperature-humidity combinations associated with sporulation, secondary infection, and lesion development was documented on the hygrothermograph chart. The duration of given temperature averages during the dew period and the expected severity of secondary infection were tabulated in Table 1. The values from 1 to 4 were called "blight severity values". These criteria are not presented here as the final, precise, rigid conditions governing the behavior of the fungus, but rather as estimates of those conditions.

The ground level climate, then, associated with the rise and fall of the late blight fungus is recorded by the hygrothermograph. Sheltered hygrothermographs sampling potato foliage climate are located at 23 weather-blight stations in the North Central Region. Data are analyzed once a week and the "blight severity value" inter-

Table 1. The relation of duration of given average temperatures during the dew period (RH⩸90%) to the severity of secondary infection of *Phytophthora infestans,* the late blight fungus. Severity values are shown in hours.

Temperature range °C	Severity values of secondary infections			
	1 0-Trace	2 Slight	3 Moderate	4 Severe
7–12	16–18	19–21	22–24	25+
13–15	13–15	16–18	19–21	22+
16–27	10–12	13–15	16–18	19+

preted. Accumulative severity value of 20 indicates blight incidence in the locality, and is stated in the weekly forecast. Positive blight forecasts are issued from then on, and fungicide treatment is recommended if a cumulative value of three or more per seven-day period occurs. Positive forecasts without control recommendations are issued if values of 1 to 2 are recorded. The low values are sufficient for the pathogen to subsist with a minimum of regeneration. The occurrence of these low values for three to four weeks is considered enough to keep the pathogen dormant, ready to grow at the onset of higher values. This happened in northern Iowa and southern Minnesota in 1956. Spraying or dusting may be discontinued for the season if there are no favorable periods for three successive weeks.

Forecast accuracy has been very high over a period of years. Seasonal accuracy, however, is most difficult to assess for the following reasons:

1. If inoculum is absent, there will be no late blight no matter how many favorable periods occur.
2. If a grower sprays weekly, with or without our forecasts, his fields may have only a trace of blight which may or may not be observed.
3. Some growers have blight and do not report it, either for business reasons or because they do not recognize it.

Forecasters must assume that the fungus is present somewhere in the area and direct the forecasts to unsprayed, susceptible potato or tomato plantings. If the forecasts are to be valid, the hygrothermographs must be set in the field during the emergence period of the earliest plantings, because at that time the pathogen is first exposed to ground level climatic conditions.

Future Possibilities

In the future, ground level or foliage zone climatic data may be applied in predicting additional diseases such as the cereal rusts, barley yellow dwarf virus of cereals, and *Cercospora* leaf spot of sugar beets. Disease predictions are useful if some action, such as chemical applications, can be taken to control the diseases. Having related ground level climate to plant disease development, predictions could advise growers that certain crops may be planted in areas where climate does not support certain diseases with the assumption that these diseases will not plague them. Epiphytological investigations of barley yellow dwarf and sugar beet leaf spot are underway to determine the climatic factors in the plant zone that lead to epiphytotics. Once identified, these factors may be used to forecast incidence and subsequent spread of these diseases.

Future epiphytological research will be directed toward establishing a link between the ground level climatic requirements of the plant diseases mentioned and the typical patterns portraying such requirements on a synoptic weather chart. The tools and concepts of modern synoptic meteorology, as well as the far-reaching facilities of the Weather Bureau network, can be utilized to great advantage. Ground level or plant zone climatic patterns were first related by Bourke to synoptic weather charts in predicting potato late blight in Ireland (Bourke, 1957, 1965) and later in the United States by Wallin and Riley (1960). Hourly dew points associated with large-scale synoptic patterns were used successfully in forecasting lima bean downy mildew by Scarpa and Raniere (1964).

In cooperation with Weather Bureau meteorologists and also with entomologists, we are studying the initiation of barley yellow dwarf virus on cereals in the North Central States by aphid vectors riding the low-level jet winds blowing from Texas and Oklahoma into the target area. Future investigations will be conducted on the relation of ground level or plant zone climate to viruliferous aphid takeoff in the area of origin.

Author's Note: This contribution is Journal Paper No. J-5346 of the Iowa Agricultural and Home Economics Experiment Station, Project 1163.

REFERENCES

Beaumont, A., 1947. The dependence of the weather on dates of outbreak of potato late blight epidemics. *Brit. Mycol. Soc. Trans., 31:* 45–53.

Bourke, P. M. A., 1957. The use of synoptic weather maps in potato blight epidemiology. *Irish Dept. Industry and Commerce, Met. Services Tech. Note, 23:* 1–35.

Bourke, P. M. A., 1965. The contribution of modern meteorology to plant disease forecasting. *Phytopathology, 55:* 943–952.

Corneli, E., 1932. On mildew warnings in central Italy. *Rivista Patologia Vegetale, 22:* 1–9.

Crosier, W. J., 1934. Studies in the biology of *Phytophthora infestans* (Mont) De Bary. *Cornell Univ. Agr. Exp. Sta. Mem. 155:* 1–40.

DeWeille, G. A., 1960. Blister blight (*Exobasidium vexans*) in tea and its relationship with environmental conditions. *Neth. J. Agr. Sci., 8:* 183–210.

Duvdevani, S., I. Reichert, and J. Palti, 1946. The development of downy and powdery mildew of cucumbers as related to dew and other environmental factors. *Palestine J. Bot. Rehovot Series, 5:* 127–151.

Forsund, E., and H. K. Flaatten, 1959. The interrelationship between climate and outbreak of late blight epiphytotics. *Sci. Rept. Agr. Coll. Norway, 38:* 1–61. Vollebekk, Norway.

Geiger, R., 1950. *The Climate Near the Ground,* translated by M. N. Stewart *et al.* Harvard Univ. Press, Cambridge, Massachusetts.

Green, V. E., Jr., 1958. Observations on fungus diseases of rice in Florida, 1951–57. *Plant Disease Rept., 42:* 624–628.

Green, V. E., Jr., and E. P. VanArsdel, 1956. Rice investigations. *Fla. Agr. Exp. Sta. Ann. Rept.,* 224–225. Gainesville, Florida.

Hart, H., 1926. Factors affecting the development of flax rust, *Melampsora lini* (Pers.) Lev. *Phytopathology, 16:* 185–205.

Hirst, J. M., and O. J. Stedman, 1956. The effect of height of observations in forecasting potato blight by Beaumont's method. *Plant Pathol., 5:* 135–140.

Hirst, J. M., I. F. Storey, W. C. Ward, and H. J. Wilcox, 1955. The origin of apple scab epidemics in the Wisbeck area in 1953 and 1954. *Plant Pathol., 4:* 91–96.

Hyre, R. A., 1960. New aids for forecasting downy mildew of lima bean. *Phytopathology, 50:* 572. (Abstract)

Hyre, R. A., 1964. High temperature following infection checks downy mildew of lima bean. *Phytopathology, 54:* 181–184.

Hyre, R. A., J. MacLeod, and S. H. Davis, Jr., 1962. Forecasting downy mildew of lima bean in Cape May County, New Jersey. *Plant Disease Reptr., 46:* 393–395.

I.R.A., 1933. *Rapport sur les fonctionnements pendant l' année 1932.* Institut des Recherches Agronomiques (I.R.A.), Paris, France.

Jensen, R. E., and L. W. Boyle, 1965. The effect of temperature, relative humidity and precipitation on peanut leafspot. *Plant Disease Reptr., 49:* 975–978.

Johannes, H., 1953. Beitrag zur Epidemiologie der *Phytophthora infestans.* I. Einführung und mikroklimatische untersuchungen. *Z. Pflanzenkrankh Pflanzenschutz, 60:* 289–307.

Keitt, G. W., and L. R. Jones, 1926. Studies of the epidemiology and control of apple scab. *Res. Bull. Wisc. Agr. Exp. Sta. No. 73.*

Kraus, G., 1911. *Boden w. Klima auf Kleinstem Raum.* Fischer, Jena, Germany.

Mattsson, J. O., 1961. Microclimatic observations in and above cultivated crops with special regard to temperature and relative humidity. *Lund Studies Geogr. Ser. A. Phys. Geogr. No. 16.* Lund, Sweden.

Melhus, I. E., 1915. Germination and infection with the fungus of the late blight of potato. *Wisc. Agr. Exp. Sta. Res. Bull. 37.*

Miller, P. R., 1959. Plant disease forecasting. *Plant Pathol. Probl. Progr. 1908–1958:* 557–565.

Miller, P. R., and M. J. O'Brien, 1952. Plant disease forecasting. *Botan. Rev., 18:* 547–601.
Miller, P. R., and M. J. O'Brien, 1957. Prediction of plant disease epidemics. *Ann. Rev. Microbiol.,* 11: 77–110.
Mills, W. D., 1944. Efficient use of sulphur dusts and sprays during rain to control apple scab. *Ext. Bull. Cornell Agr. Exp. Sta., 630.*
Mills, W. D., and A. A. LaPlante, 1954. Diseases and insects in the orchard. *Ext. Bull. Cornell Agr. Exp. Sta., 711:* 20–22.
Mischke, W., 1960. Untersuchungen uber den Einfluss des Bestundsklimas auf die Entwicklung der Ruben-Blattfleckenkrankheit (*Cercospora beticola* Sacc.) im Hinblick auf die Einrichtung eines Warndienstes. *Bayer. Landwirtsch. Jahrb., 37:* 197–227.
Molga, M., 1958. *Agricultural Meteorology.* Part II. *Outline of Agrometeorological Problems,* Centralny Inst. Inform. Naukowo-Tech. Ekon., Warsaw. Translation, 1962: Nat. Sci. Found.-U.S. Dept. Agr., Washington, D.C.
Pool, U. W., and M. B. McKay, 1916. Climatic conditions as related to *Cercospora beticola. J. Agr. Res., 6:* 21–60.
Post, J. J., and C. Richel, 1951. Possibilities for the reorganization of the Dutch potato-blight warning service. *Landbouwk. Tijdschr., 63:* 77–95.
Post, J. J., C. C. Allison, H. Burckhardt, and T. F. Preece, 1963. The influence of weather conditions on the occurrence of apple scab. *World Meteorological Organization Tech. Note, 55:* 1–14.
Preece, T. F., and L. P. Smith, 1961. Apple scab infection weather in England and Wales, 1956–60. *Plant Pathol., 10:* 43–51.
Rotem, J., and I. Reichert, 1964. Dew—A principal moisture factor enabling early blight epidemics in a semiarid region of Israel. *Plant Disease Reptr., 48:* 211–215.
Rotem, J., J. Palti, and E. Rawitz, 1962. Effect of irrigation method and frequency on development of *Phytophthora infestans* on potatoes under arid conditions. *Plant Disease Reptr., 46:* 145–149.
Roussakov, L. F., 1924. Peculiarities of the microclimate in the midst of plants in connection with the development of cereal rusts. *Trans. 4th All Russian Entomo-Phytopath. Congr. Moscow 1922:* 201–216.
Scarpa, M. J., and L. C. Raniere, 1964. The use of consecutive hourly dewpoints in forecasting downy mildew of lima bean. *Plant Disease Reptr., 48:* 77–81.
Schnathorst, W. C., 1957. Microclimates and their significance in the development of powdery mildew of lettuce. *Phytopathology, 47:* 533. (Abstract)
Schrodter, H., and G. M. Hoffmann, 1961. Der Einfluss der Witterung und des Mikroklimas auf den Befall des Leins durch *Polyspora lini* Laff. *Zentr. Bakteriol. Parasitenk., Abt. II, 114:* 15–44.
Thomas, W. D., Jr., 1946. Two aids for the study of potato late blight epidemiology. *Phytopathology, 36:* 322–324.
Ullrich, J., 1957. Die Biologie und Epidemiologie von *Phytophthora infestans* (Mont.) de By. *Nachrbl. Deut. Pflanzenschutzdienst (Berlin), 9:* 129–138.
Ullrich, J., 1962. Beobachtungen uber die Infektionsbedingung waeh-

rend der Ausbreitung von *Phytophthora infestans* in Kartoffelfeld. *Nachrbl. Deut. Pflanzenschutzdienst (Berlin), 14:* 149–152.

Van Arsdel, E. P., 1961. Some forest overstory effects on microclimate and related white pine blister rust spread. *Bull. Am. Meteorol. Soc., 42:* 739–740. (Abstract)

Van Arsdel, E. P., A. J. Riker, T. M. Kouba, V. E. Suomi, and R. A. Bryson, 1961. The climate distribution of blister rust on white pine in Wisconsin. *U.S. Dept. Agr., Lake States Forest Exp. Sta. Paper 87:* 1–34. St. Paul, Minnesota.

Van Arsdel, E. P., A. J. Riker, and R. F. Patton, 1956. The effects of temperature and moisture on the spread of white pine blister rust. *Phytopathology, 46:* 307–318.

Van Eimern, J., 1964a. Zum Begriff und zur Messung der potentiellen Evapotranspiration. *Meteorologische Rundschau, 17:* 33–42.

Van Eimern, J., 1964b. Untersuchungen uber das Klima in Pflanzenbestanden. *Ber. Deut. Wetterdienstes, 96:* 1–76.

Van Everdingen, E., 1926–1927. Het Verband Tusschen de Weersgesteldheid en de Aardappelziekte (*P. infestans*). *Tijdschr. Plantenziekten, 32:* 129–140.

Ventskevich, G. Z., 1958. *Agrometeorology.* Leningrad.

Vestal, E. F., and F. G. Bell, 1931. A preliminary study of some environmental factors on the spread of *Cercospora* leaf spot and yield in checked and drilled sugar beets. *Am. J. Botany, 18:* 705–716.

Vitkevich, V. I., 1960. *Agricultural Meteorology.* Moscow.

Waggoner, P. E., 1950. Temperature lapse rates over bare ground and over potato plots on peat and mineral soils. *Bull. Am. Meteorol. Soc., 31:* 326–329.

Waggoner, P. E., 1960. Forecasting epidemics. In *Plant Pathology,* edited by J. G. Horsfall and A. E. Dimond; vol. 3, pp. 291–312. Academic Press, New York.

Waggoner, P. E., and R. H. Shaw, 1952. Temperature of potato and tomato leaves. *Plant Physiol., 27:* 710–724.

Wallin, J. R., 1963. Dew, its significance and measurement in phytopathology. From Symposium on Requirements and Interpretations of Biometeorological Observations. *Phytopathology, 53:* 1198–1216.

Wallin, J. R., and J. A. Riley, Jr., 1960. Weather map analysis—an aid in forecasting potato late blight. *Plant Disease Reptr., 44:* 227–234.

Wallin, J. R., and R. H. Shaw, 1953. Studies of temperature and humidity at various levels in crop cover with special reference to disease development. *Iowa State J. Sci., 28:* 261–267.

Wallin, J. R., and P. E. Waggoner, 1950. The influence of climate on the development and spread of *Phytophthora infestans* in artificially inoculated potato plots. *Plant Disease Reptr. Suppl., 190:* 19–33.

Wiltshire, S. P., 1931. The correlation of weather conditions with outbreaks of potato blight. *Roy. Meteorol. Soc. London Quart. J., 57:* 304–316.

Yarwood, C. E., 1939. Relation of moisture to infection with some downy mildews and rusts. *Phytopathology, 29:* 933–945.

Yarwood, C. E., 1959. Microclimate and infection. *Plant Pathol. Probl. Progr. 1908–1958:* 548–556.

Microclimatic Gradients in Mixed Grass Prairie

WARREN C. WHITMAN AND GALE WOLTERS, *Botany Department, North Dakota State University, Fargo, North Dakota*

PHENOLOGICAL STUDIES of native range plants in the mixed grass prairie of the Northern Great Plains, carried on over a period of years at the Dickinson Experiment Station in southwestern North Dakota, have served to indicate the need for information on the actual effective climate in which the grasses exist. Measurements of important environmental factors at a standard weather station about a mile from the study area failed to show a close relationship with observed phenological events. Rather the results obtained seemed to emphasize the truth of the seventh axiom of Platt and Griffiths (1964): "Environmental data obtained in one area cannot be used directly for the understanding of experimental units in another area, 40 feet or 40 miles away." To provide on-the-spot microclimatic measurements for use in interpreting phenological data, a microclimate station was set up in native mixed grass prairie at the Dickinson Station in 1962 (Fig. 1).

Sprague and his associates (1954, 1955) have demonstrated the nature of the temperature and atmospheric moisture gradients over a Kentucky bluegrass sod maintained at a height of about 1½ inches. These measurements, made at State College, Pennsylvania, showed that while the average daily and monthly temperatures at various heights up to eight feet above the sod were practically the same, greater extremes occurred at the lower levels, where temperatures were generally higher in daytime and lower at night. Both daily and monthly temperature ranges were greater near the ground than farther above it.

Fig. 1. Microclimate study area in native mixed grass prairie at the Dickinson Experiment Station in southwestern North Dakota. In the left foreground are the anemometers; in the left background are the supports and holders with the Livingston atmometers. Can-like objects on the pole in the center are housings for the relative humidity units. The slender pole on the right supports the air-temperature thermocouples.

The average moisture content of the air decreased progressively with height above the sod. Greater vapor pressure deficits occurred with increasing heights above the ground, and relative humidities were found to be greater near ground level than above during both maximum and minimum air temperatures. The macroclimate was considered to begin at 60 inches above the ground surface. Members of the Regional Forage Crops Technical Committee (NE-29) (1959) have reported similar relations in the microclimatic stratum above sod in northeastern United States.

Biel (1959) stated that the existence of environmental gradients in the microclimatic layer is no surprise to anyone, but, "The order of magnitude of the differences is amazing indeed." The nature of the environmental gradients in the microclimatic layer above either grazed or ungrazed native grassland seems to have had very little investigation, even though the importance of the microclimate in determining the composition and productivity of grassland has been cited many times (Ellison, 1960; Sprague, 1959; Tomanek, 1959).

As Sprague (1959) has pointed out, the microclimate depends to a large extent on the nature of the plant cover involved: "Thus there may be many different microclimates within short distances of each other, all of which are determined by, and yet have an influence on, the vegetation." The average foliage height of the native mixed grass prairie of the Northern Plains is about six to eight inches, with the flowering stalks of the major grasses attaining average heights of 18 to 24 inches. On this basis it would be expected that the principal microclimatic influences in this grassland normally would be effective from the soil surface to a height not exceeding 2 to 2½ feet.

The native mixed grass prairie of the Northern Great Plains is a continually varying mosaic of species composition and productivity, with major changes in structure and composition varying with topography, soil texture, moisture relations, salts, and various biotic influences, of which grazing by domestic livestock is generally of prime importance. Over extensive areas the principal differences in the cover may consist largely of variations in the relative percentages of the same major grass species, six to eight in number, and in the degree to which minor associated species are present. The mosaic nature of the grassland has been emphasized by Hanson and Whitman (1938), Dyksterhuis (1949), and Ayad and Dix (1964).

The general climate of the mixed grass prairie is characterized as continental, semiarid, and subject to the characteristic variability detailed by Thornthwaite (1941) and Borchert (1950). The long-time climatic averages at the Dickinson station in southwestern North Dakota near the microclimatic study area might be considered as representative, though not average, for the region as a whole. The 73-year average annual precipitation at this station is 15.63 inches, with April–July precipitation averaging 9.26 inches (59 percent of the total), and April–September precipitation 12.26 inches (78 percent of the total). The greatest precipitation on record, 31.16 inches, occurred in 1944, and the least, 6.72 inches, in 1936. Snowfall is usually light, varying from a total of 12 inches to 74 inches, and snow may be expected from October through April.

The average annual temperature at the station is 44°F, with the January average 11.0°, and the July average 69.0°F. The December–

February mean is 13.8°F, and the June–August mean is 65.7°F. The maximum temperature thus far recorded by standard Weather Bureau instruments is 114°F, and the minimum recorded temperature is 47° below zero. Over the period of record the minimum temperatures have dropped below zero an average of 46 times a year, while during the winter period maximum temperatures of over 32°F have been reached an average of 36 times each year. Temperatures of 90°F or warmer occur on 22 days per year, but temperatures of over 100°F are rare.

Open-pan evaporation during the growing season has averaged 31.90 inches, and the average total wind for the April–September period has been about 16,500 miles. Greatest wind velocities are reached in March, April, and May, although tornadic winds of high velocity are experienced occasionally in the summer period. No direct data on sunshine are available, but Rosenberg (1964) pointed out that over the area as a whole the hours of sunshine average 60 to 70 percent of the total possible, and in July and August often 75 percent or more of the maximum possible.

Soil Moisture

Precipitation occurring in the macroclimate comes into direct contact with plant parts in the microclimatic zone, and becomes an integral part of the grassland microclimate as soil moisture. Biel (1959) referred to the "utter" importance of soil moisture. Tomanek (1959) stated that the composition and productivity of Great Plains grassland depend almost entirely on climatic and grazing influences. Ellison (1960) more specifically stated that the two most important factors affecting range productivity are available soil moisture and intensity of grazing. Soil moisture has probably been given more attention as a microclimatic factor in semiarid grasslands than any other single environmental influence because of its importance in relation to seasonal production. Rogler and Haas (1947) and Smoliak (1956) found high correlations between available soil moisture and grassland production in the Northern Plains.

The data given in Table 1 are presented to exemplify the nature of precipitation and soil moisture relations in the mixed grass prairie of the Northern Great Plains and to illustrate their influence on grassland production. The potentially effective precipitation values

Table 1. Potentially effective precipitation, available soil water, use of water in major growth period, and production of vegetation in the mixed grass prairie of southwestern North Dakota, 1962–1964.

Year	Potential effective precipitation[1] (inches)	Inches available water in soil to 48-inch depth					Inches water used in major growth period[2]	Yield of grass—lbs./acre[3]	Lbs. of grass per inch of water used[4]
		May	June	July	Aug.	Avg.			
1962	18.67	4.21	2.02	1.31	0.25	1.95	9.07	2101	232
1963	17.42	3.85	3.48	1.18	0.24	2.19	9.51	3195	336
1964	18.38	2.31	2.06	1.50	0.26	1.53	12.35	2488	201
Avg.	18.16	3.46	2.52	1.33	0.25	1.89	10.31	2595	256

[1] Sept. and Oct. of previous year, March through Aug. of current year.
[2] Major growth period: May 1–July 31. Values are approximate.
[3] Oven-dry weight of all grasses and forbs from experimental plots.
[4] Water used during major growth period.

for the three-year period, 1962–1964, are above the longtime average, and it would be expected that values for available soil water and grass yields also would be above average, as they are. The general tendency for available soil moisture values to be relatively high in the spring and to approach exhaustion by the end of July or early August is well illustrated by the data for inches of available water in the soil to a depth of 48 inches. The general maturity of the natural grass crop corresponds to the exhaustion of available soil water between mid-July and early August.

The inches of water used by the grass crop (actual evapotranspiration) during the major phenological period of May 1 to July 31, given in the table, should be considered as approximations. However, for the particular period of this trial, it seems apparent that about 18 inches of potentially effective rainfall provided an average of about 10 inches of water to be used during the major growth period of the native vegetation. Total production of vegetative material averaged about 250 pounds (dry weight) per inch of water used during the major growth period under the particular microclimatic conditions existing on the experimental site. Granting the "utter" importance of soil moisture, the variability in production indicates that moisture distribution, its availability in relation to times of development of different species in the cover, and temperature conditions prevailing during the principal phenological period of the natural vegetation are also important factors in determining overall productivity of the mixed grass prairie.

Ellison (1960) pointed out that grazing reduces both standing herbage and the accumulation of mulch, with the result that evaporative losses are encouraged, and a lighter, warmer, and drier microenvironment is created. Studies in western North Dakota (Whitman *et al.,* 1964) have shown that mulch accumulations may be reduced by over 50 percent even by moderate grazing of the mixed grass prairie. Duley (1939), Dyksterhuis and Schmutz (1947), Tomanek and Albertson (1953), Hopkins (1954), Osborn (1954), Klemmedson (1956), Rauzi (1960), Reed and Peterson (1961), Johnston (1962), Zeller (1963), and many others have discussed the influence of grazing on mulch removal and subsequent reduction in the rate of water infiltration into the soil.

Hopkins (1954) considered soil temperatures, evaporation from the soil surface, and available moisture to a depth of four feet in relation to the mulch layer in Kansas grassland. He found the mulch layer to be extremely important in reducing soil temperatures, retarding evaporation when the surface soil was moist, and increasing the amount of available moisture in the soil. However, a careful investigation of the influence of forage and mulch removal on the microclimate of mixed grass prairie in the Northern Plains has not been made. The influence of the changing microenvironment associated with forage and mulch removal on competitive relations between species remains as a practically unexplored area of study in natural grasslands.

Another little-studied aspect of precipitation and soil moisture relations in the microclimatic zone near the surface of the soil is the interception of precipitation by growing vegetation and by mulch accumulations. Clark (1940) in Nebraska grassland found that up to 50 percent of one inch of water artificially applied did not reach the soil surface. This seems to be a very high interception value, and observation would indicate that the degree of interception would normally be lower in the mixed grass prairie of the Northern Plains. The scarcity of data regarding interception of precipitation by grassland cover indicates the need for further study of the fate of varying amounts of precipitation falling on grassland cover of varying density and state of development at different times during the year.

Temperature Relations

The most obvious and striking features of the temperature relations in the microclimate above grassland sod are the temperature gradients which can be observed at almost any time of the day or night. Baum (1949), Sprague *et al.* (1954), the Regional Forage Crops Technical Committee (NE-29) (1959), Geiger (1965), and others have shown the general nature of these gradients. Ordinarily the gradient is cooler from the soil surface upward during the day and warmer upward during the night. Maximum gradient ranges are established on warm, bright days and cool, clear nights with minimum air movement (Biel, 1959).

Data from the microclimate study area in the mixed grass prairie of southwestern North Dakota indicate the existence of the same general types of gradient. Figures 2 and 3 illustrate the nature of the gradients that might be expected under extreme conditions. Figure 2 indicates the situation in the mixed grass prairie 1 inch and 1 foot in the air and at 1 inch and 2 feet in the soil on a clear, bright day in late summer, August 9, 1964. On this day the 1-inch air temperature ranged from a low of 57°F at 4:00 A.M. to a high of 122°F by 11:00 A.M. At the same time the 1-foot air temperature went from 59°F to a high of 101°F, the 1-inch soil temperature from 69° to 95°F, while the 2-foot soil temperature stayed nearly constant throughout the day at 72°F.

Figure 3, representing the gradients on a cold day, January 19, 1963, shows that the air temperature at 1 foot ranged from a low of −34°F at 4:00 A.M. to a high of 17°F at 5:00 P.M. At the same time the 1-inch air temperature reached a low of only −16°F and a high of 12°F. There was a 2-inch snow cover on the ground at the time, which obviously had an insulating effect on the soil and air layers near the surface. The soil temperature at 2 feet showed a slight decline during the day, from a relatively warm 25° to 24°F.

The net effect of gradients such as those shown in the figures is to make the range of extremes much greater near the soil surface than it is above. Data from a hot, clear day, August 19, 1963, serve to illustrate this. At 5 feet above the ground the minimum observed temperature was 54°F and the maximum observed was 98°F. At 4 feet the minimum was 54°F and the maximum 98°F. At the 3-foot level the corresponding temperatures were 52° and 101°F; at 2 feet,

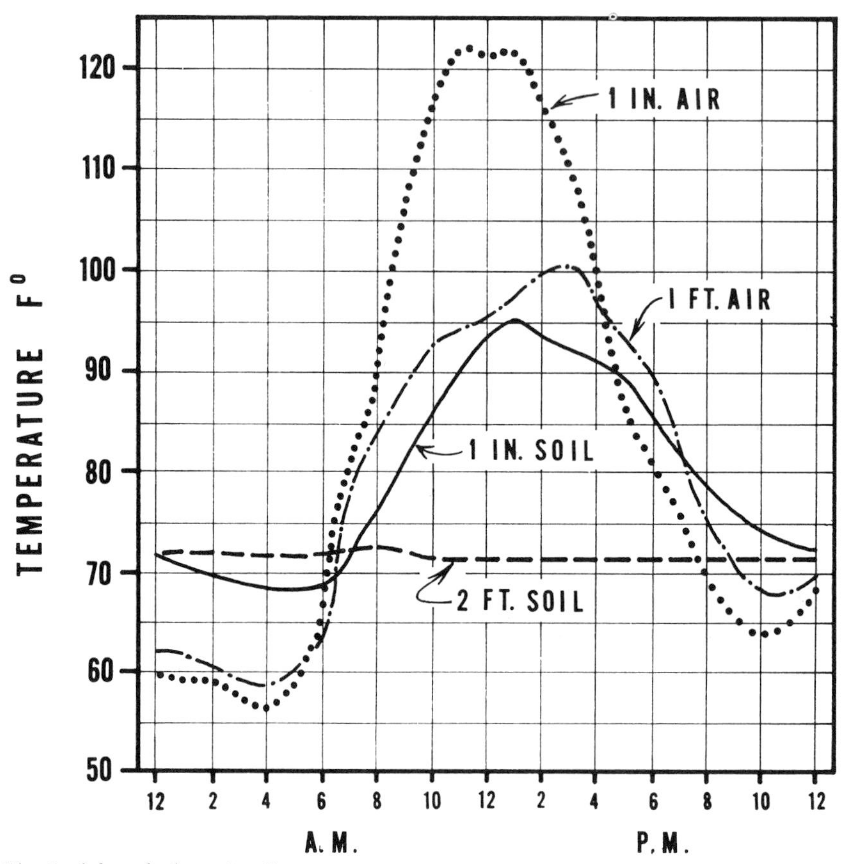

Fig. 2. Selected air and soil temperatures at the microclimate station on a clear, hot day, August 9, 1964.

50° and 99°F; at 1 foot, 49° and 114°F; and at 1 inch above the soil surface a minimum of 48°F and a maximum of 127°F were registered on this date. These data emphasize that with this type of vegetation in its natural state the principal temperature gradient effects are manifested within the 2-foot vertical distance above the soil surface.

The increased severity of the environment as the surface of the ground is approached is well illustrated by the data given in Table 2. For the months of June through September during the 1962–1964 period the air temperature at 5 feet was 90°F or higher an average of 26 times. At 1 foot this temperature was reached an average of 37

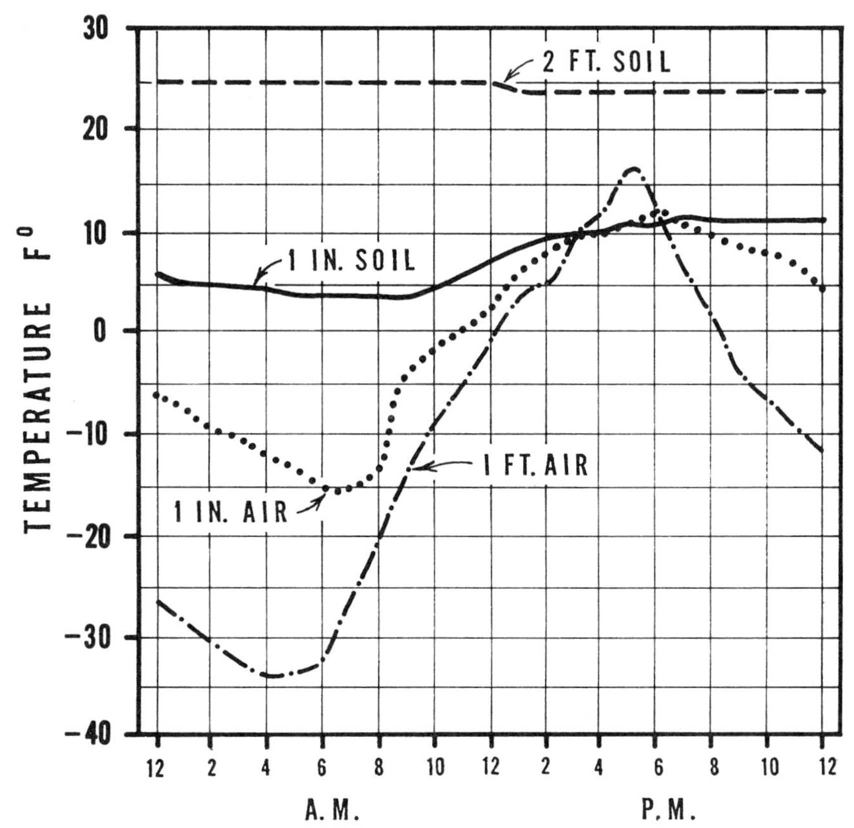

Fig. 3. Selected air and soil temperatures at the microclimate station on a clear, cold day, January 19, 1963.

times; at 6 inches, 46 times; at 3 inches, 54 times; and at 1 inch, 83 times. Since the average leaf-height of the grasses is about 6–8 inches, with stalks extending to a height of about 2 feet, it is apparent that the aerial parts of the plants are subjected to a wide range of temperature conditions, with the major portions of the plants being in the zone of maximum severity.

Diurnal variations in soil temperatures near the surface of the ground have been described by Baver (1961), Geiger (1965), and others. The diurnal variations are apparent mostly in the upper six inches in the soil, while the soil temperatures at greater depths show a progression toward warmer or cooler conditions, depending primarily on season of the year. The general nature of these changes

Table 2. Number of days on which maximum temperatures exceeded 90°F at different heights above native grassland sod during the months June–September.

Height above ground	1962	1963	1964	Average
5 ft.	17	34	28	26
1 ft.	26	47	37	37
6 in.	36	61	42	46
3 in.	41	79	42	54
1 in.	77	97	75	83

is well known, and the nature of the average soil temperature gradients in the mixed grass prairie is shown in Figure 4.

Data for the curves in Figure 4 are from hourly measurements made at ½-inch, 1-inch, 3-inch, 6-inch, 1-foot, 2-foot, 3-foot, and 4-foot depths in the soil under the grassland sod. The weekly averages, all from the 1963 season, represent a cold week, January 13–19; a week when temperatures are nearly the same throughout the profile, March 31–April 4; a week when insolation attains its maximum, June 16–22; and a week when environmental heating has reached the maximum for the season, August 18–24. It is apparent from these data that the subterranean parts of the plants, like the aboveground parts, are operating through an appreciable temperature gradient at most times of the year, with the gradient during the major phenological period being from cooler below to warmer above and varying over an average range of difference of 10 or more degrees Fahrenheit.

Wind

The influence of frictional drag on the movement of the wind over the vegetation of the earth's surface is well known. Presumably, in the grass cover very near the surface of the earth wind movement would be near zero, and air currents would be convectional rather than oriented to the direction of mass air movements. No data are available on direct movement of air in the layer very close to the earth's surface in the mixed grass prairie of the North-

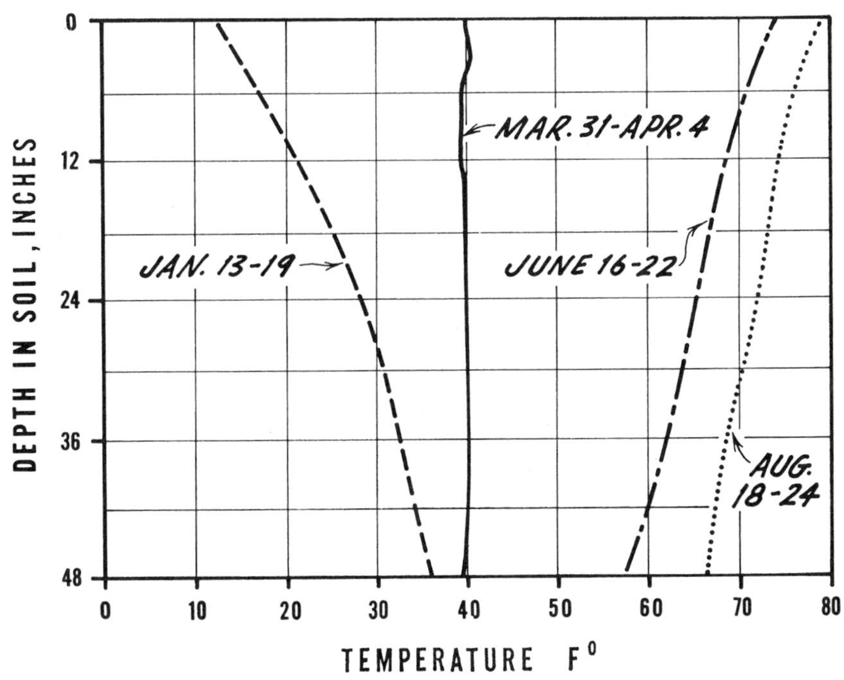

Fig. 4. Soil temperature gradients under native grassland sod from the surface to a depth of 4 feet for selected weeks in the 1963 season.

ern Plains. Observations at the microclimate station at Dickinson over a period averaging 110 days from late May to mid-September during the three-year period, 1962–1964, serve to illustrate the general nature of the wind gradient over the undisturbed native grass sod. The average miles of wind per day at a height of 6 inches above the soil surface was 22.7; at 12 inches, 46.7; at 36 inches, 99.8; and at 5 feet, 126.3. The average velocities thus ranged from less than 1 mile per hour at 6 inches to 5.3 miles per hour at 5 feet.

The average annual wind velocity reported in Weather Bureau records is about 10 miles per hour and the prevailing direction of the wind in all months of the year is from the northwest. Over the three-year period of observation at the microclimate station it was apparent that wind movement over the grassland sod during the 110-day period from late May to mid-September was not so great, even at a height of 5 feet, as that reported as the average for the area.

Figure 5 shows the general nature of the wind gradient as typified by data for the month of July, 1963. Actual measurements, recorded on the basis of total miles of wind movement over a 24-hour period, were made at heights of 6 inches, 1 foot, 3 feet, and 5 feet above the soil surface. In this month, the average velocity of the wind at a height of 6 inches in the well-developed native grass crop was 0.43 miles per hour, while at a height of 5 feet above the sod the average velocity was 4.95 miles per hour.

Evaporation

Data obtained with Livingston atmometer bulbs placed at different heights over the native grassland sod have shown the existence

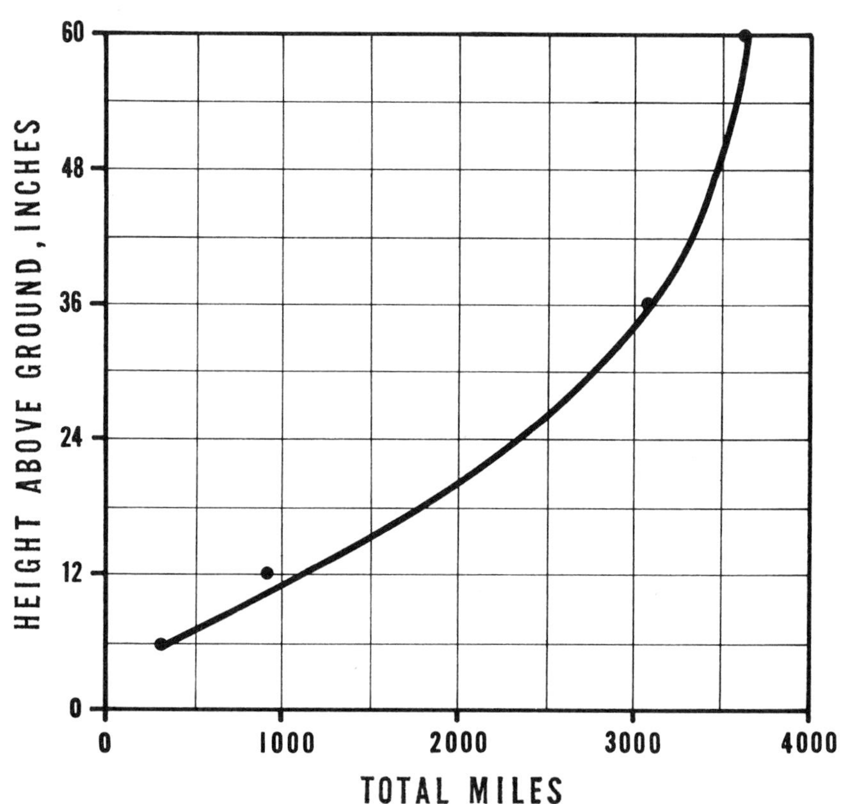

Fig. 5. Total miles of wind in relation to height above ground surface at the microclimate station for the month of July, 1963. Anemometers were located at 6 inches, 12 inches, 36 inches, and 60 inches above the ground. Actual values for total miles of wind were 323 at 6 inches, 923 at 12 inches, 3,145 at 36 inches, and 3,686 at 60 inches.

of a distinct evaporation gradient during the summer months. Table 3 presents a summary of daily evaporation rates from white bulbs at heights of 6 inches, 1 foot, 2 feet, 3 feet, 4 feet, and 5 feet above the sod during the months of June, July, August, and the first half of September. Limited comparative data between white-bulb and black-bulb evaporation are also available from the study.

Evaporation increased progressively with increase in height throughout the 5-foot vertical distance. Daily evaporation at 5 feet averaged about 80 percent greater than at 6 inches in the case of the white bulbs. Black-bulb evaporation rates were about 50 percent greater at 5 feet than at 6 inches. In general black-bulb evaporation averaged about one-third greater than white-bulb evaporation. The steeply rising gradients of evaporation are typified by the curves in Figure 6, where total white-bulb and black-bulb evaporation at the different heights are given for the month of July, 1963.

The shape of the curves in Figure 6 indicates that evaporation rates probably continue to increase for some distance above the height of 5 feet. The increase in evaporation beyond the 5-foot height is probably not related to increased radiant energy or to increased atmospheric evaporative demand, but to greater air movement, as indicated by the wind movement curve shown in Figure 5.

It has been pointed out (Oosting, 1956) that atmometer losses

Table 3. Average daily evaporation from white Livingston atmometer bulbs in native grassland during summer months for the period 1962–1964 in relation to height of bulb above the soil surface. (Loss in cc per 24-hour period.)

Height above surface	June	July	Aug.	Sept.*	Avg.
6 in.	23.9	27.2	37.2	25.1	28.3
1 ft.	31.7	37.1	47.3	33.1	39.5
2 ft.	35.0	41.0	51.0	35.6	40.6
3 ft.	37.9	43.9	54.7	39.2	43.9
4 ft.	39.6	46.1	56.4	40.6	45.7
5 ft.	42.1	47.8	58.9	42.0	47.7
Avg.	35.0	40.5	50.9	35.9	40.9

* Daily average for the first 15 days of the month.

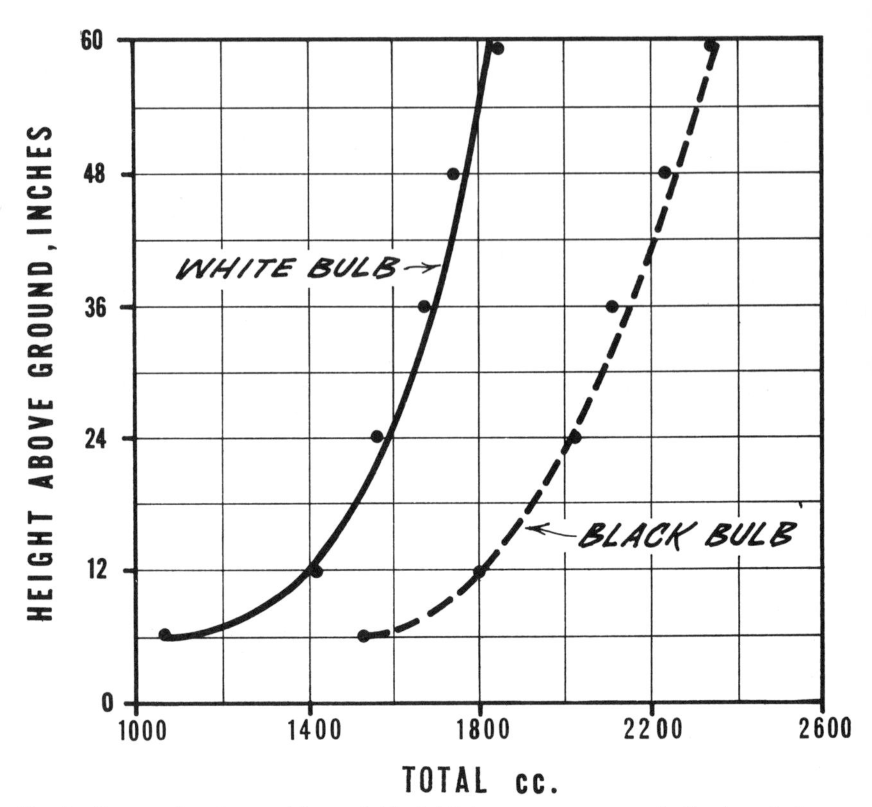

Fig. 6. Evaporation from white and black Livingston atmometer bulbs in relation to height above the ground surface at the microclimate station for the month of July, 1963. Evaporation losses are given in total cc for the month.

are primarily valuable in providing comparative data, and no immediate relation between bulb evaporation and losses by evapotranspiration from the native grass sod would be expected. Tanner and Lemon (1962) stated that where water is plentiful, the evaporative process is restricted only by the supply of energy available. Gerard *et al.* (1959) reported losses of water from grass-covered soil in Texas to be over 0.20 inches per day in July and August. The reported losses were highly correlated with open-pan evaporation and with soil and air temperature.

In the native mixed grass prairie of the Northern Plains water obviously is not plentiful, even during important portions of the major phenological period (May 1–July 31), as shown in Table 1. As the season progresses, more and more of the radiant energy falling on the prairie goes to raising the temperature in the microenvironment and less to the evaporation of water from soil and vegetation, primarily because of scarcity of water in the soil, dry soil surfaces, and physiological maturity of the vegetation.

The average daily evapotranspiration loss during the 91-day major phenological period (1962–1964) at the Dickinson microclimate station was 0.11 inches. The average value given must be considered to represent relatively large early-season losses, when available soil moisture was relatively high and vegetation was green and rapidly growing, summed with later-season losses, when available soil water was practically nonexistent and vegetation was near, if not at, physiological maturity. The transfer of solar radiation from supplying energy for the evaporation of water from the native grass sod to the heating of the soil and the air mass of the general environment is a phase of the description of the grassland microclimate which is of basic importance, as pointed out by Denmead *et al.* (1962). Data are being gathered on solar radiation at the microclimate station, but they are not yet available for interpretation.

Relative Humidity

Sprague (1955) found that atmospheric moisture decreased with increase in height over a Kentucky bluegrass sod in Pennsylvania. In general the same relationship holds for atmospheric moisture over the native grass sod in the mixed grass prairie of the Northern Plains. A distinct gradient was found to exist in relative humidity values recorded hourly during the summer period at heights of 6 inches and 5 feet above the ground surface. The 6-inch level had a higher daily average relative humidity and a higher daily maximum relative humidity with less day-to-day variation than the 5-foot level.

Differences between 6-inch and 5-foot relative humidity values were found to be as much as 25 percentage units or more, but the average was about 5 percentage units. On the season-long basis average relative humidity values at the two heights were found to be closest together at 8:00 A.M., with the three-year average at both heights at this hour being 63 percent. Maximum relative humidity at both heights occurred most frequently at 5:00 A.M. Minimum daily relative humidity values at both heights occurred most frequently between 2:00 P.M. and 4:00 P.M.

Figure 7 shows the general nature of observed relative humidity values at different times during the season, with hourly values at both heights for June 6, July 14, and August 20, 1963. The curves show the progressively lower hourly levels of relative humidity that occur as the season becomes warmer and drier, as soil moisture is depleted, and as the grassland vegetation reaches and passes physiological maturity. The generally higher humidity values at the 6-inch level are also apparent from the curves.

Relative humidity values at the Dickinson grassland microclimate station were recorded hourly from psychrometric elements operating

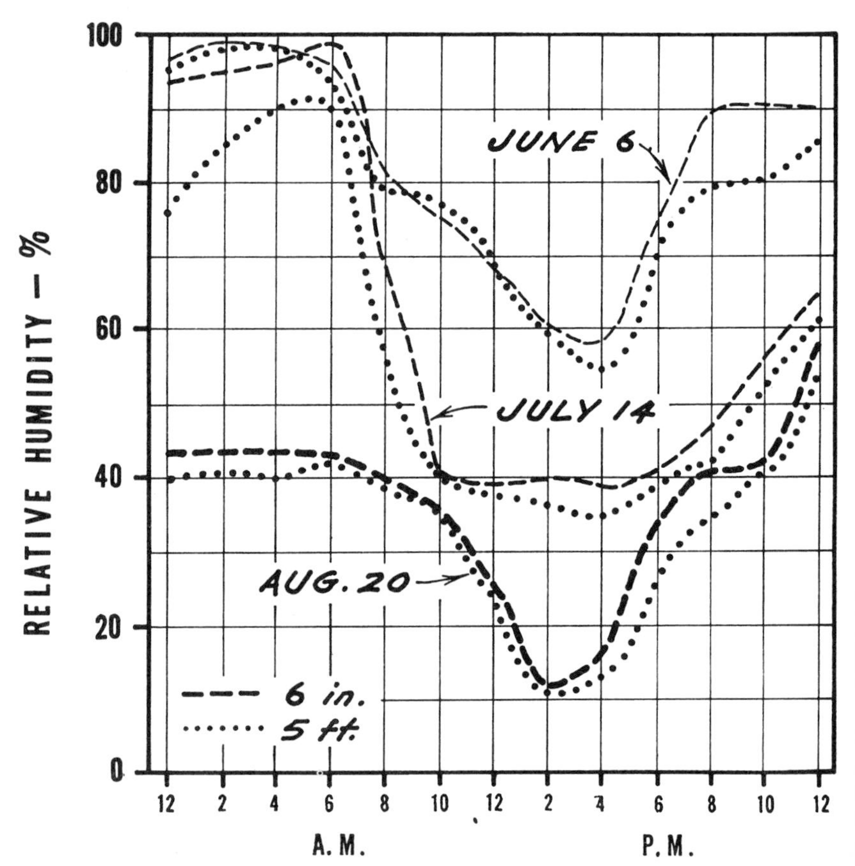

Fig. 7. Representative relative humidity values at 6 inches and 5 feet above native grass for selected days in the months of June, July, and August during the summer of 1963.

on the Dunmore principle, and readings of air temperatures made at the same time permit the conversion of these values to vapor pressure deficits. Vapor pressure deficits provide a better indication of the evaporative potential of the air than relative humidity readings, since the evaporative stresses indicated by the saturation deficit values are valid irrespective of temperature (Oosting, 1956; Sprague, 1955). Table 4 gives the average saturation deficits in mm of mercury for average maximum, average minimum, and average daily relative humidity values during the June-July-August-early September period at the 6-inch and 5-foot heights above the grassland sod.

These data show that while the evaporative potential of the air is generally greater on the average at 5 feet than it is at 6 inches and is also greater at the time of maximum relative humidity, it is not greater at the time minimum relative humidity occurs. Thus the average minimum daily relative humidity value at a height of 6 inches above the sod occurred at an average temperature of 87.9°F with an average vapor pressure deficit of 18.65 mm of mercury. The average minimum relative humidity value at a height of 5 feet above the sod occurred at an average temperature of 82.6°F with an average vapor pressure deficit of 16.52 mm of mercury. Obviously the average minimum relative humidity value of 44.7 percent

Table 4. Average daily maximum, average daily minimum, and average daily relative humidity values at 6 inches and 5 feet above prairie sod in relation to average temperatures and vapor pressure deficits.[1]

Height above ground	Relative humidity		Avg. temperature at time of RH value	Vapor pressure deficit-mm Hg
	Factor	%	(F)	
6 inches	Avg. maximum	92.1	51.4	0.78
	Avg. minimum	44.7	87.9	18.65
	Avg. daily	67.6	68.6	5.82
5 feet	Avg. maximum	88.6	55.8	1.30
	Avg. minimum	42.4	82.6	16.52
	Avg. daily	64.2	68.6	6.40

[1] Averages of relative humidity values and temperatures at time of occurrences are for the summer months, June, July, August, and first half of September over the period 1962–1964.

at the 6-inch height, contrasted to the average minimum relative humidity value of 42.4 percent at the 5-foot height, did not indicate a more favorable evaporative stress at the 6-inch height.

Implications of Studies

The initial studies of microclimate in the Northern Great Plains grassland have served to reveal obvious gaps in our overall knowledge regarding the actual effective climate in which the grass plants live. It might well be desirable to reproduce the grassland microclimate under controlled environmental conditions, so that specific studies of species response to varying treatments, such as defoliation, regulated moisture availability, or adjusted light intensities, could be made. It is doubtful, however, whether such studies could be started effectively now because of our general lack of knowledge of the seasonal dynamics of microclimatic gradients in native grassland.

There do not seem to be any organized bodies of semiarid or arid grassland microclimatological data available for comparative purposes. In order to achieve greater comprehension of reactions by grassland to varying effective climatic conditions it would seem essential to establish a number of microclimatological stations throughout the natural grassland region in each of the major grassland types. Without the availability of data obtained from such stations, the interpretation of primary productivity data in grasslands may be seriously hampered.

The significance of modification of the grassland microenvironment by grazing is an area which requires much more intensive investigation. Sprague (1959) pointed out that the influence of height of foliage removal and systems of grazing management on the modification of moisture, temperature, and light conditions in the microenvironment of tame grass pastures needs to be studied. Certainly such studies applied to the native grasslands of the Northern Plains would have practical as well as theoretical value.

The possibility of the modification of the microenvironment as an aid to securing successful grass seedings in the arid and semiarid grassland regions is very great indeed, and has already received considerable attention. Glendening (1942) in New Mexico made use of a chopped burroweed mulch, straw, and gauze to increase germination and emergence of native grasses. Ellison (1949) attributed slow colonization of bare spaces in depleted subalpine herbland to unfavorable microclimate and concluded that modifications which would increase available soil moisture and decrease surface soil temperatures would be effective in revegetation of such areas. Army and Hudspeth (1960) used sprays of aluminum and white paint, and sheets of polyethylene plastic, roofing paper, and aluminum foil to alter the microclimate in the seed zone for better germination and seedling establishment of grasses. Bement *et al.* (1961) used asphalt-emulsion mulches successfully to hasten establishment of native grasses.

In all such studies a careful evaluation of the degree of microenvironmental modification achieved and an evaluation of the critical levels of the interacting environmental influences are needed. Furthermore, the measurement of the modification of the microenvironment by the developing grass stands and the influence of such modifications on the survival and development of the different grass species is needed for a full understanding of the biology of grass seedling establishment.

Authors' Note: Data reported in this paper were obtained in a study supported in part by National Science Foundation Grants G-17523 and GB-2246. Publication is approved by the Director, North Dakota Agricultural Experiment Station.

REFERENCES

Army, T. J., and E. B. Hudspeth, Jr., 1960. Alteration of the microclimate of the seed zone. *Agron. J., 52:* 17–22.

Ayad, M. A. G., and R. L. Dix, 1964. An analysis of a vegetation-microenvironmental complex on prairie slopes in Saskatchewan. *Ecol. Monographs, 34:* 421–442.

Baum, W. A., 1949. On the relation between mean temperature and height in the layer of air near the ground. *Ecology, 30:* 104–107.

Baver, L. D., 1961. *Soil Physics, 3rd Ed.* John Wiley and Sons, New York.

Bement, R. E., D. F. Hervey, A. C. Everson, and L. O. Hylton, Jr., 1961. Use of asphalt-emulsion mulches to hasten grass seedling establishment. *J. Range Management, 14:* 102–109.

Biel, E. R., 1959. Microclimate and grassland. In *Grasslands,* edited by H. B. Sprague; pp. 263–274. American Association for the Advancement of Science, Washington, D.C.

Borchert, J. R., 950. The climate of the central North American grassland. *Ann. Assoc. Am. Geog., 40:* 1–39.

Clark, O. R., 1940. Interception of rainfall by prairie grasses, weeds, and certain crop plants. *Ecol. Monographs, 10:* 243–277.

Denmead, O. T., L. J. Fritschen, and R. H. Shaw, 1962. Spatial distribution of net radiation in a corn field. *Agron. J., 54:* 505–510.

Duley, F. L., 1939. Surface factors affecting the rate of intake of water by soils. *Soil Sci. Soc. Am. Proc., 4:* 60–64.

Dyksterhuis, E. J., 1949. Condition and management of range land based on quantitative ecology. *J. Range Management, 2:* 104–115.

Dyksterhuis, E. J., and E. M. Schmutz, 1947. Natural mulches or "litter" of grasslands: with kinds and amounts on a southern prairie. *Ecology, 28:* 163–179.

Ellison, L., 1949. Establishment of vegetation on depleted subalpine range as influenced by microenvironment. *Ecol. Monographs, 19:* 95–121.

Ellison, L., 1960. Influence of grazing on plant succession of rangelands. *Botan. Rev., 26:* 1–78.

Geiger, R., 1965. *The Climate Near the Ground, Rev. 3rd Printing.* Harvard Univ. Press, Cambridge, Massachusetts.

Gerard, C. J., M. E. Bloodworth, and W. R. Cowley, 1959. Effect of tillage, straw mulches, and grass upon soil moisture losses and soil temperatures in the lower Rio Grande Valley. *Texas Agr. Exp. Sta. Misc. Publ., 382:* 1-15.

Glendening, G. E., 1942. Germination and emergence of some native grasses in relation to litter cover and soil moisture. *J. Am. Soc. Agron., 34:* 797–804.

Hanson, H. C., and W. C. Whitman, 1938. Characteristics of major grassland types in western North Dakota. *Ecol. Monographs, 8:* 57–114.

Hopkins, H. H., 1954. Effect of mulch upon certain factors of the grassland environment. *J. Range Management, 7:* 255–258.

Johnston, A., 1962. Effects of grazing intensity and cover on the water-intake rate of fescue grassland. *J. Range Management, 15:* 79–82.

Klemmedson, J. O., 1956. Interrelations of vegetation, soils, and range conditions induced by grazing. *J. Range Management, 9:* 134–138.

Oosting, H. J., 1956. *The Study of Plant Communities. 2nd Ed.* W. H. Freeman & Co., San Francisco.

Osborn, B., 1954. Effectiveness of cover in reducing soil splash by raindrop impact. *J. Soil Water Conserv., 9:*70–76.

Platt, R. B., and J. Griffiths, 1964. *Environmental Measurement and Interpretation.* Rheinhold Publ. Co., New York.

Rauzi, F., 1960. Water-intake studies on range soils at three locations in the Northern Plains. *J. Range Management, 13:* 179–184.

Reed, M. J., and R. A. Peterson, 1961. Vegetation, soil, and cattle responses to grazing on Northern Great Plains range. *U. S. Dept. Agr. Forest Serv. Tech. Bull., 1252:* 1–79.

Regional Forage Crops Management Technical Committee (NE-29), 1959. Forage climates in the Northeast. (N.E. Reg. Publ. 43). *Penn. State Univ. Agr. Exp. Sta. Bull., 653:* 1–33.

Rogler, G. A., and H. J. Haas, 1947. Range production as related to soil moisture and precipitation on the Northern Great Plains. *J. Am. Soc. Agron., 39:* 378–389.

Rosenberg, N. J., 1964. Solar energy and sunshine in Nebraska. *Nebraska Univ. Agr. Exp. Sta. Res. Bull., 213:* 1–31.

Smoliak, S., 1956. Influence of climatic conditions on forage production of shortgrass rangeland. *J. Range Management, 9:* 89–91.
Sprague, M. A., 1959. Microclimate as an index of site adaptation and growth potential. In *Grasslands,* edited by H. B. Sprague; pp. 49–57. American Association for the Advancement of Science, Washington, D.C.
Sprague, V. G., 1955. Distribution of atmospheric moisture in the microclimate above a grass sod. *Agron. J., 47:* 551–555.
Sprague, V. G., H. Neuberger, W. H. Orgell, and A. V. Dodd, 1954. Air temperature distribution in the microclimatic layer. *Agron. J., 46:* 105–108.
Tanner, C. B., and E. R. Lemon, 1962. Radiant energy utilized in evapotranspiration. *Agron. J., 54:* 207–212.
Thornthwaite, C. W., 1941. Atlas of climatic types in the United States 1900–1939. *U.S. Dept. Agr. Misc. Publ., 421.*
Tomanek, G. W., 1959. Effects of climate and grazing on mixed prairie. In *Grasslands,* edited by H. B. Sprague; pp. 371–377. American Association for the Advancement of Science, Washington, D.C.
Tomanek, G. W., and F. W. Albertson, 1953. Some effects of different intensities of grazing on mixed prairie near Hays, Kansas. *J. Range Management, 6:* 299–306.
Whitman, W. C., D. Zeller, and A. J. Bjugstad, 1964. Influence of grazing on factors affecting water intake rates of range soils. *Proc. N. Dakota Acad. Sci., 18:* 71.
Zeller, D., 1963. *Certain Mulch and Soil Characteristics on Major Range Sites in Western North Dakota as Related to Range Condition.* M.S. Thesis, N. Dakota State Univ., Fargo, North Dakota.

III. Ground Level Climate and Animals

Climatic Effects on Physiology and Productivity of Cattle

H. D. JOHNSON, *Department of Dairy Husbandry, University of Missouri, Columbia, Missouri*

A DISCUSSION OF the environmental influence on the physiology and productive capacity of animals should emphasize the aspects of the physiology underlying production and the effect of the microenvironment. It is important to point out the integrated efforts of micrometeorologists, environmental physiologists, and personnel concerned with the productivity of animals.

This paper will be limited to environmental studies on the whole-animal physiology of cattle using lactation as a measure of production. A physiological interpretation of the climatic or environmental effects on the animals will be presented from the point of view of heat balance with the modifying influence of various hormones, and the effects of these factors on production. Because a greater amount of physiological research data is available from warm climates, high environmental temperature conditions will be emphasized.

Environment

The climatic environment, consisting principally of temperature, humidity, radiation, and air velocity, affects all domestic species ranging from the smaller poultry to the largest cattle (Johnson, 1965a). The surrounding microenvironment and the animals' ability to adjust physiologically to the extremes in the microclimate vary with the species. Of course the regional climate sets the limits for the microclimate unless shelters are used for modification.

Figure 1 shows climatographs relating temperature to relative humidity and to wind of various localities in the United States.

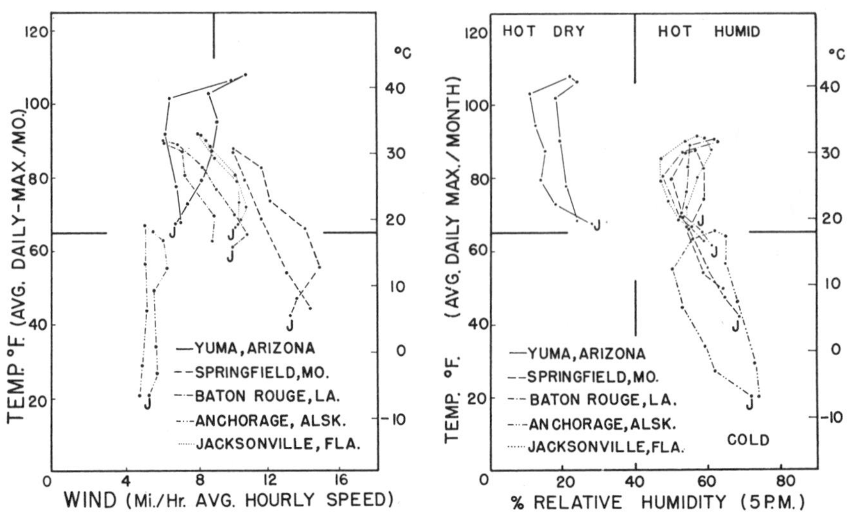

Fig. 1. Climatographs relating temperature to wind in the left section and to humidity in the right section for various climatic regions in North America (J refers to the mean monthly value for January).

The ideal temperature for most domestic species is, generally, within the range of 4° to 24°C. All of these species can normally survive in climatic regions where mean temperatures are greater or less than these, but they must adjust physiologically and, as a result, there are losses in productivity.

Other factors of the natural environment, such as wind, humidity, diurnal cycles, and an environment modified by shelters, alter the physiological compensations required by the animals. An area in the center of each climatograph would be most favorable for productivity. The humidity, temperature above 24°C, the air velocity, and radiation below 4° and above 24°C ambient temperature are of special concern. The advantages or disadvantages of these various combinations to the physiological status and productivity of domestic animals have been studied extensively only for temperature and humidity (Johnson *et al.*, 1962). The relative effects of all the varied combinations remain to be studied on all domestic animals.

Microclimatic Influence on Physiology and Productivity

The controlled climatic conditions provided by a laboratory are essential to further understanding of the mechanisms by which various environmental complexes may influence physiological functions and behavior.

Figure 2 shows how environmental heat and cold produce physiological compensations and adjustments necessary to maintain heat balance within tolerable limits by the organism and, as a result, to modify productivity.

The relationship of the environment to productivity is emphasized in this paper. There are numerous excellent reviews describing environmental influences on physiological mechanisms of temperature regulation (Carlson, 1964; Hammel, 1965, 1966; Hardy, 1961, 1965; Lind, 1964).

It is generally known that cold, either of the skin or through the hypothalamus, will increase heat production by shivering or nonshivering thermogenesis and by stimulation of endocrine-releasing factors in the hypothalamus such as TSH, ACTH, and STH, which are calorigenic hormones (Carlson, 1964; Hammel, 1965; Hardy,

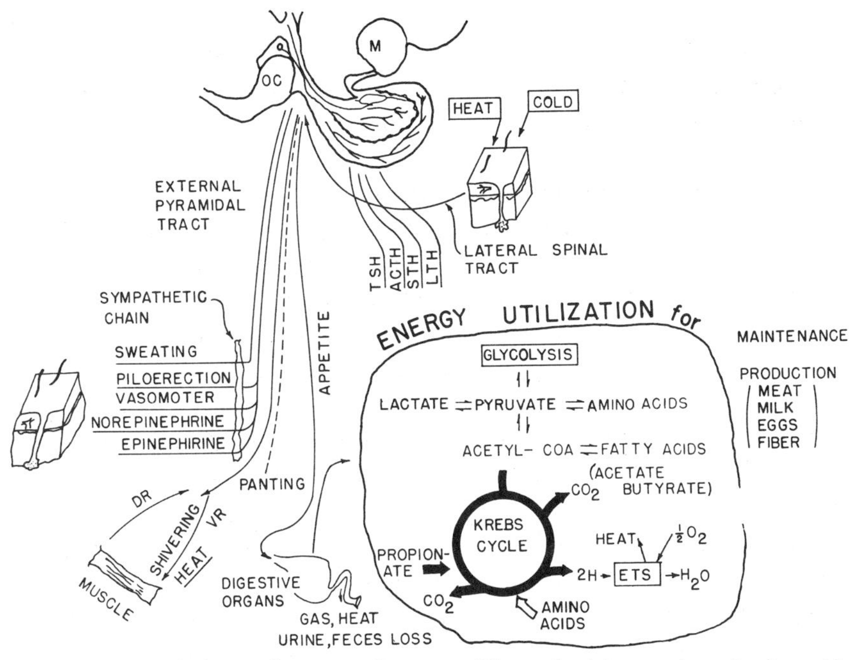

Fig. 2. Scheme relating environment (heat or cold) to physiology and production with emphasis on physiological mechanisms involved in temperature regulation and subsequent influence on production of a homoiothermic animal.

1961). Cold also increases the appetite (Brobeck, 1960; Stevenson, 1962), and the greater appetite will provide more substrate for heat production through energy utilization.

The action of hot environmental temperatures through the skin or the hypothalamus will activate heat-loss mechanisms such as panting, sweating, surface moisture diffusion, and urination. These compensate for the lessened ability of the animals to dissipate heat from body surfaces by non-evaporative cooling. The appetite decreases (Hamilton, 1965; Johnson *et al.*, 1963) and there is less synthesis of calorigenic hormones such as thyroxine, adrenal cortical hormones, growth hormone, and possibly others. The lowered feed substrate at high temperatures will result in less heat production or energy utilization and aid in maintenance of heat balance. The increase in efficiency of phosphorylation, principally by the electron transport system, may also theoretically lower the quantity of heat that must be dissipated. If heat production does not equal heat dissipation, body temperature will change. A higher body temperature, as previously suggested, will lower feed substrate to cells and lessen the calorigenic hormone levels. This decreased hormone production may aid in producing less heat per unit of O_2 consumption by influencing the phosphorylation mechanisms (Yousef and Johnson, 1966).

At high environmental temperatures the animal compensates by lowering its input into the energy-utilizing system, resulting in less O_2 consumption and less energy for maintenance and production. Cold has essentially the opposite effects on the functions described. Productivity normally reflects only the physiological compensations the organism undergoes under various environmental situations.

Specific areas in the hypothalamus respond to the temperature of the microclimate surrounding the animal. Figure 3 is a diagram of coordinates taken from De Groot (1959) which will be used to describe some of the centers. The major nuclei of the hypothalamus are shown and the areas responsible for heat production, heat loss, and related functions of thirst and appetite are indicated. Pertinent publications are Andersson (1964) and Hardy (1961). The areas controlling the releasing factors for various tropic hormones such as TSH, ACTH, growth, LH, and LTH are shaded on the diagram. These factors or functions were previously summarized by Meites

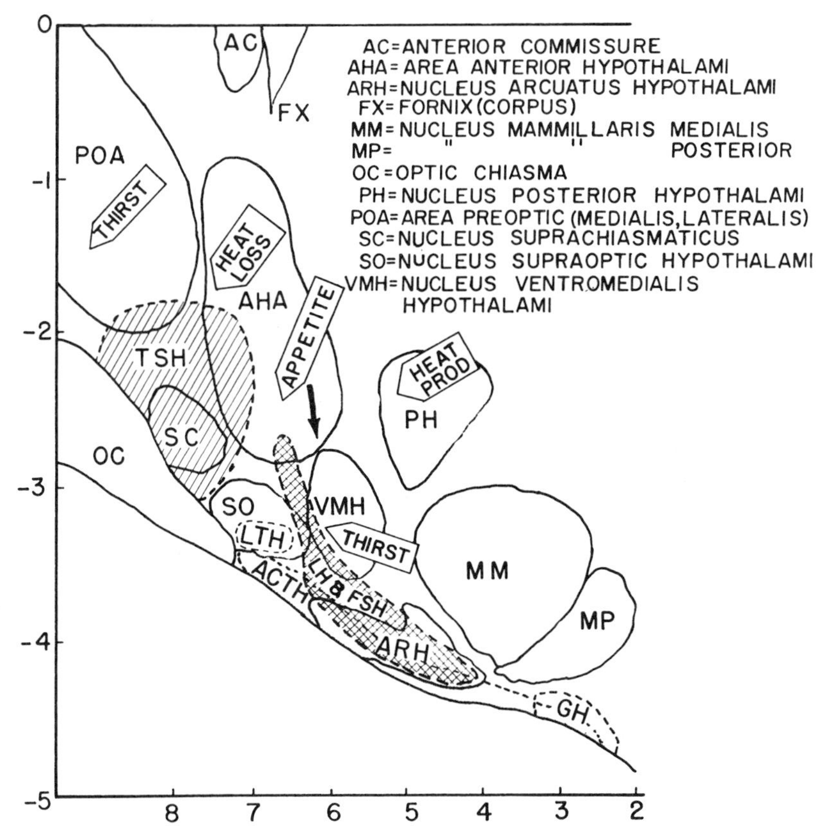

Fig. 3. Diagram of major areas of the hypothalamus with areas that are generally believed to be responsible for functions indicated (De Groot, 1959).

et al. (1963), Reichlin (1964), and Smith (1965). The relation of these releasing factors to energy utilization and its resultant effect on heat balance was suggested in Figure 2.

Heat Balance

Holstein animals, representative of domestic European cattle, showed a rise in rectal temperature around 25°C (Fig. 4), primarily because of increasing skin temperature which prevents loss of heat by non-evaporative cooling. Respiratory rates increased because of the rising body or hypothalamic temperature at 20°–25°C environmental temperature.

Total vaporization, which includes both respiratory and surface vaporization, shows a tremendous increase above 20°C. Water intake

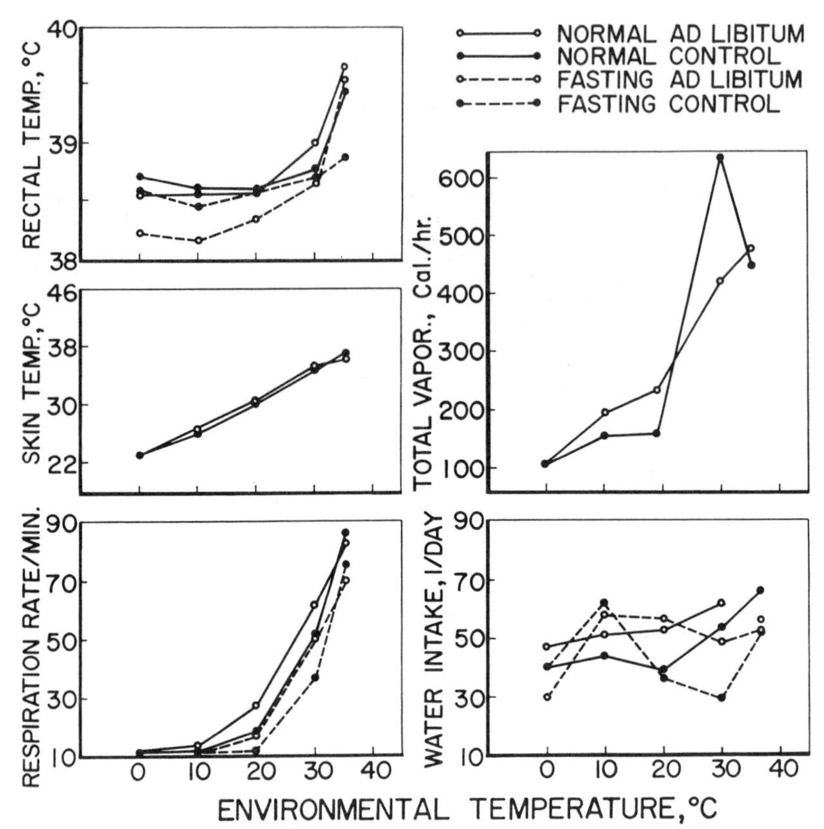

Fig. 4. Major functions of cattle that relate to heat dissipation of fed and fasting animals. "Normal" refers to animals that were fed. "Control" refers to a fixed level of feeding at all temperatures (the amount normally consumed at 18°C). The feed refused by a control-fed animal was added through a rumen cannula.

increases to provide moisture for increased vaporization and urination (Fig. 4). More detailed data on water balance of cattle were published by Johnson and Yeck (1964).

The dotted lines in Figure 4 refer to data obtained on these animals which were fasted approximately 24 hours. Animals fed *ad libitum* had a complete ration consisting of 40 percent grain mixture and 50 percent alfalfa. The control-fed animals were fed typical dairy grain and supplement mixture and were restricted or force-fed to their voluntary level of feed intake at 18°C by the rumen cannula at all temperatures (Fig. 5).

With fasted animals the heat production and energy utilization

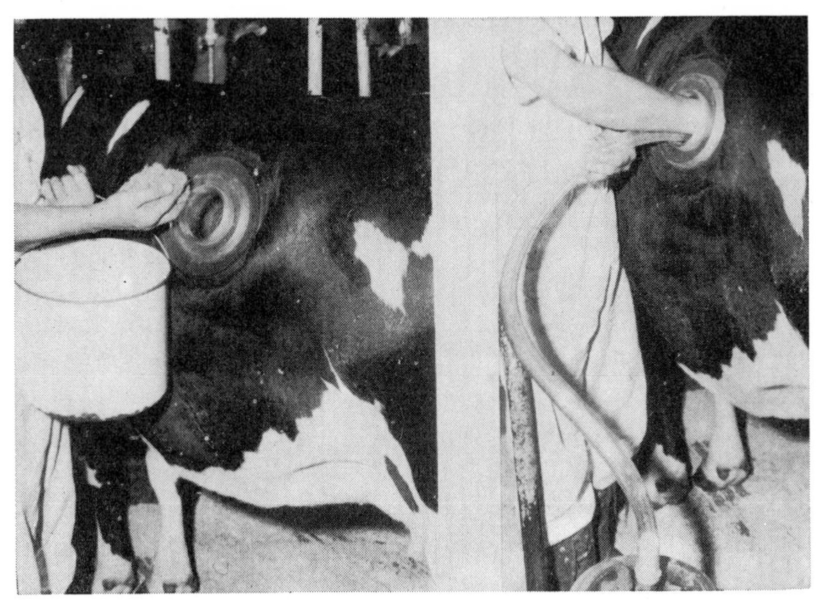

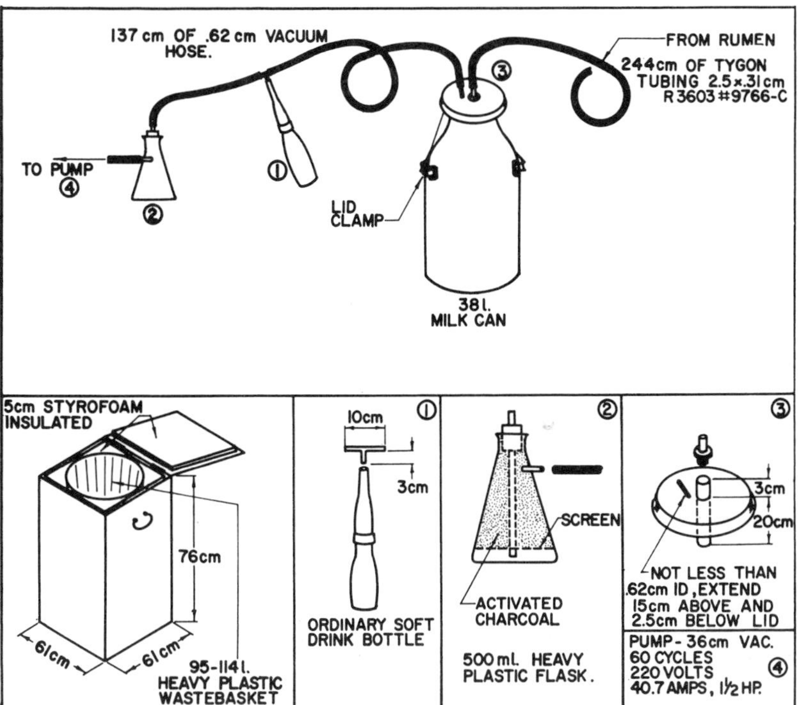

Fig. 5. The technique of force-feeding and fasting of Holstein animals. The lower section describes the apparatus for removal of rumen contents.

was much lower, resulting in considerably less hyperthermia at the higher temperatures and even somewhat lower body temperatures below environmental temperatures of 18°C. Animals were fasted by removal of rumen contents through the rumen fistula (Fig. 5).

Heat production and related functions of these same animals are shown in Figure 6. At temperatures below 18°C, *ad libitum*-fed animals had a higher heat production because of greater feed intake. The control-fed animals increased heat production considerably at temperatures below 18°C, presumably because of shivering and non-shivering thermogenesis. Upon exposure to these colder temperatures most animals shivered somewhat for 24 to 48 hours. This was especially true of fasting animals, as is shown by the pronounced increase in heat production at 1°C.

At temperatures above 18°C the control-fed animals tended to

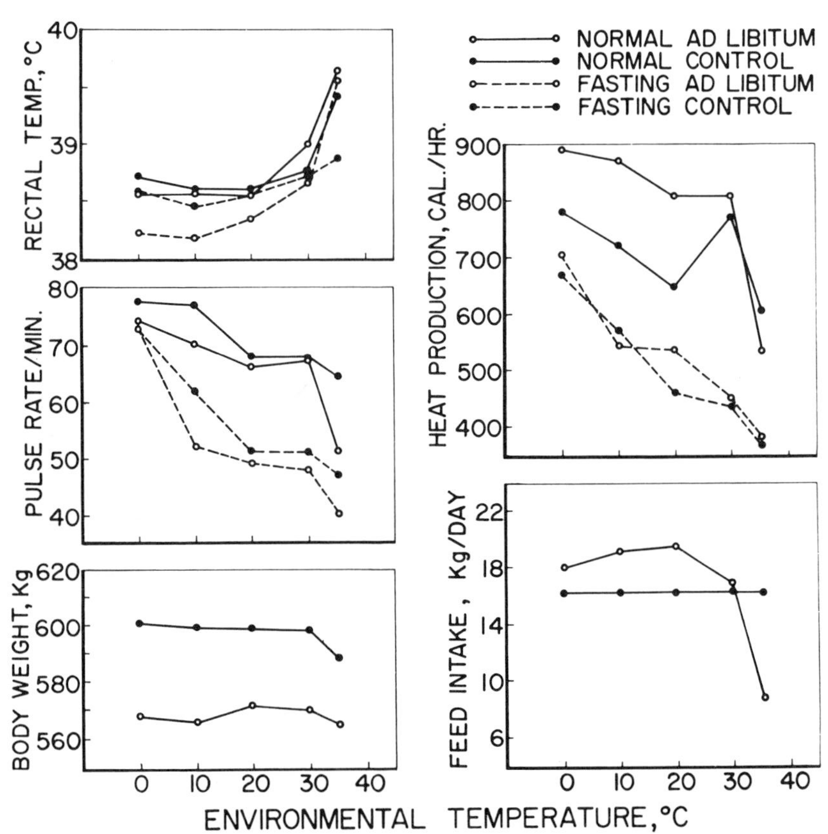

Fig. 6. Some functions of cattle that relate to heat production.

decline less in heat production than the *ad libitum*-fed animals. At 35°C the heat production of the control-fed animals was even higher than that of the *ad libitum*-fed animals. Pulse rates tended to verify the responses observed in heat production.

All of these data related to heat production serve to emphasize the influence of caloric intake on heat balance and the effect of environmental temperature on voluntary feed intake.

Hormonal Effects on Heat Balance

Information on the rate of hormonal output as it relates to heat balance is rather limited. Macfarlane (1963) has an excellent review on the effects of hot environments on endocrine functions. He described the available data on effects of environmental heat on cortical steroids and catecholamines of human subjects and suggested that a generally lowered level of these hormones exists after considerable duration of exposure to heat. A lowered excretion of 17-OHCS (17-hydroxycorticosteroids) in sheep was also reported by Macfarlane.

These lowered values as a result of prolonged exposure to heat are in agreement with recent data on cattle (Bergman and Johnson, 1963) and rats (Kotby and Johnson, unpublished). Peripheral utilization of thyroxine I^{131} by *ad libitum*-fed animals (Fig. 7) showed an elevation at 1°C and declines at temperatures above 18°C. A calorigenic hormone in this manner aids in maintenance of heat balance.

More limited data on plasma hydrocortisone of cattle suggest a lowered functional level of this hormone which has some calorigenic action (Yousef, 1966). Much more information is needed to clarify the secretory function of this gland at both hot and cold environmental temperatures.

Catecholamines, which play a role in both heat loss and heat production, are important, but again little information is available for hot and cold temperatures. Data by Alvarez and Johnson (1966) suggest that urinary excretion of noradrenaline is increased at higher environmental temperatures, although adrenaline appears to be the most potent sudomotor drug (Findlay and Robertshaw, 1965).

The relationship of other hormones to heat balance and the environment awaits intensive investigation by environmental physiologists.

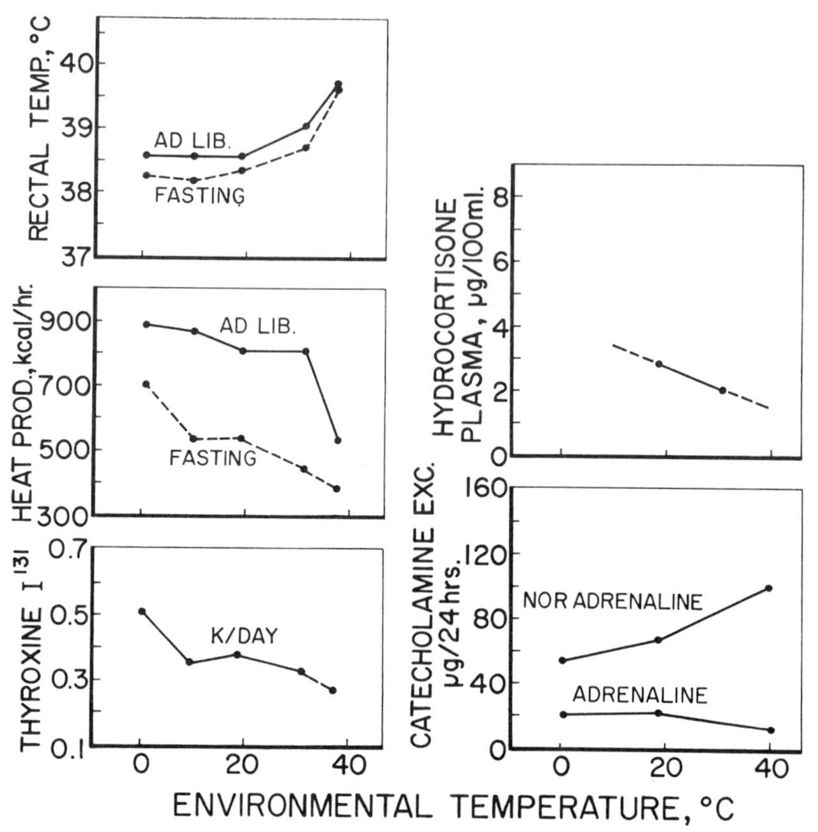

Fig. 7. Relationship of some endocrine functions to heat production at various environmental temperatures. From data of Bergman (1963) on plasma hydrocortisone and Alvarez (1966) on catecholamine excretion.

Calorigenesis

Since the relation of hormones to heat production may also relate to heat balance and higher environmental temperatures, a series of studies was initiated by this laboratory. Three hormones of special interest at high environmental temperatures are hydrocortisone, growth hormone, and thyroxine. The results, summarized in Figure 8, illustrate the time and percentage of increase in heat production for each of the intravenously injected hormones.

The metabolic effects of hydrocortisone, growth hormone, and thyroxine are manifested at approximately 3, 10, and 48 hours respectively at 18°C, and somewhat sooner at the hot temperatures (32° and 38°C). The effective time of the hormones seems to be

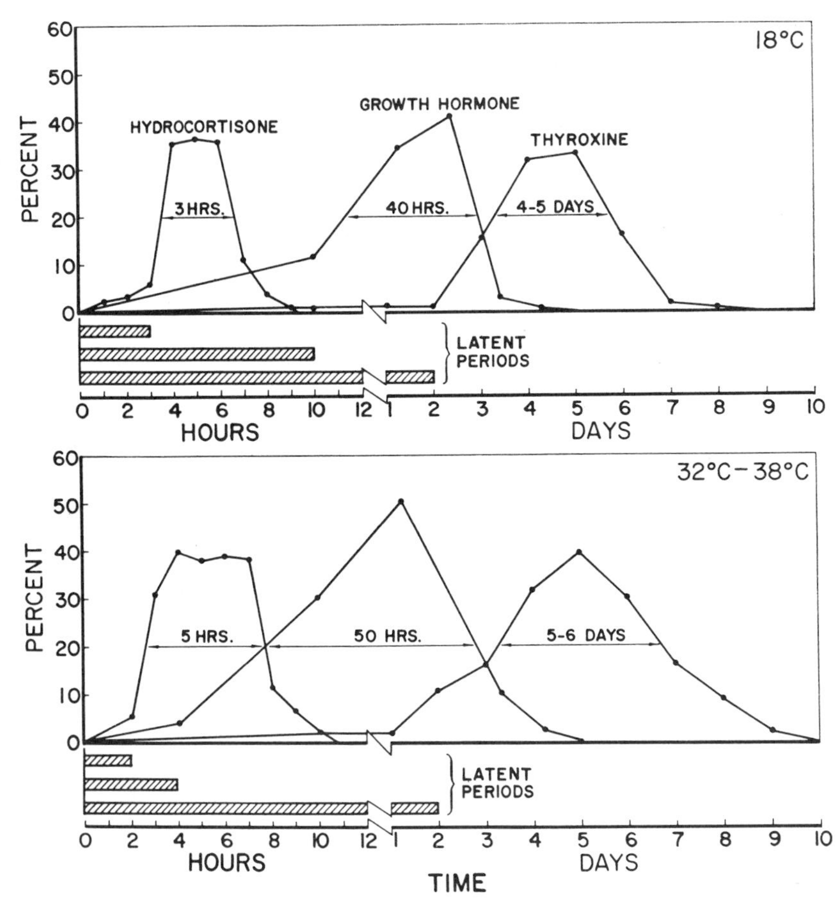

Fig. 8. A summary of effects of calorigenic hormones on heat production in cattle at various environmental temperatures (Data from Yousef, 1966).

greater at the higher environmental temperatures, indicating a slower utilization of the hormones. The full importance of the sequence of hormonal action and their role in physiological adjustment of cattle suddenly exposed to a high environmental temperature requires further study. Since a period of time is required for the cellular utilization of a normal secretory level at 18°C, the ability for rapid acclimation may be altered by the relative secretory levels of these hormones. This may account for some of the initial discomfort observed in laboratory animals when suddenly exposed to heat. We have observed that after a period of three to four days, licking and excessive panting tend to subside although the body temperatures remain elevated. Cattle are observed to display these actions even though they may not have attained their maximum body temperature following exposure to an environmental temperature which elevates the rectal temperature approximately 3°C.

Lactation as a Measure of Production

One may consider the use of hormones or force-feeding to maintain an elevated metabolism at a high environmental temperature as a means of promoting greater lactation, providing the calorigenic actions would not limit this function. Rather than use hormones, this laboratory several years ago used a force-feeding technique on lactating cattle which were fitted with a rumen cannula (Wayman *et al.,* 1962). This permitted feeding through the rumen cannula, at a higher temperature, the same amount of feed the animal would have eaten voluntarily at 18°C. The objective was to determine if the amount force-fed would be used by the animal for maintenance and lactation; normally both would have declined. Figure 9 illustrates that the force-fed or control-fed animals declined significantly less in lactation than *ad libitum*-fed animals. Force-feeding did not help maintain thyroid function; it declined even further at the high temperature (Lundgren and Johnson, 1964). Perhaps a combination of specific hormones and feed would be even more effective in maintenance of lactation. However, this maintenance of lactation at an elevated ambient temperature may cause deterioration of other physiological mechanisms as described by Johnson (1965b). Except for practical difficulties, the technique of force-feeding is useful in clarifying many interrelated mechanisms associated with temperature regulation and performance, for example lactation or growth. Although lactation was somewhat greater in control-fed cattle, the ratio of TDN (total digestible nutrients) in feed to FCM (fat-corrected 4 percent milk) was greater, suggesting less efficiency (Fig. 10). Furthermore, one may speculate that the lactogenic and related hormones may be depressed by the heat, thus reducing the animals' use of the fixed-feed intake. There is evidence that the physiological activity of the rumen is lessened at the higher environmental temperatures (Kelley *et al.,* 1965).

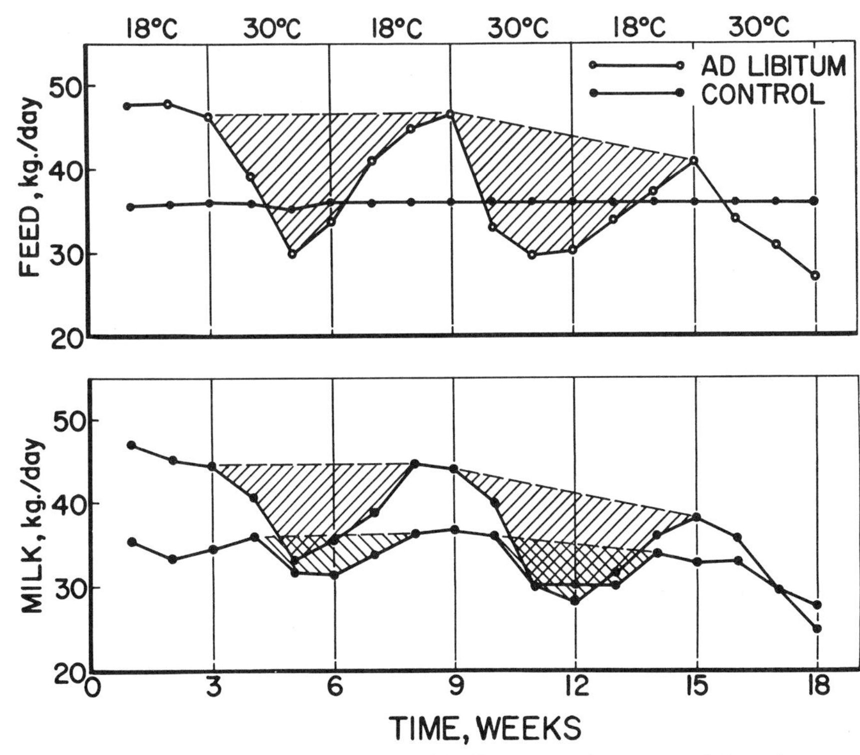

Fig. 9. Effect of *ad libitum-* and control-feeding on maintenance of lactation at a higher environmental temperature of 30°C. Control-fed animals were fed by rumen cannula the same amount at 18° and 30°C.

Energy Utilization as Related to Environment and Productivity

In reference to the general scheme of Figure 2, with special attention to energy utilization (Fig. 11) as related to the microclimate, we observe that a cow with a high level of lactation has approximately twice the level of heat production or O_2 consumption of a fasting cow and much more than non-lactating cattle.

Temperatures for Minimum Heat Production

Some data which show minimum values show no distinct minimum zone of heat production. The minimum heat production values for these animals are near lethal rectal temperatures. The control-fed animals appeared to increase heat production at 35°C.

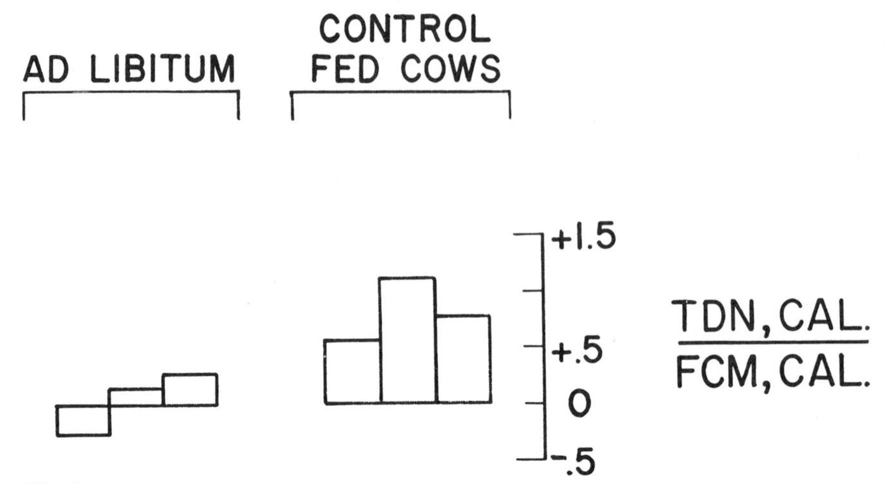

Fig. 10. A gross estimation of conversion of TDN to milk energy by the two groups of cows. The ratio TDN/FCM is based on the difference in the ratio between 65° and 88°F environmental temperatures. TDN refers to total digestible nutrients in the feed. FCM to the milk energy, i.e., fat-corrected milk (fat calculated at 4 percent).

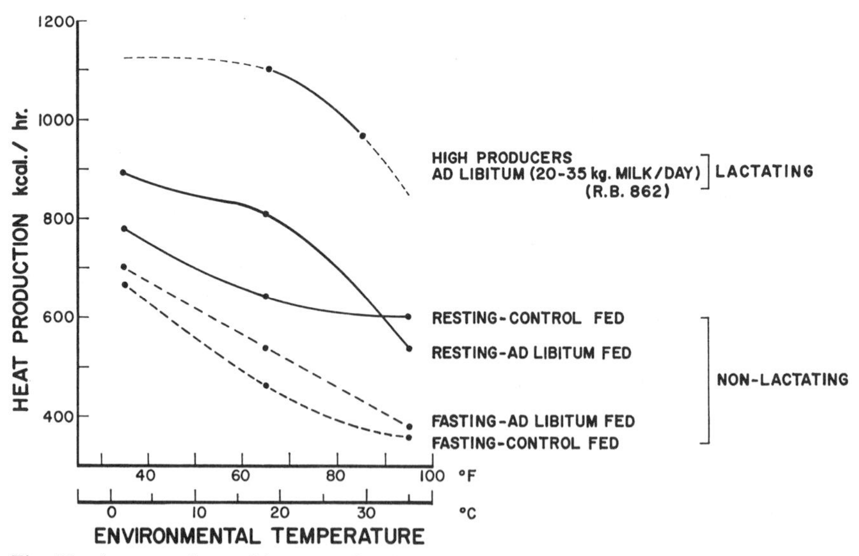

Fig. 11. A comparison of heat production of lactating and non-lactating cattle (Holstein), and a comparison of *ad libitum*-fed and fasting animals at various environmental temperatures.

At temperatures below 18°C the fasting animals increased heat production considerably more than normal lactating animals.

Thus the zone of minimum heat production is not in the "thermoneutral zone" or "comfort zone". The caloric requirements for maintenance of body function are shown by the fasting data to be much less at the higher environmental temperatures.

Theoretical Estimates of Heat Loss Requirements for Lactation at High Environmental Temperature

Figure 12 aids in quantitation of heat balance and helps visualize the magnitudes involved in maintaining heat balance at a high environmental temperature.

Using a lactating Holstein cow as an example, we find that if heat balance (no increase in rectal temperature) is to be maintained at a high environmental temperature an extra 398 kcal of heat must be dissipated as effective vaporization if heat production is to remain stable. This would probably require drinking approximately an extra 16 liters of water a day. Heat balance in this manner may

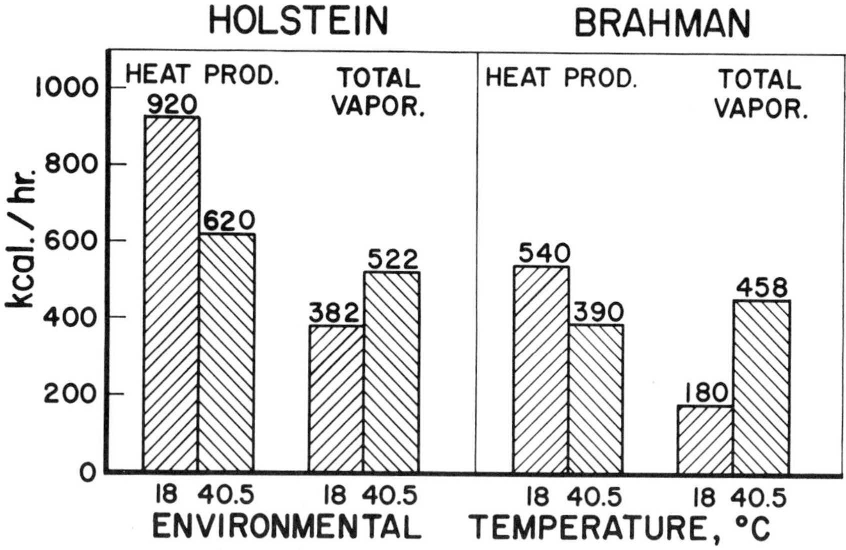

Fig. 12. Heat production and total vaporization of Holstein and Brahman animals at 18° and approximately 40°C. The illustration is for purposes of estimating the magnitude of vaporization or heat loss necessary to maintain heat production of lactating cows at a high environmental temperature (Data from Kibler and Brody, 1950, 1951, 1952).

conceivably be possible in a hot (40.5°C) microclimate, if the peripheral temperature effect does not depress needed physiological functions normally associated with lactation, feed intake, etc., at the more favorable microenvironment of 18°C. Rather than suggest that it is physically, physiologically, or genetically impossible, it may be regarded as a challenge to environmental physiologists and engineers to search for means by which an animal may maintain productivity and heat balance.

Those factors which influence heat balance may be evaluated by determining the full potential of an animal's ability to drink, involving the possible control of neurohormonal and other mechanisms, greater efficiency of heat production mechanisms and heat utilization, and stimulatory actions on heat dissipation by the skin. Note that a lactating Brahman animal (Fig. 12) would need only approximately 100 kcal as vaporization to accomplish heat balance at 40°C.

Conclusion

Productivity depends on the microclimate, particularly its temperature, and an integrated concept of the physiology involved. To maintain domestic animals in an unfavorable microclimate (outside the climate zone where homoiothermy is maintained) requires compensations in heat production and heat-loss mechanisms. Greater knowledge of these compensations and interactions would permit a basis to increase productivity under adverse microclimates.

Some functions of the central nervous system pertaining to appetite, heat regulation, and hormonal involvement are most important in maintaining efficient energy utilization. Climatologists, engineers, physiologists, production specialists, and others must cooperate in investigating the environment-physiology-production complex and jointly develop engineering, bioengineering, or physiological methods of maintenance of the organism in the most favorable microclimate for physiological efficiency of energy conversion.

Author's Note: Special acknowledgment is made for the assistance of the staffs of Agricultural Engineering Research Division (AERD), Agricultural Research Service (ARS), U. S. Department of Agriculture, at Beltsville, Maryland, and Columbia, Missouri. I am particularly indebted to H. H. Kibler, Leroy Hahn, M. D. Shanklin, and M. K. Yousef, in the Department of Agricultural Engineering and Dairy, University of Missouri, for the use of unpublished data.

REFERENCES

Alvarez, M., and H. D. Johnson, 1966. Urinary excretion of adrenaline and nor-adrenaline in cattle during heat and cold exposure. *4th Intern. Biometeorol. Congr.,* New Brunswick, New Jersey.

Andersson, B., 1964. Hypothalamic temperature and thyroid activity. In *Brain-Thyroid Relationships,* edited by M. P. Cameron and M. O'Connor; pp. 35–50. Little Brown and Co., Boston, Massachusetts.

Bergman, R. K., and H. D. Johnson, 1963. Temperature effects on plasma cortisol of cattle. *J. Animal Sci., 22:* 854.

Brobeck, J. R., 1960. Food and temperature. In *Recent Progress in Hormone Research,* edited by Gregory Pincus; vol. 16, pp. 439–466. Academic Press, New York.

Carlson, L. D., 1964. Reactions of man to cold. In *Medical Climatology,* edited by Sidney Licht; vol. 8, pp. 196–228. Waverly Press, Inc., Baltimore, Maryland.

DeGroot, J., 1959. The rat hypothalamus in stereotaxic coordinates. *J. Comp. Neurol.,* vol. 113: 389–400.

Findlay, J. D., and D. Robertshaw, 1965. The role of the sympathoadrenal system in the control of sweating in the ox (*Bos taurus*). *J. Physiol., 179:* 285–297.

Hamilton, C. L., 1965. Control of food intake. In *Physiological Controls and Regulators,* edited by W. S. Yamamoto and J. R. Brobeck; pp. 274–294. W. B. Saunders Co., Philadelphia, Pennsylvania.

Hammel, H. T., 1966. *The Regulator of Body Temperature.* VI Brody Lecture. Spec. Rept. Missouri Univ. Agr. Exp. Sta.

Hammel, H. T., 1965. Neurons and temperature regulation. In *Physiological Controls and Regulators,* edited by W. S. Yamamoto and J. R. Brobeck; pp. 71–97. W. B. Saunders Co., Philadelphia, Pennsylvania.

Hardy, J. D., 1961. Physiology of temperature regulation. *Physiol. Rev., 41:* 521–606.

Hardy, J. D., 1965. The "set-point" concept in physiological temperature regulation. In *Physiological Controls and Regulators,* edited by W. S. Yamamoto and J. R. Brobeck; pp. 98–116. W. B. Saunders Co., Philadelphia, Pennsylvania.

Johnson, H. D., 1965a. Response of animals to heat. *Meteorol. Monographs, 6:* 109–122.

Johnson, H. D., 1965b. Environmental temperature and lactation (with special reference to cattle). *Intern. J. Biometeorol., 9:* 103–116.

Johnson, H. D., and R. G. Yeck, 1964. Age and temperature effects on TDN, water consumption and balance of dairy calves and heifers exposed to environmental temperatures of 35 to 95°F. *Missouri Univ. Agr. Exp. Sta. Res. Bull., 865:* 1–37.

Johnson, H. D., A. C. Ragsdale, I. L. Berry, and M. D. Shanklin, 1962. Effect of various temperature-humidity combinations on milk production of Holstein cattle. *Missouri Univ. Agr. Exp. Sta. Res. Bull., 791:* 1–39.

Johnson, H. D., A. C. Ragsdale, I. L. Berry, and M. D. Shanklin, 1963.

Temperature-humidity effects including influence of acclimation in feed and water consumption of Holstein cattle. *Missouri Univ. Agr. Exp. Sta. Res. Bull., 846:* 1–43.

Kelley, O., F. A. Martz, and H. D. Johnson, 1965. Effect of environmental temperature on the volatile fatty acid (VFA) content of rumen fluid from cows receiving constant feed intake. *J. Dairy Sci., 48:* 819.

Kibler, H. H., and S. Brody, 1950. Effects of temperature, 50° to 105°F and 50° to 9°F, on heat production and cardiorespiratory activities in Brahman, Jersey and Holstein cows. *Missouri Univ. Agr. Exp. Sta. Res. Bull., 464:* 1–18.

Kibler, H. H., and S. Brody, 1951. Influence of increasing temperature, 40° to 105°F, on heat production and cardiorespiratory activities in Brown Swiss and Brahman cows and heifers. *Missouri Univ. Agr. Exp. Sta. Res. Bull., 473:* 1–16.

Kibler, H. H., and S. Brody, 1952. Relative efficiency of surface evaporative, respiratory evaporative, and non-evaporative cooling in relation to heat production in Jersey, Holstein, Brown Swiss and Brahman cattle, 5° to 105°F. *Missouri Univ. Agr. Exp. Sta. Res. Bull., 497:* 1–31.

Lind, A. R., 1964. Physiologic responses to heat. In *Medical Climatology,* edited by Sidney Licht; vol. 8, pp. 164–195. Waverly Press, Baltimore, Maryland.

Lundgren, R. G., and H. D. Johnson, 1964. Effects of temperature and feed intake on thyroxine I^{131} disappearance rates of cattle. *J. Animal Sci., 23:* 28–31.

Macfarlane, W. V., 1963. Endocrine functions in hot environments. In *Reviews of Research;* pp. 153–222. UNESCO, Paris.

Meites, J., C. S. Nicholl, and P. K. Talwolker, 1963. The central nervous system and the secretion and release of prolactation. In *Advances in Neuroendocrinology;* p. 238. Univ. Illinois Press, Urbana, Illinois.

Reichlin, S., 1964. Function of the hypothalamus in regulation of pituitary-thyroid activity. In *Brain-Thyroid Relationships,* edited by M. P. Cameron and M. O'Connor; pp. 17–32. Little Brown and Co., Boston, Massachusetts.

Smith, G. P., 1965. Neural control of the pituitary-adrenocortical system. In *Physiological Controls and Regulators,* edited by W. S. Yamamoto and J. R. Brobeck; pp. 117–134. W. B. Saunders Co., Philadelphia, Pennsylvania.

Stevenson, J. A. F., 1962. The regulation of food intake. *XXII Intern. Congr. Physiol. Sci.,* vol. 1, part 2. Leiden, Netherlands.

Wayman, O., H. D. Johnson, C. P. Merilan, and I. L. Berry, 1962. Effect of *ad libitum* or force-feeding of two rations on lactating dairy cows subject to temperature stress. *J. Dairy Sci., 45:* 1472–1478.

Yousef, M. K., and H. D. Johnson, 1966. Calorigenesis of dairy cattle as influenced by thyroxine and environmental temperature. *J. Animal Sci., 25:* 150–156.

Yousef, M. K., 1966. *Hormonal Effects on Gaseous Metabolism and Thyroid Function of Cattle at Various Temperatures.* Ph.D. Thesis. Univ. Missouri, Columbia, Missouri.

Microclimate and Livestock Performance in Hot Climates

T. E. BOND, *Agricultural Engineering Research Division, Agricultural Research Service, U. S. Department of Agriculture, Davis, California*

ACCORDING TO THE DEFINITION of Geiger (1959), the microclimate of livestock means the conditions within the microenvironment closely surrounding the animal. Livestock performance in a hot climate is easy to measure in terms of weight gain, efficiency of feed utilization, milk or egg production, or some other appropriate variable. The real problem is knowing what the microclimate really is and how to evaluate it, or how to compare the microclimates of two locations.

The temperature and humidity of the air surrounding an animal can easily be measured, as can the air velocity and the thermal radiation to which an animal is exposed—these are the primary variables constituting the microclimate. How can these variables be combined into some form that will represent a value for the microclimate? There is no really satisfactory answer at present.

The problem of relating microclimate and animal production can be approached in terms of the influences of individual microclimatic factors under controlled laboratory conditions. Such studies have produced a wealth of valuable information.

Yet controlled laboratory studies cannot be relied upon entirely, because it is still difficult to duplicate the conditions of solar radiation, variable winds, and changing air temperatures, among other things, that are normally present where numbers of animals are raised in hot climates.

Another approach is to study livestock production and performance in hot climates. This does not eliminate the problem of defining the microclimate, but over the years these studies have led to a better understanding of the problem. This paper discusses the production of livestock under field conditions in a hot climate, and indicates how animal performance and some of the factors of the microclimate are related.

Air Temperature

Laboratory studies provide data showing how constant air temperatures influence livestock production and performance. Figure 1 shows typical trends of the influence of air temperature on the production response of a Holstein dairy cow, a 150-pound pig, and a laying hen. The point to note is how much more rapidly production declines with high temperatures than with low temperatures. However, the low temperatures shown are not extremely cold.

Usually such production data are obtained when the wall, floor, and ceiling of the laboratory are at the same temperature as the air. This is a condition seldom encountered under field conditions, where it is difficult to separate the influence of air temperature from other variables of the microclimate.

Activity studies were made at Davis, California, to investigate the use swine made of shades, wallows, and an air-conditioned house

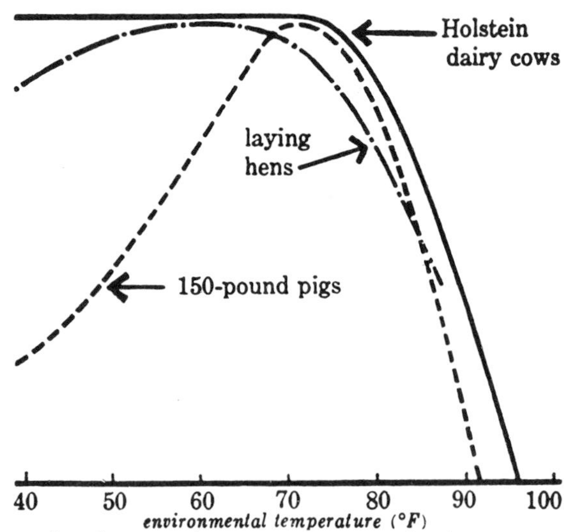

Fig. 1. Influence of environmental temperature on production trends of farm animals (Bond and Kelly, 1960).

during hot weather (Heitman *et al.,* 1962). Table 1, showing the percentage of pigs using these three relief measures at some time during the day, indicates that they started to feel the stress of air temperature at about 70°F. Also evident is the increased use of these cooling devices as air temperature increased. Figure 2 shows that the hogs started using the air-conditioned house when the air temperature was about 68°F. Of course, each of these thermal relief methods changed the animal's microclimate in a different way. The

Table 1. Percentage of pigs having access to one cooling device using it during a 50-day summer observation period at Davis, California, between the hours of 7:00 A.M. and 3:00 P.M. (From Heitman *et al.,* 1962).

Temperature	61°–70°F	71°–80°F	81°–90°F	91°–100°F	101°–110°F
Pig location:					
Air-conditioned house	15.6	57.2	77.9	84.3	86.4
Fabric shade	5.4	14.4	33.3	43.4	43.8
Wallow	4.9	8.4	12.1	19.4	28.8

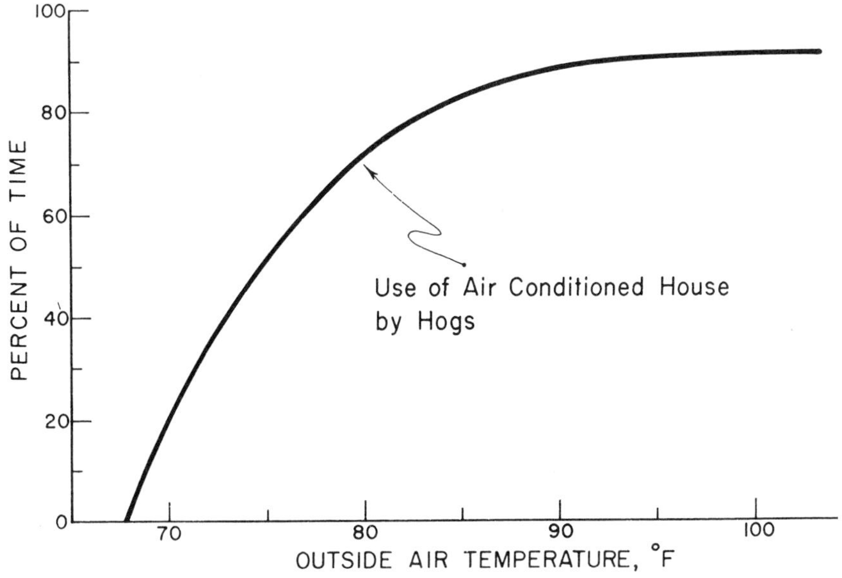

Fig. 2. Influence of outside air temperature on the use of an air-conditioned house by swine at Davis, California.

shades altered the radiation environment rather than the air temperature. The air-conditioned house altered air temperature, air movement, and radiation. The wallow, by wetting the skin, altered the animals' microclimate completely. Although these relief measures altered the microclimate in different ways, there were no significant differences between them in the effects on animal production during a summer period when the average mean, maximum, and minimum temperatures were 75°, 94°, and 59°F. A control group with none of these relief measures, however, had significantly less weight gains (Heitman *et al.,* 1959).

The effect of lowered air temperature on the weight gains of beef cattle was measured in tests at El Centro, California (Kelly *et al.,* 1959). Five Herefords and two Brafords had access to a three-sided shelter cooled by air from an evaporative cooler installed at one end of the structure. The north end, opposite the cooler, was open to the corral. Even though the air temperature inside the shelter was rarely more than 10°F cooler than the outside air, which averaged 91°F during a 54-day feeding trial, the cooled Herefords gained 0.36 pound more per day than uncooled Herefords. Braford gains were not influenced by the cooled air. The lower air temperature was not the only change in the animal microclimate. The walls of the shelter altered the radiation environment, and the blower of the evaporative cooler increased the air movement over the animals.

In recent tests with dairy cattle in Arizona, animals had access to a shade with evaporatively cooled air blown through it (Wiersma and Stott, 1966). The air temperature was 9° to 10°F lower under this shade than under a similar but uncooled shade. Cows produced an average of four pounds more milk per animal daily under the cooled shade than under the uncooled shade. The greater production may have been due to reduced air temperature, increased air movement, or both.

Air Movement

Five field production tests with swine were conducted at three locations in California to study the effect of increased air movement on the growth rate of swine during hot weather (Bond *et al.,* 1965). Fans increased the air movement to two to six miles per hour (Fig. 3) from the average natural airflow at the field locations of one to

Fig. 3. Swine exposed to increased air movement at Davis, California.

two miles per hour. Mean air temperatures during the five test periods were 90°, 78°, 76°, 75°, and 71°F, and, even though some of these are considered stressing air temperatures, increased air velocity did not promote any increase in animal production during any of the test periods.

In studies at El Centro, gains of cattle were found to be much better in wire corrals than in wood plank corrals (Fig. 4) (Ittner *et al.*, 1955). The reason was probably the lower radiation environment or increased air movement in the wire corrals, or perhaps both. Detailed studies during several days showed that the radiant heat load per square foot of animal surface was about 10 BTU less per hour in the wire pen. Figure 5 shows the air temperature, wind velocity, and radiation in the wood and wire corrals during one day. During an 84-day feeding trial, the average respective air velocities in the wood and wire corrals were 1.1 and 2.4 miles per hour. Air temperatures averaged 3.8°F less in the wire corral than in the wood. The microclimate for animals differed enough between the

Fig. 4. Wire-fence and wood-fence cattle corrals used at El Centro, California, in tests on the influence of airflow on cattle production (Ittner *et al.*, 1955).

two locations that seven Herefords weighing about 814 pounds initially gained 0.43 pound more per day in a wire pen than a similar group in a wood pen.

When fans were added to a wood corral to increase average airflow over the animals from 0.7 to 3.7 miles per hour during a summer feeding period, seven Herefords averaging 670 pounds initially gained an average of 2.3 pounds per day, compared to 1.3 pounds per day for an unfanned group (Bond *et al.*, 1957). In this case, air temperature and radiation load were the same in the two wood pens, so the difference in animal gain, as far as is known, was a result only of the difference in airflow around the animals.

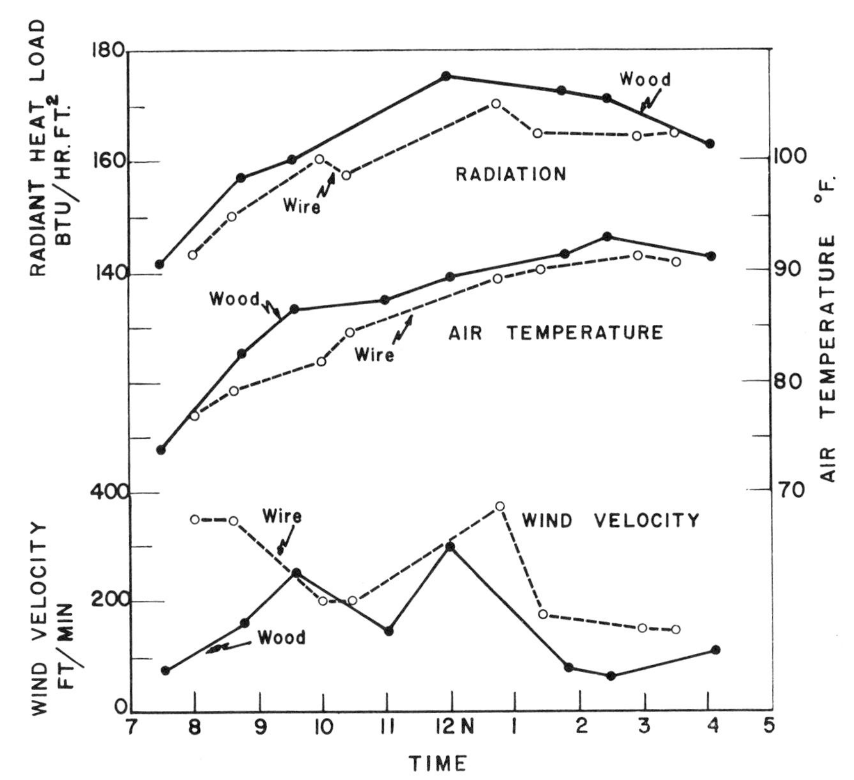

Fig. 5. Air temperature, wind velocity, and animal radiant heat load in wood-fence and wire-fence cattle pens (Ittner *et al.*, 1955).

A test with Hereford steers at El Centro was designed to separate the influences of air movement and radiation. Animals in wire pens had four treatments, consisting of no shade, shade only, fan only, or fan and shade (Table 2). Figure 6 shows a trial with a fan when average air temperature was 91°F and average relative humidity was 37 percent. Steers weighing about 620 pounds at the start gained an average of 1.63 pounds per day without shade or fans. Steers with no shade but with a fan that increased to 5.5 miles per hour a natural airflow of 2.75 miles per hour gained 1.85 pounds per day. With shade alone, the average daily gain was 2.28 pounds. Figure 7 compares surface and rectal temperatures, respiration, and pulse rate during a period when the air temperature was 107°F. The lowered radiant heat load from the shade appears more effective than the increased air velocity. This may be misleading, because

Table 2. Weight gain and feed conversion of cattle during 84-day summer feeding trial at El Centro, California (From Garrett *et al.*, 1960).

	No shade	Shade only	Fan only	Fan and shade
Av. initial wt., lb.	619	630	613	627
Av. daily gain, lb.	1.63	2.28	1.85	2.15
Feed/100 lb. gain	994	851	940	869

Fig. 6. Beef cattle exposed to increased air movement from a fan—El Centro, California (Garrett *et al.*, 1960).

the natural airflow in the control pen (no shade) was 2.75 miles per hour, great enough so that a further increase to 5.5 miles per hour might not be as effective as an increase from a lower initial level might have been.

Radiation

In work at the University of California at Davis, some scientists feel that radiation is the most neglected of the microclimatic vari-

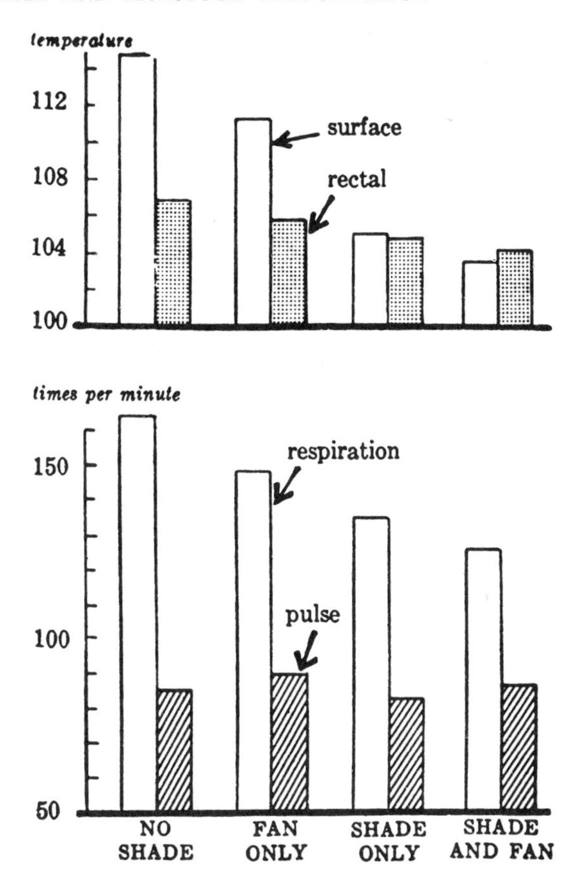

Fig. 7. Surface and rectal temperatures and pulse and respiration rates of beef cattle at El Centro, California, when air temperature was 107°F (Bond and Kelly, 1960).

ables. Its importance is emphasized in Figure 8, which shows cattle in Arizona under two shades. It is doubtful that there was any difference in air temperature or air velocity under these shades, because they were so close to each other. The material of one shade provided a solid shadow. The other shade, of slatted boards, allowed some sun to reach the ground. The primary difference between the two microclimates was thermal radiation, and it is obvious from the figure that the animals preferred the solid shade.

Figure 9 shows the radiant heat load received by a shaded and unshaded animal on a typical August day in El Centro (Bond *et al.*, 1954). This figure also shows the relative magnitude of radiation from various sources surrounding an animal.

Fig. 8. Shaded beef cattle in Arizona. Shade on left provides solid shadow; slatted shade provides only a partial shadow.

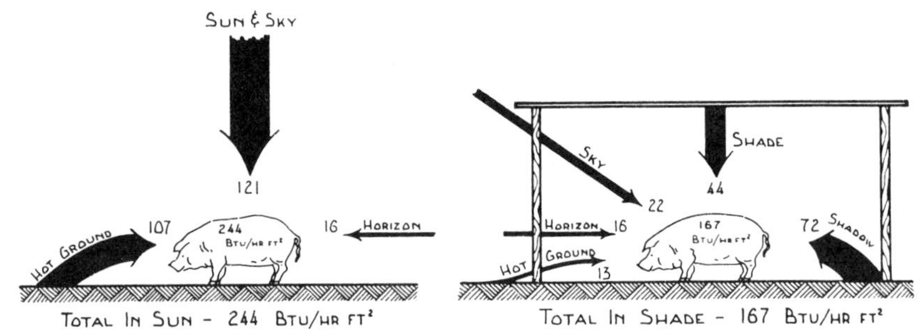

Fig. 9. Radiation heat loads (BTU/hr per sq. ft. of animal surface) received by shaded and unshaded animals on a typical cloudless summer day in El Centro, California (Bond *et al.,* 1954) .

While a shade may reduce the radiant heat load on an animal, it cannot be assumed that a shade will always improve gains of all livestock in hot climates. Table 2 shows that shaded beef cattle in the Imperial Valley of California gained 0.65 pound more per day, with 143 pounds less feed per 100 pounds of gain, than unshaded beef cattle (Garrett *et al.*, 1960). During the summers of 1964 and 1965, however, the performance of Hereford cattle at Davis was not improved by shades (Garrett *et al.*, 1966a). McCormick *et al.* (1963) found no benefits from shades in Georgia for Hereford steers fattened in a drylot or grazed on pastures. In tests reported by Johnson *et al.* (1960), unshaded Jersey cows in Georgia seemed to suffer more from heat (higher rectal temperature) than shaded Jerseys, but there was no evidence of any significant effect on feed and water intake, efficiency of feed conversion, or milk production. Much seems left to be learned about how simple shades affect the microclimate of an animal.

In recent California studies, the radiation an animal receives was divided and measured as shortwave energy (up to 5 μ) and longwave energy (greater than 5 μ). Figure 10 shows some measured values for short- and longwave radiation from sources surrounding an animal under shade during August. The values shown are radiant-flux rates from surrounding sources. The amount of energy the animal receives from each source depends on the shape factor of the animal with respect to the source. The important point here is the surprisingly high percentage of shortwave radiation under shade. Kelly *et al.* (1954) showed that white pigs reflect 51 percent of the solar energy that is between 0.41 and 1 μ, whereas a black pig

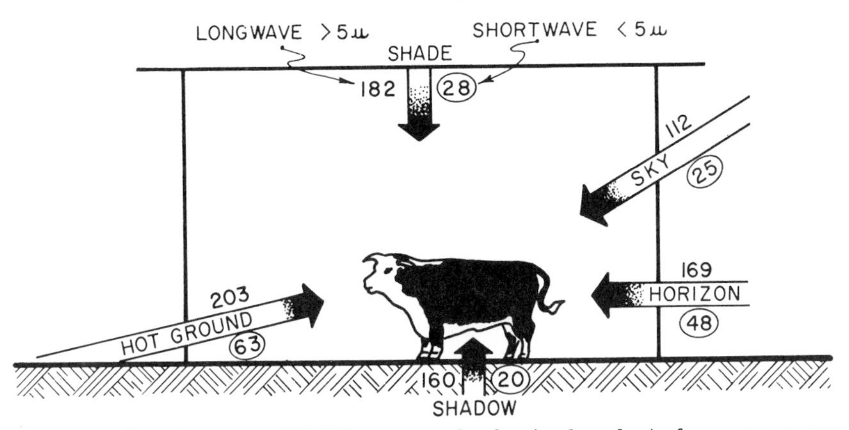

Fig. 10. Radiant-flux rates (BTU/hr per sq. ft of animal surface) from sources surrounding a shaded animal on a typical cloudless summer day. Shortwave radiation shown by circled numbers; longwave radiation values are not circled.

reflects only about seven percent. The reflectance for longwave energy is about the same for both colors of pigs, about five percent. A knowledge of the spectral distribution of incoming radiant energy might be useful in helping define the microclimate of an animal in the field.

Even the height of a shade influences the microclimate of an animal. Measurements during the summer of 1965 at Davis and El Centro under shades 6, 9, and 12 feet high with the same surface area proved that the microclimate was cooler under a high shade than under a low shade. The difference was due primarily to the change in radiation. At noon in El Centro in August, the respective radiant heat loads under the three shades were 180, 176, and 168 BTU per hour for each square foot, while the radiant heat load in the sun was 247 BTU. At Davis, the surface and rectal temperatures of Hereford steers at the center of the shadows differed significantly among these three shades; it was highest under the six-foot shade and lowest under the twelve-foot shade (Garrett *et al.*, 1966b).

The foregoing results were true in California with its clear sky and low humidity. Givens (1965) obtained completely different results in Georgia, where both relative humidity and degree of cloudiness were relatively high. Under his conditions, animal radiant heat load was least under a six-foot shade and highest under a twelve-foot shade. According to Givens, clouds, because of their water-vapor content, tend to increase atmospheric radiation from clear sky conditions. Exposure of animals to the sky, to take advantage of its low temperature as a radiation sink, becomes less important in the presence of clouds. It seems reasonable to expect that the amount, frequency, and type of clouds could dictate the optimum height of shades in a particular area.

Humidity

There is little that can be said about a fourth variable of the microclimate—humidity, or vapor pressure. There has been little opportunity to study the influence of humidity on livestock production in the field. In most of the California tests mentioned above, the humidity was relatively low, generally below 35 percent. In some earlier tests in the Imperial Valley of California, Hereford steers with access to a shower operated by an electric eye gained about 0.36 pound more per day during one 66-day feeding period, and 0.22 pound more per day during a second 80-day test, than steers without the showers. Two tests with fogging nozzles giving mist-type sprays slightly depressed daily gains. The possible gain from the water was probably reduced because of increased vapor pressure of the air around the animals.

Conclusion

From the varied results presented, it is obvious that animal performance can often be influenced by one or several of the microclimatic factors discussed. Unless each of these factors can be controlled closely, it is nearly impossible to be certain that results with farm animals are not biased by some factor of the microclimate. Whether or not such a test is concerned directly with some animal-environmental relationship, one must either account for or somehow eliminate the separate effects of the microclimatic variables of air temperature, humidity, wind, and radiation.

At present no single index accurately describes the microclimate of an animal, and care must be exercised in assessing the environmental conditions surrounding an animal.

It is hoped that the examples and discussion of this paper emphasize the possible presence and importance of certain microclimatological factors which have effects often disregarded or unrecognized on animal response.

REFERENCES

Bond, T. E., C. F. Kelly, and N. R. Ittner, 1954. Radiation studies of painted shade materials. *Agr. Engr., 35:* 389–392.

Bond, T. E., C. F. Kelly, and N. R. Ittner, 1957. Cooling beef cattle with fans. *Agr. Engr., 38:* 308–309.

Bond, T. E., and C. F. Kelly, 1960. *Environment of Animals;* pp. 231–242. U. S. Dept. Agr. U. S. Government Printing Office, Washington, D. C.

Bond, T. E., H. Heitman, and C. F. Kelly, 1965. Effects of increased air velocities on heat and moisture loss and growth of swine. *Trans. Am. Soc. Agr. Engr., 8:* 167–174.

Garrett, W. N., T. E. Bond, and C. F. Kelly, 1960. Effect of air velocity on gains and physiological adjustments of Hereford steers in a high temperature environment. *J. Animal Sci., 19:* 60–66.

Garrett, W. N., R. L. Givens, T. E. Bond, and J. L. Hull, 1966a. Obser-

vations on the need for shade in beef feedlots. *Proc. Western Sect. Am. Soc. Animal Sci., 17:* 349–355.
Garrett, W. N., T. E. Bond, and N. Pereira, 1966b. *The Influence of Shade Height on Physiological Responses of Cattle during Hot Weather. Paper No. 66–909,* Am. Soc. Agr. Engr., Chicago.
Geiger, R., 1959. *The Climate Near the Ground.* Harvard Univ. Press, Cambridge, Massachusetts.
Givens, R. L., 1965. Height of Artificial Shades for Cattle in the Southeast. *Trans. Am. Soc. Agr. Engr., 8:* 312–313.
Heitman, H., C. F. Kelly, T. E. Bond, and L. Hahn, 1959. Modified summer environment and growing swine. *Proc. Western Section Am. Soc. Animal Prod., 10(48):* 1–4.
Heitman, H., L. Hahn, T. E. Bond, and C. F. Kelly, 1962. The effects of modified summer environment on swine behavior. *Animal Behavior, 10:* 15–19.
Ittner, N. R., T. E. Bond, and C. F. Kelly, 1955. Environment comparisons and cattle gains in wood and wire corrals. *J. Animal Sci., 14:* 818–824.
Johnson, J. C., R. L. Givens, and B. L. Southwell, 1960. *Hot Weather Performance of Jersey Cows with and without Shade in South Georgia.* Paper presented at Annual Meeting, Am. Soc. Animal Prod., Chicago. (Mimeograph)
Kelly, C. F., T. E. Bond, and H. Heitman, 1954. The role of thermal radiation in animal ecology. *Ecology, 35:* 562–569.
Kelly, C. F., T. E. Bond, and N. R. Ittner, 1959. Cooling of livestock in hot climates. *Applications and Industry, AIEE, 40:* 512–517.
McCormick, W. C., R. L. Givens, and B. L. Southwell, 1963. Effects of shade on rate of growth and fattening of beef steers. *Georgia Agr. Exp. Sta., Tech. Bull. N. S. 27.*
Wiersma, F. and G. H. Stott, 1966. Microclimate modification for hot-weather stress relief in dairy cattle. *Trans. Am. Soc. Agr. Engr., 9:* 309–311.

Livestock Production in Cold Climates

C. M. WILLIAMS, *Department of Animal Science, University of Saskatchewan, Saskatoon, Saskatchewan, Canada*

The temperature of the living body, like that of an inanimate object, tends to come into heat equilibrium with the environmental temperature by conduction, convection, and radiation.
Samuel Brody (1945)

LIVESTOCK-PRODUCING AREAS in the temperate zones usually have periods of lowered ambient temperatures associated with rain or snow, high humidities, and wind. These impose a potentially stressful condition on livestock which may result in severe economic losses to the owner through decreased production, disease, and death. Various systems of management have been developed to offset at least the extremes of winter conditions, but economic considerations have kept building construction to a minimum and have discouraged physiologists and engineers from turning more attention to this important area of study.

In the past the usual compromise between the requirements imposed by the changing seasons and the great variety of age and species on any farm has been the multipurpose barn designed for economy and convenience. More recently livestock production has become more specialized and efficient so that interest in providing optimum winter housing is growing. This interest has created a demand for information on how animals will respond to different environmental conditions. Unfortunately much of the data required to fill this need have yet to be collected.

Several authors have noted that an animal in a cold environment obeys the physical laws governing radiation, conduction, and convection (Blaxter, 1962; Hensel, 1959; Scholander *et al.,* 1950a). The animal in the cold maintains a relatively constant core temperature by reducing overall heat loss to a minimum and making up the deficit by increased heat production. The heat to maintain homoiothermy must ultimately come from dietary sources or radiant heat gain from the environment, but may initially come from either the heat increment of feeding, muscular activity (including shivering), or the expenditure of energy directly from dietary sources or body stores (non-shivering thermogenesis). Heat losses may be reduced by reducing the exposed surface area, reducing the respiratory rate or volume, increasing insulation, avoiding rapid air flows, and avoiding wetting the body surface.

Certain species, particularly the laboratory rat, have been demonstrated to have an ability to respond to a period of low temperatures in such a manner that their survival rate is greater when exposed to severe cold stress (Hart, 1957). The precise metabolic processes are still being investigated, but they involve the thyroid-adrenal axis and an elevated heat production and oxygen consumption. This acclimation has never been adequately demonstrated in large animals; however, there are changes which do occur in large animals in response to lower temperatures that aid them in coping with winter conditions. Increased hair growth, skin thickening, and changes in the composition of certain fat deposits are some of the relatively permanent changes. Of a more temporary nature, but still requiring a positive response to cold, are changes in respiration and in blood flow to the periphery. Blood flow may be increased to exposed tissues that are to be maintained at or near the temperature of the main body mass such as the teats or scrotum, while blood flow may be reduced to tissues that are allowed to drop well below the core temperature, such as the legs and face and to a lesser degree the surface of the trunk. These latter surfaces receive periodic vasodilations to restore the starved tissues (Blaxter, 1962).

The surface of the animal's body is complex in terms of insulation and temperature and, therefore, of heat loss to the environment. In the cow and sheep, which are typical of animals having a heavy coat of insulation, the heaviest part of the hair coat does not extend over the legs, face, or underside. This would appear to be a requirement of an animal that uses insulation to reduce heat loss but periodically may need to dissipate heat as a result of elevated ambient temperatures or violent exercise. Scholander *et al.* (1950b) stated that, ". . . a resting, heavily insulated arctic mammal or bird . . . is able to change its heat dissipation by a factor of eleven."

The study of domestic animals in a cold environment provides an opportunity to observe many different types of adaptation. Physiologists studying the basic responses to cold may well find some definite advantages in shifting some of their attention from the laboratory animals to farm animals. There is the newborn animal with responses which border on the poikilothermic, the big-bodied ruminant with its capacity for heat production, the bare-skinned pig, and the heavily insulated sheep. All are similar in many of their responses to cold but each has some unique feature as well.

The Newborn Animal

The newborn animal has some special problems in coping with low temperatures: a large ratio of surface area to body mass, dormant methods for increasing heat production, limited energy reserves, and a body surface wet from amniotic fluids. It has an initial body temperature at or near that of its dam, but this usually falls for a period following birth and the fall can be accentuated by an ambient temperature below the critical temperature. The newborn may be described as poikilothermic during this period because it will tolerate a decrease in body temperature—as much as 10°C under some circumstances—without responding by increasing heat production by either shivering or non-shivering thermogenesis. This period may also be characterized by a drop in oxygen consumption which indicates an actual reduction in heat production. It is tempting to interpret this early response as an adaptive mechanism; however, observations on newborn lambs (Alexander and McCance, 1958) and piglets (Pomeroy, 1953) indicate that the animal with the greatest likelihood of survival is the one that permits the least drop in body temperature for the shortest period. Lambs seem to have well-developed thermoregulatory mechanisms at birth and often establish a reasonably stable body temperature in a few hours through non-shivering heat production, in spite of being wet. Piglets, on the other hand, are less well developed at birth and are not in control of body temperature until the sixth to ninth day (Holub,

1957). Both lambs and piglets may have greater than adult fluctuation in body temperature until about the twentieth day (Hamdy and Weaver, 1958; Holub, 1957).

The nutrition of the very young animal has a direct effect on how rapidly and how effectively it establishes itself as a homoiotherm. McCance and Mount (1960) reported that undernourished pigs have a diminished ability to adjust to low ambient temperatures. Lower ambient temperatures will stimulate milk consumption (Walters and Boaz, 1963). McCance (1959) noted an increased protein catabolism in newborn pigs in response to low temperatures. This protein catabolism is most pronounced with weanling pigs receiving a high protein intake previous to the cold stress (Bauer and Filer, 1959) and survival is greatest with those having the greatest fat stores.

A most interesting nutritional disease of piglets is associated with low temperatures (Lucas, 1954; Naftalen and Howie, 1949). It is known as "nutmeg liver" and develops in piglets on cold, damp floors. The liver is enlarged by vascular congestion and fatty infiltration, and erythrocytes escape into the tissue spaces. This condition can be confused with nutritional anemia since they both result in pale tissues and respiratory distress ("thumps").

It may be concluded that the livestock man must often assist the newborn through the critical period of adjustment to full homoiothermy. This usually involves providing an external heat source and ensuring that the animal nurses. If the newborn becomes seriously chilled, the first requirement will be a source of food energy followed by the application of external heat. The rationale is that if the body temperature is elevated, the metabolic rate will also rise before there is energy to support it. The result is hypoglycemia, convulsions, and death.

Swine

Swine are widely distributed and have demonstrated considerable ability to cope with winter conditions. Calorimetric studies with mature swine indicate that the critical temperature is approximately 21°C, or not much below that for man (Clapstick and Wood, 1922). Ambient temperature, however, must drop to 0°C to require a doubling of the metabolic rate. By comparing this with the data of Scholander *et al.* (1950a) on arctic and tropical animals, the pig is above the tropical animal but well below the arctic animal in ability to withstand low temperatures before elevating heat production.

Irving (1956) suggested that the true critical temperature of mature swine is much below 20°C and more nearly 0°C. He explained that the discrepancy arises because the swine studied by other investigators would not react normally after the long period of fasting and confinement that was imposed to establish basal metabolic conditions. Blaxter (1962) indicated his concern about extrapolating to the out-of-doors from studies made in chambers, and Hart (1957) positively differentiated between studies under natural conditions and those under constant laboratory conditions.

It is tempting to assume that the insulative subcutaneous fat layer of swine is the complete solution to maintaining a constant body temperature; however, to quote Irving (1956), "Although a layer of fat covers the warm interior of swine, a fixed insulation alone cannot properly serve a mammal which must be able to increase its metabolic heat production greatly and suddenly or which may meet large changes in temperature from night to day."

The maintenance of homoiothermy in the bare-skinned swine is achieved by combining the protection of a subcutaneous fat layer with a reduced blood flow to the periphery and making up any deficiencies by increasing heat production. Most species can regulate somewhat their blood flow to the body surface, but swine have this ability highly developed. Irving (1956) reported that regression of skin temperature on core temperature became steeper as ambient temperature decreased. The regression line was curvilinear, indicating that the insulation was less effective in the deeper tissues because of less restricted circulation.

In practice, swine have two more effective methods of coping with low temperatures than circulation. They will huddle together to make essentially one large animal or burrow under bedding to gain insulation. If swine are individually penned, or provided with insufficient bedding, or exposed to drafts and dampness they will have difficulty with low temperatures (Lucas and Thompson, 1953). Bowland *et al.* (1962) found that pigs housed in colony houses at acceptable temperatures would not perform up to expectations because they would not go out into the cold to eat often enough. Hicks (1965) noted that growing pigs individually penned, without bedding and with ambient temperatures at either 40° or 60°F, reduced daily gains in response to the lowered temperatures by 0.06 pound at 100 pounds body weight and 0.15 pound at 200 pounds body weight, or 4 percent and 11 percent, respectively. Feed efficiency was reduced by 0.3 pound of feed per pound of gain at 100 pounds of body weight and 0.1 pound of feed per pound of gain at 200 pounds body weight, or 11 percent and 2 percent, respectively.

Beef Cattle

The beef animal is usually provided with overhead shelter during winter in areas having heavy snowfall or winter rains. In the ranching areas of western Canada and the United States this protection may vary from a barn, to open sheds, to board fence windbreaks, to clumps of trees. The beef animal's greatest problems with winter conditions are precipitation, high humidity, and wind, for singly or in combination they interfere with the hair coat which otherwise is adequate for all but the most extreme temperatures encountered.

Given a situation with uncomplicated low temperatures, the beef animal is well equipped to maintain a constant body temperature without greatly increasing heat production. Besides its low ratio of surface area to body mass and protective hair coat, it has the advantage of considerable waste heat from rumen fermentation and digestion to use for maintaining body temperature.

Since beef animals do not usually huddle or burrow to conserve heat they are very dependent upon their hair coat insulation. Scholander *et al.* (1950b) reported that large arctic mammals are able to experience ambient temperatures down to −40°F without increasing metabolic rate. Lentz and Hart (1960) reported that the caribou, a large arctic ruminant, has hair coats averaging 3,900 hairs per square centimeter. Peters and Slen (1964) gathered comparative data on the hair coats of cattalo (*Bison americanus* × *Bos taurus*), Herefords, and Brahman cows which indicated that in clipped hair samples cattalo had ten times as much weight of coat as the tropically adapted Brahman, with the temperate zone Herefords intermediate. Additional studies on the differences in hair coats between breeds was reported by Williams and Noy (1961). In this case the hair coats of steers sired by Hereford, Aberdeen Angus, and Charolais bulls differed in weight and density as well as length and diameter of fiber. In general these domestic cattle had about one-half the hair density of the arctic caribou examined by Lentz and Hart (1960).

Several studies have confirmed the general observation that cattle will be more productive if protected from wind and dampness, but where shelters are poorly designed so as to create a humidity problem the results have favored abandoning the buildings. Williams (1958) found that beef steers being fattened in ambient temperatures as low as −27°F grew more rapidly if sheltered by a ten-foot windbreak than by an open-fronted shed that elevated the relative humidity. Straw bedding which turned into a fermenting manure pack increased growth rate 30 percent over steers without bedding.

The latest trend in beef cattle housing is to provide complete environmental control, termed "confinement housing". Confining fattening steers to 20 feet of slatted floor area per steer in a well-ventilated building may seem the approach that should have been obvious long before this, but this development had to wait until increase in nutritional knowledge made steer feeding efficient enough to justify the high cost of the confinement housing.

Sheep

Sheep are particularly well adapted to withstand low temperatures, provided their wool is not dampened or disturbed by strong winds (Hutchinson and Wodzicka-Tomaszewska, 1961). A problem is created, however, when the wool is clipped off and inclement weather occurs. The critical temperature for sheep changes from approximately 33° to −0.3°C as the fleece lengthens from 0.0 to 12 centimeters (Blaxter *et al.*, 1959a, b; Graham *et al.*, 1959).

An interesting aspect of maintaining a constant body temperature in sheep was reported by Hicks (1961) and Bailey *et al.* (1962). Cold water introduced into the rumen caused a sharp drop in rumen temperature and a corresponding smaller fall in the rectal temperature. Although variations in rectal temperature were quickly corrected, the rumen remained below normal for up to one hour.

One can surmise the effect such a drop in temperature would have on the rumen microflora. Blaxter (1962) considered that warming the ingested feed and water usually represented a small fraction of the total heat production but could be important under special conditions.

Dairy Cattle

Considerable literature has accumulated on the response of dairy cattle to different ambient temperatures and has been reviewed by Hancock (1954), Findlay and Blakley (1954), Brody (1956), Hess and Bailey (1961), and others. The "comfort zone" for European breeds of dairy cattle is 30° to 50°F and for Indian breeds 50° to 80°F. These are estimates made in a chamber and may well be higher than would be true for cows conditioned to low temperatures. It is most valuable to know the temperature that gives an important economic depression in production with changes in the environment.

Ragsdale *et al.* (1949) reported that milk production decreased and butterfat percentage and feed intake increased as ambient temperatures declined from 50° to 4°F. He observed that the effect was greater with the small Jersey breed than the large Holsteins, indicating the importance of relative surface area. In repeating this experiment he found the effects were not noted in the Holsteins, thus suggesting that the heat increment of feeding became sufficient to offset any need for using additional energy to maintain body temperature. MacDonald and Bell (1958) studied Holstein cows in a loose-housing-type barn in which temperatures fell as low as −5°F. They noted that there is not a marked drop in milk production until ambient temperatures reached 25°F, but it becomes very pronounced below 10°F. The minimum temperature for the day seems to affect milk production more than the average temperature for the day. In a follow-up study Williams and Bell (1963) found that by altering the barn so that relative humidity was reduced from the previous 90 to 100 percent down to 72 to 79 percent conditions were established in which milk production did not decline with falling ambient temperatures. The conclusion drawn was that when relative humidity is high the diurnal fluctuation of temperature in the barn passes through the dew point so that moisture settles on the cows' hair coat, reducing its insulative capacity.

Conclusion

Only a few research groups are examining the applied problems of cold physiology and shelter engineering with farm animals. Most such studies are on man or one of the laboratory species. Although it is possible to extrapolate from species to species some of the information now required for improved livestock shelters, more data must be taken on the same species to which it will later be applied. There is a need for more research into the most efficient methods of managing farm livestock in cold climates.

REFERENCES

Alexander, G., and I. McCance, 1958. Temperature regulation in the newborn lamb. I. Changes in rectal temperature within the first six hours of life. *Australian J. Agr. Res., 9(3):* 339–347.

Bailey, C. B., R. Hironaka, and S. B. Slen, 1962. Effects of the temperature of the environment and the drinking water on the body temperature and water consumption of sheep. *Can. J. Animal Sci., 42(1):* 1–8.

Bauer, L. S., and L. J. Filer, 1959. Influence of body composition of weanling pigs on survival under stress. *J. Nutr., 69(2):* 128–134.

Blaxter, K. L., 1962. *The Energy Metabolism of Ruminants.* Hutchinson and Co., Ltd., London.

Blaxter, K. L., N. McC. Graham, F. W. Wainman, and D. G. Armstrong, 1959a. Environmental temperature, energy metabolism and heat regulation in sheep. II. The partition of heat losses in closely clipped sheep. *J. Agr. Sci., 52(1):* 25–40.

Blatxer, K. L., N. McC. Graham, and F. W. Wainman, 1959b. Environmental temperature, energy metabolism and heat regulation in sheep. III. The metabolism and thermal exchanges of sheep with fleeces. *J. Agr. Sci., 52(1):* 41–49.

Bowland, J. P., F. V. MacHardy, and V. E. Mendel, 1962. *Effect of Winter Climate and Type of Shelter on Growing-Finishing Swine.* 41st Annual Feeders' Day; p. 7. Univ. Alberta, Edmonton, Alberta, Canada.

Brody, S., 1945. *Bioenergetics and Growth.* Reinhold Publishing Corp., New York.

Brody, S., 1956. Climatic physiology of cattle. *J. Dairy Sci., 39:* 715–725.

Clapstick, J. W., and T. B. Wood, 1922. The effect of change of temperature on the basal metabolism of swine. *J. Agr. Sci., 12:* 257–268.

Findlay, J. D., and W. R. Blakley, 1594. Progress in the physiology of farm animals. In *Environmental Physiology of Farm Animals;* ch. 6. Butterworth Scientific Publications, London.

Graham, N. McC., F. W. Wainman, K. L. Blaxter, and D. G. Armstrong, 1959. Environmental temperature, energy metabolism and heat regulation in sheep. I. Energy metabolism in closely clipped sheep. *J. Agr. Sci., 52(1):* 13–24.

Hamdy, A. H., and C. R. Weaver, 1958. Body temperature of young lambs. *Am. J. Physiol., 193(3):* 539–540.

Hancock, J., 1954. The direct influence of climate on milk production. *Dairy Sci. Abst., 16(2):* 89–102.

Hart, J. S., 1957. Climatic and temperature induced changes in the energetics of homeotherms. *Rev. Can. Biol., 16(2):* 133–174.

Hensel, H., 1959. Heat and cold. *Ann. Rev. Physiol., 21:* 91–116.

Hess, E. A., and C. B. M. Bailey, 1961. Comparative physiological effects of cold on farm and laboratory animals. *Animal Breed. Abst., 29(4):* 379–392.

Hicks, A. M., 1961. *Physiological Response to Ingestion of Cold Water by Sheep.* Master's thesis, McGill Univ., Montreal, Quebec, Canada.

Hicks, A. M., 1965. *Physiological Responses of Growing Swine to Low Temperatures.* Ph.D. thesis, Univ. Saskatchewan, Saskatoon, Saskatchewan, Canada.

Holub, A., 1957. Development of chemical thermoregulation in piglets. *Nature, 180 (4591):* 858–859.

Hutchinson, J. C. D., and M. Wodzicka-Tomaszewska, 1961. Climate physiology of sheep. *Animal Breed. Abst., 29(1):* 1–14.

Irving, L., 1956. Physiological insulation of swine as bare-skinned mammals. *J. Appl. Physiol., 9(3):* 414–420.

Lentz, C. P., and J. S. Hart, 1960. The effect of wind and moisture on heat loss through the fur of newborn caribou. *Can. J. Zool., 38:* 679–688.

Lucas, I. M., 1954. Some observations upon pigs reared in cold pens. *J. Agr. Sci., 44(4):* 369–376.

Lucas, I. M., and W. Thompson, 1953. Effect of flooring on pigs reared in an otherwise cold environment. *J. Agr. Sci., 43:* 192–198.

MacDonald, M. A., and J. M. Bell, 1958. Effects of low fluctuating temperatures on farm animals. IV. Influences of temperature on milk yield and milk composition. *Can. J. Animal Sci., 38:* 160–170.

McCance, R. A., 1959. The effect of lowering the ambient temperature on the metabolism of the newborn pig. *J. Physiol. London, 147:* 124–134.

McCance, R. A., and L. E. Mount, 1960. Severe undernutrition in growing and adult animals. 5. Metabolic rate and body temperature in the pig. *Brit. J. Nutr., 14:* 509–518.

Naftalin, J. M., and J. W. Howie, 1949. Hepatic changes in young pigs reared in a cold damp environment. *J. Pathol. Bacteriol., 61(3):* 319–328.

Peters, H. F., and S. B. Slen, 1964. Hair coat characteristics of bison, domestic × bison hybrids, cattalo, and certain domestic breeds of beef cattle. *Can. J. Animal Sci., 44(1):* 48–57.

Pomeroy, R. W., 1953. Studies on piglet mortality. I. Effect of low temperature and low plane of nutrition on the rectal temperature of the young pig. *J. Agr. Sci.,* 43(2): 182–191.

Ragsdale, A. C., D. M. Worstell, H. J. Thompson, and S. Brody, 1949. Environmental physiology with special reference to domestic animals. VI. Influence of temperature, 50° to 0°F and 50° to 95°F, on milk production. Feed and water consumption and body weight in Jersey and Holstein cows. *Missouri Univ. Agr. Exp. Sta. Res. Bull. 449.*

Scholander, P. F., V. Walters, R. Hock, and L. Irving, 1950a. Body insulation of some arctic and tropical mammals and birds. *Biol. Bull., 99(2):* 225–236.

Scholander, P. F., R. Hock, V. Walters, F. Johnson, and L. Irving, 1950b. Heat regulation in some arctic and tropical mammals and birds. *Biol. Bull., 99(2):* 237–258.

Walters, A. A., and T. G. Boaz, 1963. Effects of temperature and birth weight on milk intake of baby pigs. *Animal Prod., 5:* 223.

Williams, C. M., 1958. *Experiments on Bedding and Shelter for Beef Cattle.* Proc. 3rd Ann. Stockman's Day. Univ. Saskatchewan, Saskatoon, Saskatchewan, Canada.

Williams, C. M., and J. M. Bell, 1963. Effects of low fluctuating temperatures on farm animals. V. Influence of humidity on lactating dairy cows. *Can. J. Animal Sci., 44:* 114–119.

Williams, C. M., and W. Noy, 1961. Certain winter coat characteristics of Hereford, Charolais × Hereford and Aberdeen Angus × Hereford steers. *Proc. Am. Soc. Animal Prod., (Western Section),* XII–1.

Climatic Effects on Physiological Functions

G. C. WHITTOW, *Department of Animal Sciences, Rutgers, The State University, New Brunswick, New Jersey*

WHEN ANIMALS ARE EXPOSED to a change of environmental temperature or humidity, the most immediate physiological adjustments they are required to make are those which ensure that the rates of heat loss and heat production are balanced with the minimum change in the temperature of deep-seated organs such as the heart, brain, and liver—the deep-body temperature. This paper is concerned with the physiological control of the mechanisms of heat loss and the physiological consequences of the activation of these thermoregulatory devices.

Regulation of Heat Loss

Earlier reports (Ingram and Whittow, 1962a, b, 1963; Ingram *et al.*, 1963) have shown that the three pathways of heat loss in the ox (*Bos taurus*)—an increased cutaneous blood flow and skin temperature, respiratory evaporative cooling, and cutaneous evaporation—can all be activated by two distinct means. Warming of the skin alone will bring about an increased heat loss, even though the temperature of the temperature-regulating center in the hypothalamus does not change. On the other hand, localized heating of the anterior hypothalamus and preoptic region of the brain by implanted heating electrodes is also an effective means of increasing heat loss along evaporative and non-evaporative channels. Simultaneous heating of the skin and the hypothalamus will also activate the three heat-loss mechanisms and, in the case of respiratory evaporative cooling, an interaction can be demonstrated between the effects of heating the skin and the hypothalamus. Thus, the increase in respiratory activity in response to heating the hypothalamus depends upon the environmental temperature. The hotter the environment, the greater will be the effect of heating the hypothalamus. The increased heat loss resulting from an increased blood flow to the skin or evaporation of moisture from the skin has not been examined quantitatively, but there is evidence that the operation of these pathways also is controlled by the integrated action of cutaneous receptors and central receptors in the hypothalamus.

These findings led to the formulation of a working hypothesis concerning the role of central and peripheral temperature changes in the regulation of heat loss. When an animal is exposed to a hot environment, its respiratory activity, peripheral blood flow, and cutaneous moisture loss increase as a result of a change in the activity of receptors in the skin. If the environment is not very hot, these peripherally activitated responses may be sufficient to compensate for the reduced facility for heat loss occasioned by the increase in environmental temperature. If the environment is very hot, however, the deep-body temperature will increase and the increase in the temperature of the hypothalamus will result in further increases in heat loss. The higher the environmental temperature the greater will be the response elicited by a given increase in hypothalamic temperature.

Physiological Consequences of an Increased Heat Loss

Cardiovascular Changes

One of the mechanisms of heat loss is an increased blood flow to the skin (Whittow, 1962). It is important to know what effect this increased blood flow has on the blood pressure and whether an increase in cardiac output is required in order to maintain the increased blood flow. In man (Koroxenidis *et al.*, 1961) and other animals (Maxwell *et al.*, 1959; Whittow *et al.*, 1964), exposure to heat causes profound changes in blood pressure, heart rate, cardiac output, and in the total peripheral resistance, which is a measure of the total resistance to blood flow through all the tissues of the body. It is possible also that during hyperthermia, particularly at very high body temperatures, the animals may be in a state of circulatory failure. Evidence will be presented to show that the panting mechanism breaks down at high deep-body temperatures, and this raises the question whether at these body temperatures the blood pressure is maintained and the heart's pumping ability is unimpaired.

Measurements (Table 1) were made of the cardiac output, blood pressure, and blood volume of the ox in a cool environment (15°C), in a hot, dry environment (40°C) and in a hot, humid environment (40°C) in which the animals became hyperthermic (Whittow, 1965).

The rectal temperature of the animals in the hot, dry environment was not significantly higher than that in the cool environment, whereas exposure to the hot, dry environment resulted in a threefold increase in respiratory rate. Associated with the increased

Table 1. Effects of heat on the body temperature, respiratory rate, and systemic circulation of the ox. Mean values (±S.E.) of six animals (Whittow, 1965).

	Environmental temperature (°C)			
	DB/WB 15/11.5	DB/WB 40/22	DB 40	WB 39.5
Rectal temp. (°C)	39.0±0.2	39.1±0.1	40.5±0.1	41.5±0.0
Respiratory rate (resps./min)	26±3	85±8	212±4	185±12
Cardiac output (l/min)	25.3±2.2	27.9±1.6	40.4±8.4	48.6±12.7
Heart rate (beats/min)	67±5	69±3	98±6	137±15
Stroke volume (ml)	390±48	409±36	428±105	230±36
Left ventricular work (kg m/min)	47.9±4.7	48.5±2.6	82.2±18.3	96.9±27.7
Mean arterial blood pressure (mm Hg)	136±3	126±2	144±4	141±6
Total peripheral resistance (dynes sec cm^{-5})	450±47	367±28	330±45	298±57
Arterial packed cell volume (%)	29.1±0.9	28.6±0.9	30.7±1.8	35.1±1.3

DB = dry bulb temperature.
WB = wet bulb temperature.

respiratory rate was an increased cardiac output while the arterial blood pressure and the calculated total peripheral resistance decreased. It is known that an increased blood flow to the skin occurs when the ox is exposed to a hot, dry environment (Whittow, 1962), and presumably the diminution in blood pressure and the decrease in the total peripheral resistance reflect the magnitude of this increased flow. The increased cardiac output would ensure that an increased blood flow to the skin be maintained. There was little change in the work the heart had to perform in this environment, and the absence of any marked change in heart rate or in the percentage of red cells in the blood testify to the fact that the hot, dry environment was not stressful.

When the humidity of the hot environment was increased the body temperature increased continuously. The respiratory rate also increased, reaching a peak value at a rectal temperature of 40.5°C and decreasing at higher rectal temperatures. This pattern of respiratory rate has been observed before in the ox (Findlay, 1957; Ingram and Whittow, 1962b; Whittow, 1965) and in other unanesthetized panting animals (Whittow *et al.*, 1964). Further increases in cardiac output, which were associated with a considerable increase in heart rate, occurred. At a rectal temperature of 41.5°C, on the other hand, the stroke volume of the heart had decreased to a level lower than that in the cool environment. It seems likely that the low stroke volume was partly the result of an inadequate filling of the heart occasioned by the rapid heart rate; the heart was contracting so rapidly that there was not sufficient time between contractions for the heart to fill as much as it might. The amount of work that the heart had to perform increased and so did the arterial blood pressure, which attained a peak value at a rectal temperature of 40.5°C. The total peripheral resistance decreased, and at the highest rectal temperature there was a significant increase in the percentage of red cells in the blood.

During hyperthermia, therefore, the heart had to work considerably harder as a result of having to pump out more blood with possibly a higher viscosity against a higher arterial pressure. The addition of red cells to the blood probably reflects a response to stress involving an increase in the activity of the sympatho-adrenal system. However, even at rectal temperatures of 41.5°C the blood pressure and cardiac output were above their normal values in a cool environment, and the animals were not, therefore, in a state of shock or circulatory failure. There were no significant differences in blood volume between the cool; hot, dry; and hot, humid environments (Whittow, 1965). There was no evidence therefore that the increases in cardiac output and blood pressure were brought about by an increase in the circulating blood volume.

Table 2 illustrates some of the changes in the pulmonary circulation during exposure to a hot environment. Interest in the pulmonary circulation stemmed from the belief that the considerable increase in respiratory activity which occurs in a panting animal, such as an ox, is likely to have some effects on the pressure and volume of blood in the pulmonary circuit. It may be seen that there was a slight decrease in the pulmonary arterial pressure and small increases in the intrathoracic blood volume and in the amount of work that the right side of the heart had to do in a hot, dry environment. During hyperthermia these changes were accentuated. One interpretation of these results would be that, associated with increased respiratory activity during panting, there is an influx of blood into the thorax and possibly a dilatation of some of the pulmonary blood vessels in order to accommodate the blood.

Table 2. Effects of heat on the pulmonary circulation of the ox. Mean results (±S.E.) from six animals (Whittow, 1965).

	Environmental temperature (°C)			
	DB/WB 15/11.5	DB/WB 40/22	DB 40	WB 39.5
Mean pulmonary arterial pressure (mm Hg)	34.9±1.6	33.0±1.5	30.2±1.9	32.4±2.7
Central blood volume (1)	6.7±1.2	7.1±1.2	10.6±3.7	12.2±4.2
Right ventricular work (kg m/min)	11.5±1.4	12.8±1.1	16.6±3.2	20.8±4.3

DB = dry bulb temperature.
WB = wet bulb temperature.

Role of the Hypothalamus

Having outlined some of the important cardiovascular changes which occur in the ox during hyperthermia, the next step was to determine to what extent these changes could be reproduced by localized heating of the anterior hypothalamus alone. Localized heating of the hypothalamus at an environmental temperature of 15°C resulted in increases in respiratory rate, cardiac output, and heart rate. The increase in systemic blood pressure was small. Presumably, in a cool environment, an increased cutaneous blood flow occurs during localized heating of the hypothalamus (Ingram and Whittow, 1962a) which would tend to offset the increase in blood pressure resulting from the increased cardiac output. This interpretation is borne out by the decrease in total peripheral resistance which occurred. The left ventricular work increased also, but the increase was not statistically significant. These changes are similar to those which occur during hyperthermia. The percentage of red cells in the arterial blood did not change significantly during localized heating of the hypothalamus, whereas during hyperthermia a significant increase in the arterial hematocrit reading occurred. The effect of hyperthermia on the hematocrit does not, therefore, appear to be mediated by the increased hypothalamic temperature.

In the pulmonary circulation, the central blood volume and the work of the right side of the heart increased, similar changes to those occurring during hyperthermia. However, the pulmonary arterial pressure increased during localized heating of the hypothalamus, whereas during hyperthermia, the pulmonary arterial pressure declined. The explanation for this difference between the effects of hyperthermia and of localized heating of the hypothalamus is not yet clear, but the direct effect of an increased temperature on the pulmonary arteries in hyperthermic animals may result in a relaxation of the arterial wall and a decrease in pulmonary arterial pressure.

In a hot, dry environment localized heating of the anterior hypothalamus again caused an increase in respiratory rate. The increases in cardiac output and heart rate were less in this environment than at 15°C, while the increase in blood pressure was greater. The greater increase in blood pressure and the smaller increase in cardiac output in the hotter environment become intelligible if it is assumed that the increased blood flow through the extremities during heating of the hypothalamus in the hot environment was less than at 15°C because the cutaneous blood flow was already at a high level. This explanation is supported by the fact that the decrease in peripheral resistance was less during localized heating of the hypothalamus in the hot, dry environment than at 15°C. The pulmonary arterial pressure and right ventricular work increased during localized heating of the hypothalamus in the hot environment, but the increase in central blood volume was not statistically significant.

The general conclusion to be drawn from these results seems to be that while many of the cardiovascular effects of hyperthermia can be simulated by raising the temperature of the anterior hypothalamus alone, there are some differences. It would, in fact, be surprising if a general increase in the temperature of the body tissues did not at least affect the responses of the tissues to stimuli reaching them by nervous and chemical means.

Thermal Polypnea

The ox is a panting animal and although in a hot environment it loses considerably more heat by evaporation of moisture from the skin than from the respiratory tract, a great increase in respiratory activity occurs (Fig. 1). At first, this increase consists of an increase in respiratory rate and minute volume, while the tidal volume diminishes. If the body temperature increases to approximately 40.5°C or more, however, a change occurs in the pattern of breathing, the respiratory rate now decreases, the minute volume continues to increase while the tidal volume increases.

Whatever the thermoregulatory value of this panting, it is necessary to consider the physiological side effects of the panting. It seems possible that during the initial increase in respiration, when the tidal volume is decreasing and the respiratory dead space is increasing (Hales, 1967), the animal might tend to shunt air backward and forward over its upper respiratory tract. While ideal for losing heat, this action could lead to the impairment of gaseous exchange between the blood and the air. In consequence, the animal would incur the risk of becoming hypoxic. The reduced tension

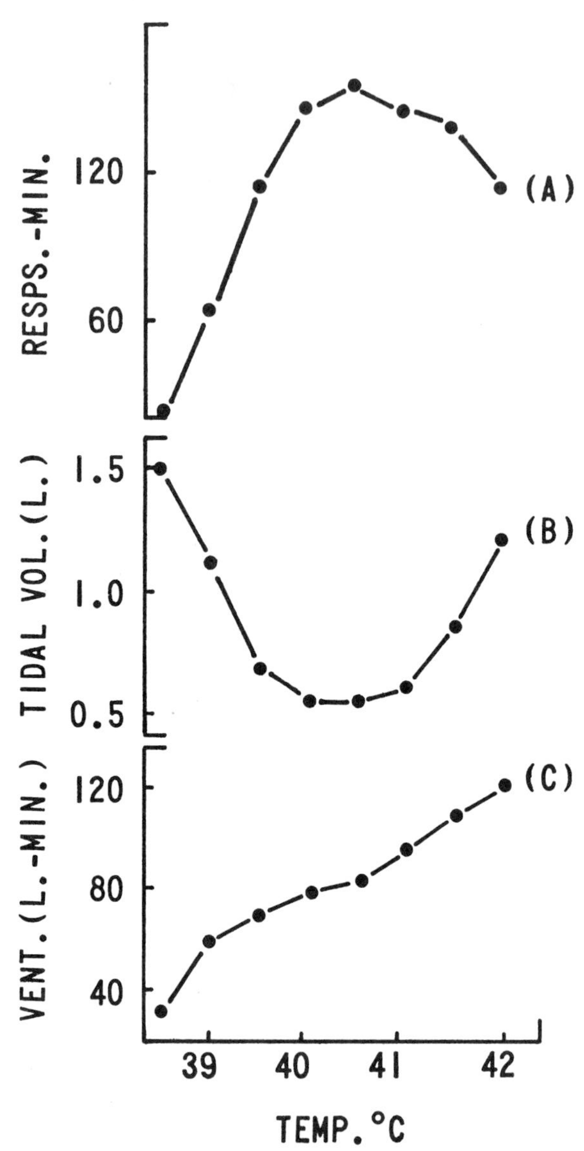

Fig. 1. Changes in the respiratory rate (A), tidal volume (B) and minute volume (C) of the ox during hyperthermia. L = liters; Temp. = rectal temperature. (Redrawn from Bianca and Findlay, 1962, courtesy of *Res. Vet. Sci.*)

of oxygen in the arterial blood might then stimulate arterial chemoreceptors which in turn would increase the depth of respiration at higher body temperatures.

This hypothesis was tested by measuring the tension of oxygen in arterial blood samples taken from animals during exposure to a cool and to a hot environment. The results are summarized in Tables 3 and 4. There was no significant difference in the tension of oxygen in arterial blood as a result of exposure to a hot, dry environment although the respiratory rate increased more than twofold. When the animals became hyperthermic, the arterial oxygen tension actually increased, thus ruling out the possibility that a lowered oxygen tension of the arterial blood resulted from thermal polypnea and could act as the stimulus for the change in the pattern of respiration at higher body temperatures (Table 4). However, some evidence was obtained that the oxygen tension of the mixed venous blood decreased during hyperthermia. While there was no hypoxemic stimulus to the arterial chemoreceptors, there might have been stimulation of chemoreceptors perfused by venous blood (Duke *et al.,* 1963). The hypoxemic venous blood presumably resulted from a tissue hypoxia which would be the consequence of an increased metabolic activity of the tissues. The increased metabolic activity would result from the increased temperature of the tissues.

Role of the Hypothalamus

In order to determine if the effects of hyperthermia could be reproduced by localized heating of the anterior hypothalamus alone, the effects of heating the hypothalamus on the arterial and mixed venous blood gas tensions were examined (Table 5). A significant increase in respiratory rate occurred during heating of the hypothalamus and both the arterial and the mixed venous blood oxygen tensions increased. There was, therefore, no evidence that the increased respiratory activity in response to localized heating of the hypothalamus resulted in a lowered oxygen tension of the blood.

ADRENO-MEDULLARY ACTIVITY

Sweating in the ox is mediated by an adrenergic mechanism (Findlay and Robertshaw, 1965). Many of the cardiovascular changes

Table 3. Rectal temperatures, respiratory rates, and arterial blood gas values of the ox in a cool (15°C DB, 12°C WB) and a hot, dry environment (40°C DB, 21°C WB). Mean (±S.E.) results from six animals (Findlay and Whittow, 1966).

	DB/WB 15/12	DB/WB 40/21
Rectal temperature (°C)	38.8±0.1	39.0±0.1*
Respiratory rate (resps./min)	29±4	76±10*
Arterial oxygen tension (mm Hg)	91±2	96±3
Arterial carbon dioxide tension (mm Hg)	47±2	42±1
Arterial pH	7.48±0.01	7.48±0.02
Arterial oxygen saturation (%)	94.4±0.9	95.5±1.3
Arterial oxygen capacity (ml %)	13.6±0.2	13.1±0.3
Arterial packed cell volume (%)	28.9±0.4	28.2±0.9

* = Statistically significant at the 5 percent level.

Table 4. Effects of a hot, dry and a hot, humid environment. Mean (±S.E.) results from six animals (Findlay and Whittow, 1966).

	Environmental temperature (°C)			
	DB/WB 40/21	DB/WB 40/39	DB/WB 40/39	DB/WB 40/39
Rectal temperature (°C)	39.0±0.1	40.4±0.1	41.0±0.0	41.5±0.0
Respiratory rate (resps./min)	76±10	204±8	196±5	190±6
Arterial oxygen tension (mm Hg)	96±3	110±4	111±3	106±2
Arterial carbon dioxide tension (mm Hg)	42±1	22±2	17±1	12±1
Arterial pH	7.48±0.02	7.72±0.05	7.81±0.06	7.90±0.05
Arterial oxygen saturation (%)	95.5±1.3	95.2±0.4	94.2±2.0	95.1±0.5
Arterial oxygen capacity (ml %)	13.1±0.3	14.0±0.2	15.1±0.3	16.3±0.6
Arterial packed cell volume (%)	28.2±0.9	29.6±0.7	31.1±1.1	34.3±1.2

DB = dry bulb temperature.
WB = wet bulb temperature.

Table 5. The effects of localized heating of the anterior hypothalamus of the ox in a cool environment (15°C DB, 12°C WB). Mean (±S.E.) results of eleven experiments (Findlay and Whittow, 1966).

	Before heating the hypothalamus	Change during localized heating of the hypothalamus
Hypothalamic temperature (°C)	38.4±0.0	+3.4±0.0
Respiratory rate (resps./min)	32±1	+38±10*
Arterial oxygen tension (mm Hg)	92±2	+10±2*
Arterial carbon dioxide tension (mm Hg)	43±1	0±0.0
Arterial pH	7.42±0.01	+0.01±0.01
Mixed venous oxygen tension (mm Hg)	34±1	+5±1*
Mixed venous carbon dioxide tension (mm Hg)	51±1	−2±1*
Mixed venous pH	7.40±0.00	0.00±0.01

* = Statistically significant at the 5 percent level.

during hyperthermia are similar to those produced by the infusion of catecholamines into other species of animals (Keck *et al.*, 1961). It was obviously important to find out what happened to the levels of circulating catecholamines in the ox during exposure to a hot environment.

Exposure to a hot, dry environment did not result in any significant change in the levels of circulating catecholamines (Fig. 2). When the animals became hyperthermic, however, increases occurred in both the adrenaline and the noradrenaline concentration. When the results from all the animals were considered, the greatest increase in adrenaline levels occurred during the initial phase of hyperthermia, that is, at rectal temperatures up to 40.5°C. At higher rectal temperatures the noradrenaline concentration increased, but there was only a small further increase in the adrenaline level. When the nerves supplying the adrenal medulla were sectioned in two animals and the animals were then made hyperthermic, there was no increase in the catecholamine levels. The source of the catecholamines appears, therefore, to be the adrenal medulla, and the stimulus to their release involves a nervous mechanism. The increased levels of catecholamines in the blood during hyperthermia suggest that

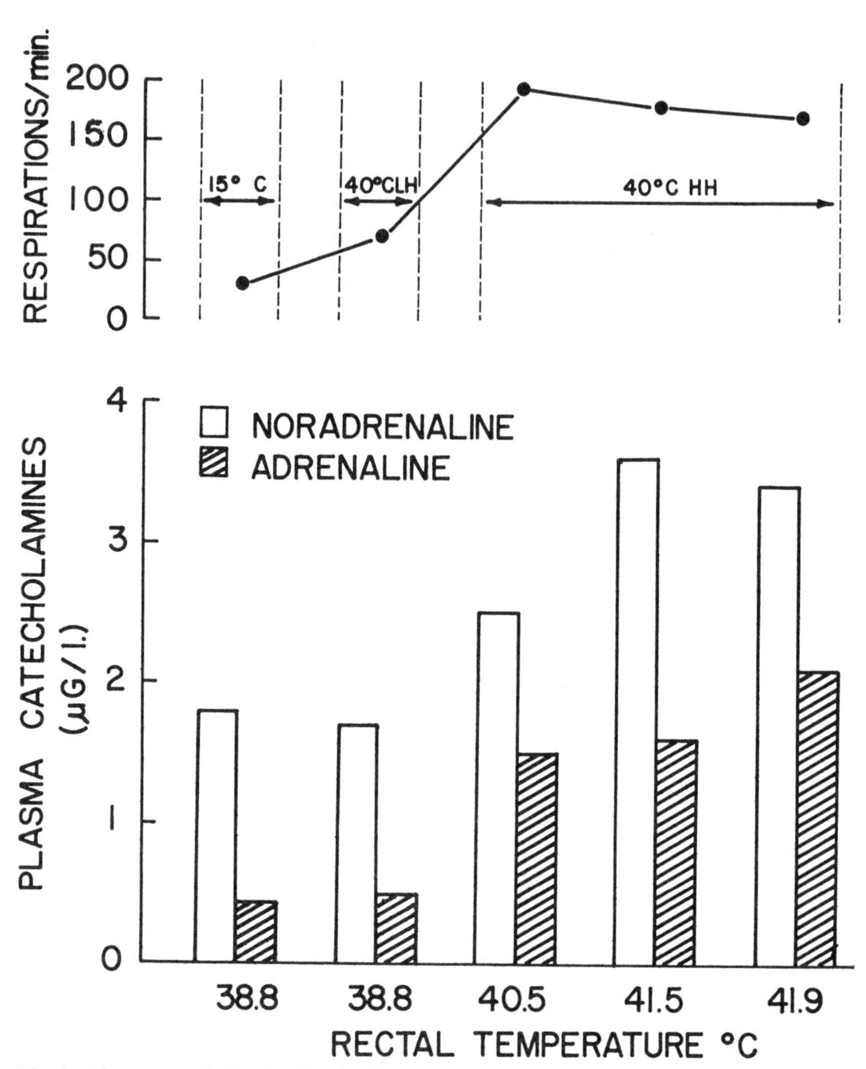

Fig. 2. Plasma catecholamine levels of a steer in a cool environment (15°C), a hot, dry environment (40°C, L.H.) and a hot, humid environment (40°C, H.H.). (Redrawn from Robertshaw and Whittow, 1966, courtesy of *J. Physiol.*)

the increase in blood pressure and cardiac output as well as the increase in the percentage of red cells in the blood could be caused, at least in part, by the catecholamines released into the blood stream.

Role of the Hypothalamus

In view of the accumulated evidence that many of the effects of hyperthermia are mediated by the increase in the temperature of the hypothalamus, the effects of localized heating of the hypothalamus on the catecholamine levels were studied. There was no effect. The stimulus to the adreno-medullary system must, therefore, have been acting on some other part of the central nervous system.

Conclusions

The heat-loss mechanisms of the ox can be activated by heating the skin alone, heating the heat-loss center in the hypothalamus alone, and by heating the skin, the heat-loss center, and other tissues simultaneously. When these mechanisms are activated they are associated with changes in the cardiovascular system, in the blood gas tensions, and in the circulating levels of catecholamines. Other physiological changes are probably also involved, but their description awaits further experimentation. These changes are likely to be of considerable importance to an understanding of how well animals withstand a hot environment.

REFERENCES

Bianca, W., and J. D. Findlay, 1962. The effect of thermally-induced hyperpnoea on the acid-base status of the blood of calves. *Res. Vet. Sci., 3:* 38–49.

Duke, H. N., J. H. Green, P. F. Heffron, and V. W. J. Stubbens, 1963. Pulmonary chemoreceptors. *Quart. J. Exp. Physiol., 48:* 164–175.

Findlay, J. D., 1957. The respiratory activity of calves subjected to thermal stress. *J. Physiol., 136:* 300–309.

Findlay, J. D., and D. Robertshaw, 1965. The role of the sympatho-adrenal system in the control of sweating in the ox (*Bos taurus*). *J. Physiol., 179:* 285–297.

Findlay, J. D., and G. C. Whittow, 1966. The role of arterial oxygen tension in the respiratory response to localized heating of the hypothalamus and to hyperthermia. *J. Physiol., 186:* 333–346.

Hales, J. R. S., 1967. The partition of respiratory ventilation of the panting ox. *J. Physiol.* (In press)

Ingram, D. L., J. A. McLean, and G. C. Whittow, 1963. The effect of heating the hypothalamus and the skin on the rate of moisture vaporization from the skin of the ox (*Bos taurus*). *J. Physiol., 169:* 394–403.

Ingram, D. L. and G. C. Whittow, 1962a. The effect of heating the hypothalamus on respiration in the ox (*Bos taurus*). *J. Physiol., 163:* 200–210.

Ingram, D. L. and G. C. Whittow, 1962b. The effects of variations in respiratory activity and in the skin temperatures of the ears on the temperature of the blood in the external jugular vein of the ox (*Bos taurus*). *J. Physiol., 163:* 211–221.

Ingram, D. L. and G. C. Whittow, 1963. Changes of arterial blood pressure and heart rate in the ox (*Bos taurus*) with changes of body temperature. *J. Physiol., 168:* 736–746.

Keck, E. W. O., M. J. Allwood, R. J. Marshall, and J. T. Shepherd, 1961. Effects of catecholamines and atropine on cardiovascular response to exercise in the dog. *Circulation Res., 9:* 566–570.

Koroxenidis, G. T., J. T. Shepherd, and R. J. Marshall, 1961. Cardiovascular response to acute heat stress. *J. Appl. Physiol., 16:* 869–872.

Maxwell, G. M., C. A. Castello, C. W. Crumpton, and G. G. Rowe, 1959. Hyperthermia: Systemic and coronary circulatory changes in the intact dog. *Am. Heart J., 58:* 854–862.

Robertshaw, D., and G. C. Whittow, 1966. The effect of hyperthermia and localized heating of the anterior hypothalamus on the sympatho-adrenal system of the ox (*Bos taurus*). *J. Physiol., 187:* 351–360.

Whittow, G. C., 1962. The significance of the extremities of the ox (*Bos taurus*) in thermoregulation. *J. Agr. Sci., 58:* 109–120.

Whittow, G. C., 1965. The effect of hyperthermia on the systemic and pulmonary circulation of the ox (*Bos taurus*). *Quart. J. Exp. Physiol., 50:* 300–311.

Whittow, G. C., P. D. Sturkie, and G. Stein, Jr., 1964. Cardiovascular changes associated with thermal polypnea in the chicken. *Am. J. Physiol., 207:* 1349–1353.

Environmental Temperature and Feed-Regulating Mechanisms

WILBOR O. WILSON, *Poultry Husbandry Department, University of California, Davis, California*

IT IS GENERALLY KNOWN that animals eat more as weather becomes colder. The intake is related to air temperature and other factors which affect heat loss such as wind, radiation, and relative humidity. Additional environmental factors not involved directly in heat loss, but which can be confounded with seasonal variations in temperature, include changes in day length and rainfall patterns.

In evaluating consumption of feed by animals, one must also consider the behavior and eating habits of the species. For example, the eating habits of the ruminants differ from those of animals with simple stomachs. The habits of birds with crops also differ. Observations in an uncontrolled environment have been made by Schmid (1965), who recently published the energy value of the crop content of mourning doves. A sampling of doves killed at different times of the day indicated that doves fill their crops twice a day (Fig. 1).

The caloric content of the ration influences the amount of feed consumed by rats exposed to cold and the length of time they spend in eating (Sellers *et al.*, 1954). Chicks fed mash used 14.3 percent of the 12-hour photoperiod eating, while chicks fed compressed pellets ate an equivalent amount in only 4.7 percent of that time (Jensen *et al.*, 1962). At the South Dakota State University, Wilson *et al.* (1945) fed free choice mash and grain to laying hens. To meet their caloric needs, the hens consumed an unbalanced ration low in vitamin A when wheat was the grain of choice. The same authors restricted the feeding time of turkeys to force them to consume approximately equal parts of mash and grain. Within a five-minute period, the turkeys ate grain in the same amount as they consumed mash the rest of the day. This occurred in the winter months with minimum sheltering for the birds.

Animal calorimeters and respiration chambers were used in much of the early work on feed requirements of animals. For an early history of energy metabolism, Swift and French (1957) and Kleiber (1961) are recommended. Basal metabolic rates and studies of energy balance, however, need to be supplemented with studies on animals kept under controlled environmental conditions. Thus, the total feed intake should include the heat equivalent of normal activity, plus the heat increment of a ration which provides the net energy sufficient for maintenance and additional energy equivalent to an acceptable weight gain.

A number of laboratories equipped with climatic chambers for

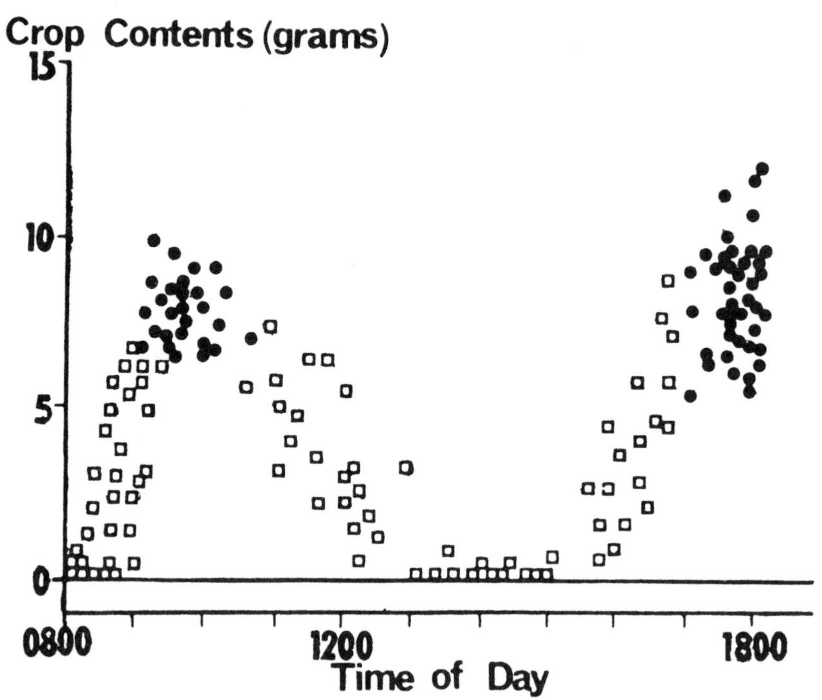

Fig. 1. Diurnal pattern of crop contents, reflecting feeding habits of doves. Dots = values obtained from doves from water holes; squares = doves from fields (After Schmid, 1965).

studying the effect of environmental factors on animals, including man, exists. A partial list of these facilities has been compiled by Henschel (1964), although he did not include the climatic chambers in the Poultry Husbandry Department nor those of the Animal Husbandry Department at the University of California at Davis.

Not only are there great differences in feed intake, based on body weight and surface area, among the various species of animals; there also is a wide difference within a given species. These differences affect feed intake indirectly, as they are associated with the heat-loss mechanism. The differences are caused by the sweating rate, age, coat thickness, color, production of milk or egg, acclimatization, and similar factors. Acclimatization can result in an adaptation to temperature which may result in an anatomical change within one generation. Figure 2 presents some data from Harrison (1963) on the growth of tails on mice reared under different temperatures. At higher temperatures tails grew longer and, except for a brief early period, grew faster. Stewart *et al.* (1951) found that the hair coat

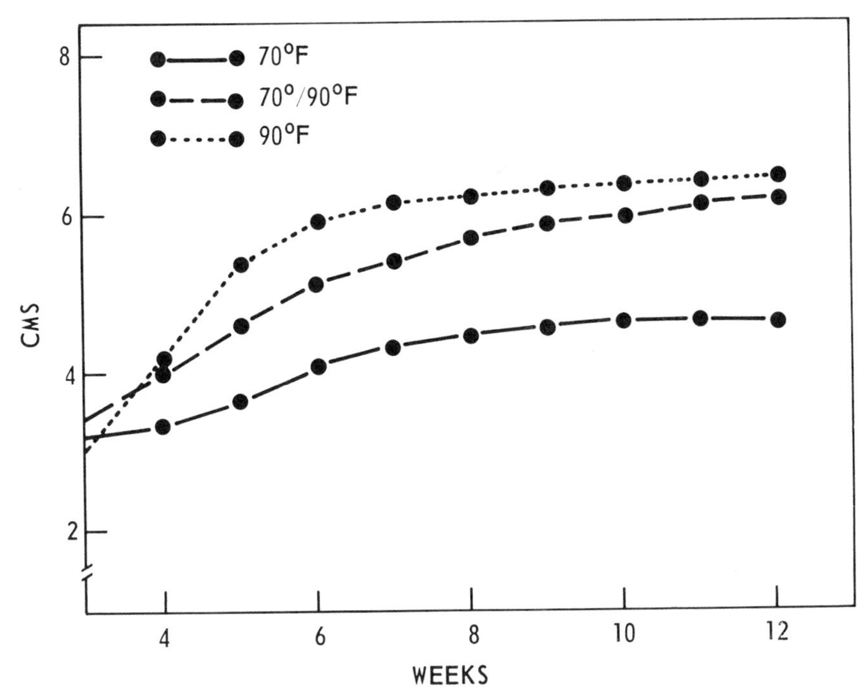

Fig. 2. Length of tails of mice kept at different temperatures (After Harrison, 1963).

of dairy calves was affected by temperature and grew darker on cattle reared at cool temperatures than on those reared in hot temperatures.

Feed Intake of Chickens at Different Temperatures

Heywang and Vavich (1962) have compiled data on the calculated caloric intake of White Leghorn hens kept in cages and exposed to normal weather conditions in Arizona (Table 1). Tremendous differences occurred in the caloric intake of fowl as the ambient temperature changed. The number of calories consumed in cold weather was approximately 50 percent greater than the amount consumed in hot weather, although part of this increase may have resulted from changes in body weight associated with the age of the bird and the rate of egg production.

In a study using poultry calorimeters at Beltsville, Maryland, White Leghorn hens at 35°C consumed 64 grams per bird and at 18°C consumed 102 grams. At the same time, water consumption was 299 ml and 207 ml for the 35°C and 18°C groups, respectively (Wilson *et al.*, 1957).

Seasonal Changes in Feed Consumption

The insulation of the animal (wool or hair, or feathers or down) and changes in production of milk or eggs have a bearing on consumption. Many species of animals grow longer coats of hair for

Table 1. Effect of temperature and caloric content of ration on energy intake of hens, based on 112 days (Heywang and Vavich, 1962).

	Daily feed intake as ME kcal/hen	
Ration ME kcal/g	Hot days $\bar{x}$ 31°C	Cool days $\bar{x}$ 12°C
2.330	252	370
2.640	243	360
2.970	250	364
3.190	242	355
3.410	241	356

ME = Metabolizable energy.

the winter months; also, in this season, changes in air temperature and wind may be quite marked. The relative monthly feed intake for laying hens has been summarized by Hill (1962) in Table 2. The data are presented as the average relative percentage of feed consumption based on the annual mean. While these data have been corrected for egg production, they do not reflect changes in body weight. The production year represented usually starts with September, so that the following months (October, November, December, *et seq.*) reflect both changes in temperature (decrease) and weight (increase).

Metabolic Rate of Domestic Animals

With decreased environmental temperature there is a dramatic increase in the metabolic rate. The number of pounds of feed required to produce a certain number of pounds of gain is the usual way of expressing feeding efficiency. It is illustrated by data from Ota and McNally (1965) of nine-week-old fryers reared in different temperatures (Fig. 3). The decrease in feeding efficiency in hot weather is nearly a linear function. Rate of growth is at a maximum around 24°C or 75°F; it decreases abruptly at higher ambient temperatures and more gradually at cooler temperatures.

Metabolic studies of sheep at three feeding levels and different ambient temperatures reported by Armstrong *et al.* (1959) are shown in Figure 4. It is evident that feed intake had an important bearing on heat production, as would be expected, and that the thermoneutrality zone is really a rather small area of the curve. There was an increase in heat production as ambient temperature rose over 32°C. The effect of shearing is also shown in Figure 4. The "critical temperature" or zone of thermal neutrality for sheep is about 27°C if the fleece length is 0.1 cm and 13°C if the fleece length is 2.5 cm. The data of Graham *et al.* (1959) on feed consumption

Table 2. Monthly feed intake of laying hens expressed as percentage of annual mean (Hill, 1962).

Month	%	Month	%	Month	%	Month	%
Oct.	95	Jan.	103	Apr.	107	July	94
Nov.	98	Feb.	107	May	100	Aug.	95
Dec.	101	Mar.	107	June	94	Sept.	95

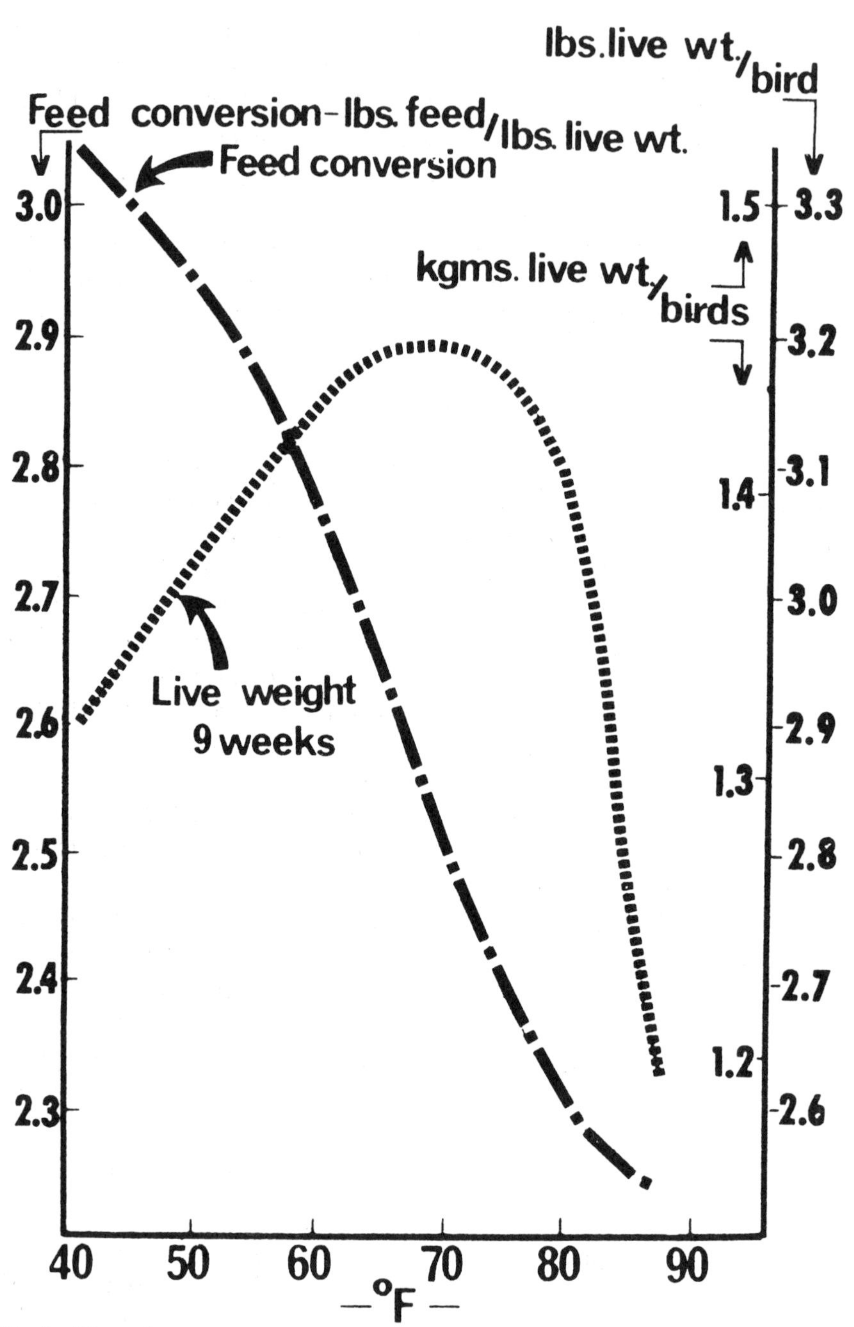

Fig. 3. Effect of temperature on growth and feed conversion of nine-week-old chickens (After Ota and McNally, 1965) .

indicate that there is an optimum temperature at which body weight gain is best, and also reveal that feed consumption goes down as temperature increases. In a study with pigs at the University of California, Heitman and Hughes (1949) found that heavier pigs eat relatively less feed at higher temperatures than do lighter weight pigs (Fig. 5).

The effect of temperature and humidity on feed intake of cows was studied by Johnson and Kilber (1963). They found that feed intake and the rate of I^{131} turnover decreased as temperature increased.

The data obtained by Romijn and Lokhorst (1961) indicate that the degree of feathering of chickens influences the basal metabolic rate throughout a wide range of temperature (Fig. 6). The data are not strictly comparable with those of Ota and McNally (1961),

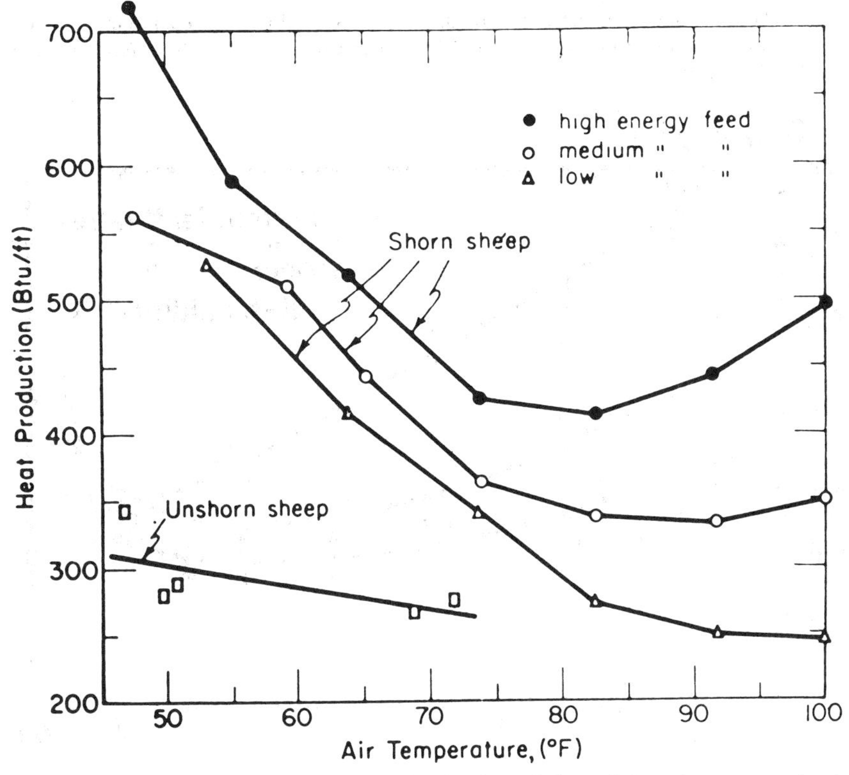

Fig. 4. Effect of air temperature on heat production of sheep fed at three energy levels (After Armstrong *et al.*, 1959).

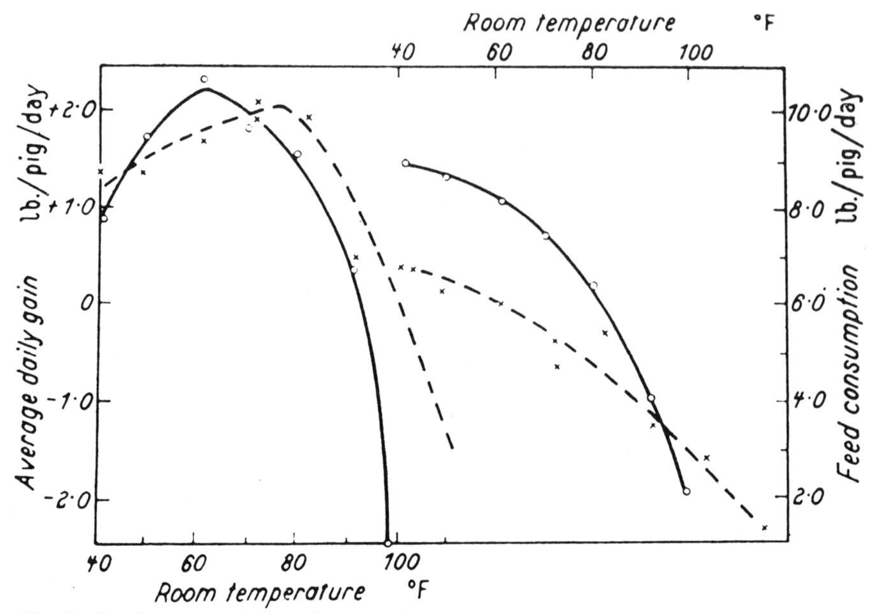

Fig. 5. Feed consumption and rate of gain of pigs at different room temperatures. Solid and dashed lines indicate heavy and lightweight pigs, respectively (After Heitman and Hughes, 1949).

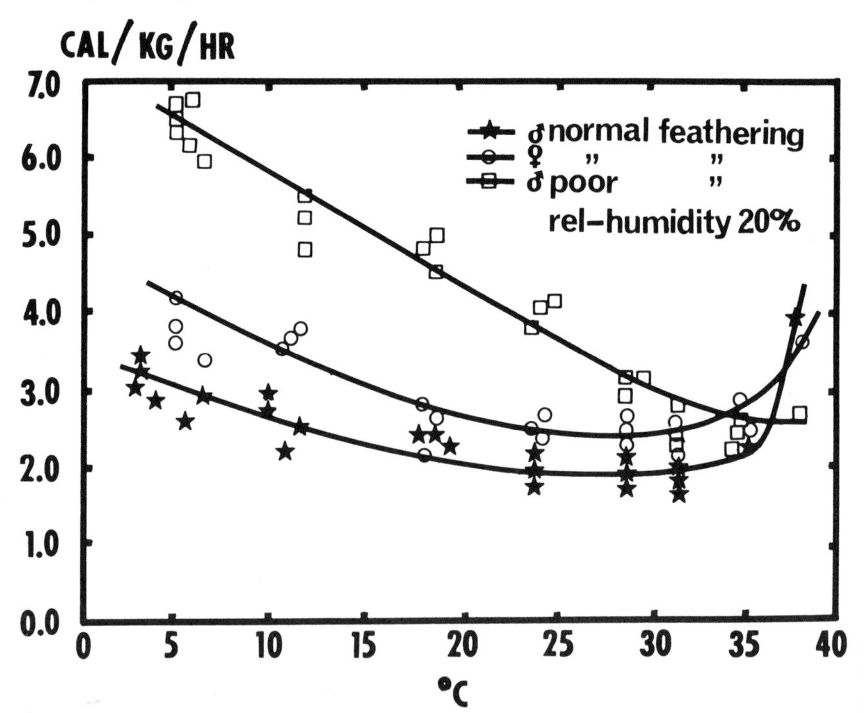

Fig. 6. Basal metabolic rate of chickens kept at different temperatures as related to the degree of feathering (After Romijn and Lokhorst, 1961).

however, because the latter were dealing with birds which had been fed.

Caloric Intake of Chickens

In a series of experiments in our climatic chambers at the University of California at Davis, we maintained four room temperatures—16°, 21°, 27°, and 32°C. In each chamber we fed three energy levels, which were formulated by Dr. F. W. Hill and were designated as high, medium, and low. The metabolizable energy (ME) in kcal/gram of ration were 3.36, 3.07, and 2.76, respectively. Table 3 shows the daily intake of the feed, expressed in kcal per bird, and also the body weight of the bird at 11 weeks of age for the three rations and four temperatures. The birds fed the ration highest in calories consumed the most total calories. As would be expected, the daily caloric intake per bird progressively decreased as temperature increased.

Feeding efficiency is a way of expressing the productivity of laying hens in terms of feed intake. Feeding efficiency often is calculated in numbers of eggs rather than weight of eggs. This can be misleading because at high temperatures, smaller eggs are produced. The feeding efficiency of Leghorns is shown for two separate experi-

Table 3. Body weight and feed intake of 11-week-old White Leghorn pullets fed rations differing in caloric content and kept at three constant environmental temperatures.

Rations ME kcal/g	Body wts. 11 wks. (g)	Daily feed intake kcal/bird
2.760	866	126
3.070	892	130
3.360	917	137
Temp. °C		
16	942	160
21	940	141
27	908	123
32	778	101

ME = Metabolizable energy.

ments in Figure 7. Experiment A was reported by Wilson *et al.* (1957) and experiment B represents previously unpublished data from my laboratory. The results shown indicate that under constant temperature conditions the optimum efficiency occurred in the range of 16° to 28°C (60° to 80°F).

Results of a series of experiments done at the U.S. Department of Agriculture by Ota and McNally (1961) with several breeds of chickens are given in Figure 8. The heat production varied widely between day and night, and was associated both with activity and previously ingested feed.

The time required for an animal to eat to satiety varies with body size and species of animal as well as with the caloric content and density of the ration. The length of the dark period when no eating normally would occur in untrained pullets may also be important. In two separate experiments at the University of California at Davis, young pullets were moved into cages under two different photoperiods. The birds were unaccustomed to the cages and therefore did not eat except during the light period. Higher mortality

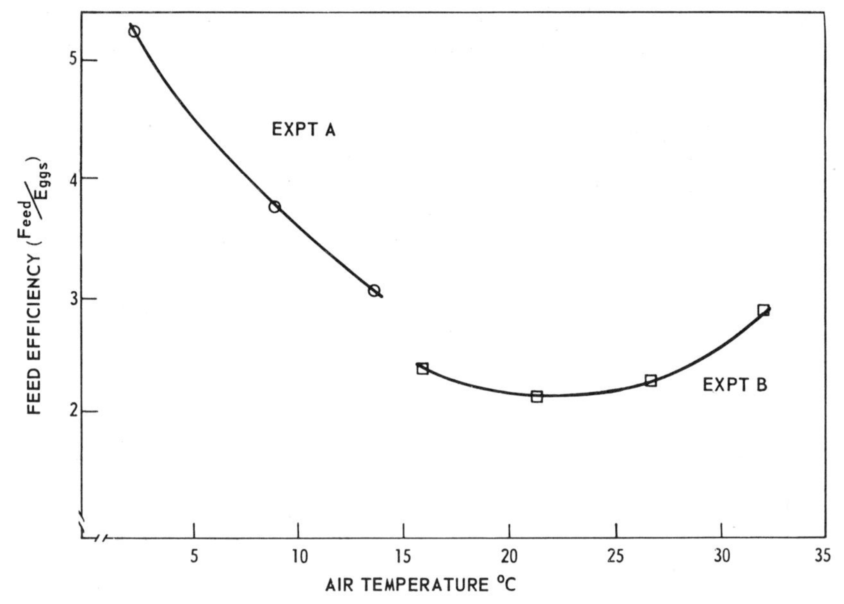

Fig. 7. Feeding efficiency of egg production of Leghorn hens kept at constant temperature. Efficiency expressed as grams of feed per gram of egg (Wilson *et al.*, 1957).

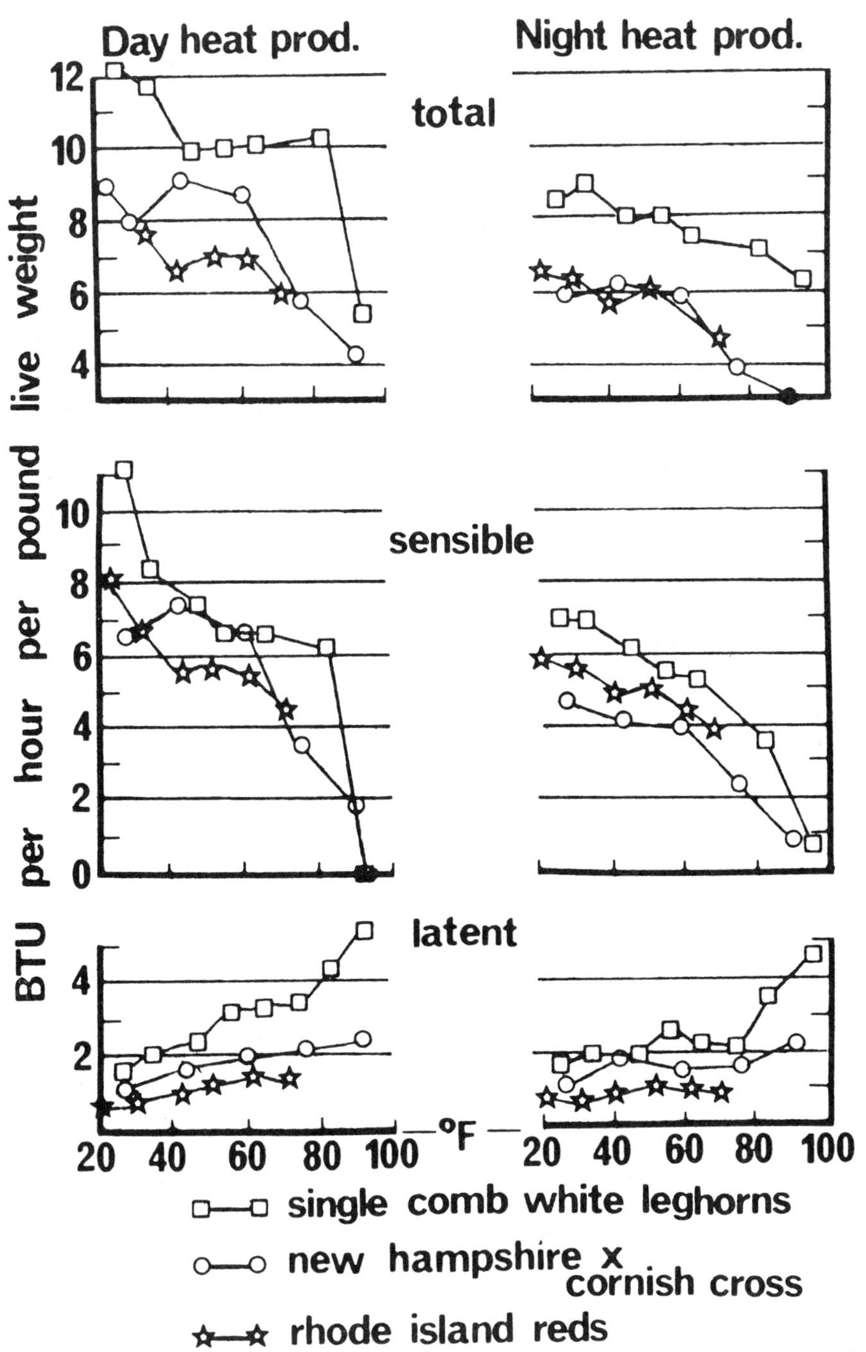

Fig. 8. Heat production of hens kept at different temperatures during the day and night periods (After Ota and McNally, 1961).

was associated with a short photoperiod of eight hours (Table 4). Results of a study by Lepkovsky *et al.* (1962) indicate that when chickens are trained, they require a period of 1½ hours to consume sufficient feed for a 24-hour day. The room temperature was approximately 24°C.

Force-Feeding at High Temperature

To determine if low feed intake associated with high temperature could cause lowered milk production in dairy cows, Wayman *et al.* (1962) force-fed cows. The cows lived for three weeks at a time at ambient temperatures of 18° and 31°C. Prior to starting the test the amount of feed consumed at the cooler temperature (18°C) was determined. Later, when exposed to a hot environment (31°C), the cows were offered their daily ration, based on their previous intake. What they did not eat was fed via a ruminal fistula. The force-feeding prevented a major portion of the decline in milk production observed in the control cows. High ambient temperature, *per se,* caused a decrease in milk production, as is illustrated in Figure 9.

We have noted that the chicken drinks more water and eats less feed as the air temperature increases. We used this knowledge to encourage birds to consume more feed by mixing the mash with either two or three parts of water. In Table 5, results are shown of an experiment where one group of White Leghorn cockerels was kept at 24°C and another at 32°C.

Regulatory Mechanisms

It has been shown that receptors in the skin respond to environmental temperature and, either through neuro-regulation of endocrine release or blood temperature, relay the message to the brain.

Table 4. The effect of length of feeding time (photoperiod) on mortality of seven-week-old pullets kept in a 5° to 10°C environment. Based on groups of 50 or more birds.

Photoperiod	Group 1	Group 2
8L:16D	10.3%	35.5%
14L:10D	00.0%	14.7%

The hypothalamus is generally thought to be the thermostat. The anterior portion of this part of the brain is concerned with heat loss; the posterior portion is concerned with heat production. It has been shown by Rampone and Shirasu (1964) that feeding will increase the cerebral temperature of rats within five minutes after the feed has been consumed. In cows a rise in brain temperature

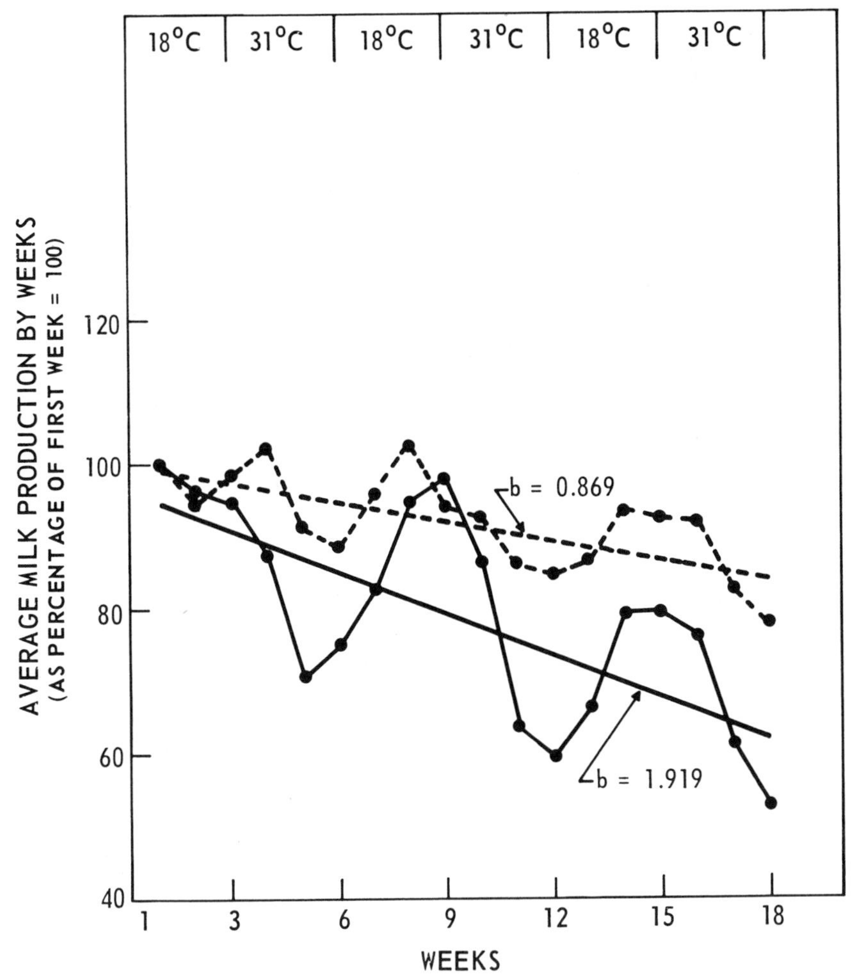

Fig. 9. Decline in milk production associated with decreased feed intake at 18° and 31°C in normal (solid line) and fistulated, force-fed (dotted line) cows. Relative humidity kept at 50 percent for both temperatures. Milk production is expressed as percentage of first week being 100 (After Wayman *et al.,* 1962).

of 0.5°C after feeding was reported by Findlay and Ingram (1961). Likewise, the localization of the feed-regulating mechanism has been demonstrated in birds; certain centers of the brain can be stimulated electrically to promote either the act of feeding or the act of drinking, as reported for pigeons (Åkerman *et al.*, 1960).

The brain also regulates other endocrine glands involved in the control of temperature, namely the thyroids and the adrenals. It is generally assumed that a high degree of correlation exists between the activity of the pituitary and thyroid glands in temperature regulation. However, the change in thyroid activity under changing thermal environment is a relatively slow process (Yousef and Johnson, 1965). Rats, sheep, and cattle have the same inverse relationship between temperature and metabolism as does man, and there are racial differences in the basal metabolic rate in livestock as in man.

Activity, ambient temperature, and conditioning all contribute to the amount of feed eaten, according to Brobeck (1960). It was suggested by Findlay (1950) that a reduction of heat production in the rumen after small meals is an adaptive mechanism protecting animals from excessive heat loads. Macfarlane (1961), however, is not in agreement with this. He pointed out that Zebu and Santa Gertrudis cattle experience little or no depression in feed intake at 28°C or even 38°C. A decrease in feed intake seems to depend on whether the body temperature rises in a hot environment. The body temperature of Zebu does not rise until the environmental temperature exceeds 38°C; then appetite is reduced. In both rabbits and cattle there is depression in intake of feed under hot environmental conditions (Johnson *et al.*, 1957).

Table 5. Consumption of water and feed mixture at room temperature of 24° and 32°C by Leghorn cockerels.

Room temp (°C)	Water/feed	Gain in 2 wk (g)	Dry feed intake 2 wk (g)
24	3:1	250	710
24	2:1	230	674
32	3:1	230	599
32	2:1	128	446

An interesting variation in the usual finding of reduced appetite and intake of hay in the tropics has been reported by Payne and Hancock (1957). Identical twin Jersey and Shorthorn calves kept in Fiji consumed less hay, but more concentrate of barley, peanut, and coconut, than did their corresponding twins in the neutral environment of the northern islands of New Zealand. The tropical cows increased the intake of concentrate proportionally to their milk production. Roughage seemed unattractive to them even in the form of lucerne (alfalfa) hay.

Hypothalamic control of feeding has been suggested by Brobeck (1960) to function as follows:

1. Specific dynamic action of feed produces heat which causes the rostral cooling center of the hypothalamus to stimulate the medial satiety center and to inhibit the lateral appetite center of the region. Feeding then ceases. If there is an external heat load, heat from the feed would work to produce a more rapid cessation of feeding. The observation that the adrenal cortex is necessary for the maintenance of appetite, even pathological appetite (Kennedy and McCance, 1958), may be important here, because adrenal cortical activity may be reduced in the heat.

2. Gastric distention and blood glucose or amino acid level probably interact with the other hypothalamic events to produce a final pattern of feedings.

All this is subject to further regulation through acclimatization. Pennycuik (1961) reared rats at 34°C and observed that after acclimatization the rectal temperature was similar to rats kept at 27° or 21°C, yet at 34°C rats consistently ate 14 percent less feed than did rats kept at 27°C and 30 percent less than rats kept at 21°C.

Metabolites circulating through the hypothalamic region may determine food intake, according to Kennedy (1953). He postulated a demands system, wherein lowered levels of circulating metabolites (during exercise, lactation, or starvation) stimulate feeding through their effect on the hypothalamus. When a region of the hypothalamus is damaged, feeding continues regardless of need. A fat depot mobilized as fatty acid could exercise control of feed intake. Probably both the heat balance and the metabolites combine in normal regulation.

In tropical sun, therefore, when the body temperature rises, it is likely that the already poor supply of feed for forage is less available for productive energy, since respiratory cooling expands energy. A raised body temperature would have the same wasteful effects in energetics of growth and production as shivering in the cold. It is probably advantageous that the thyroid and adrenal activity of mammals in hot environments is reduced, and endogenous heat production is low.

The effect of high temperatures on decreasing normal activity of animals has been shown by numerous workers (Wilson, 1948). This behavior response is mediated through the nervous system. Muscles are relaxed and unnecessary movements are eliminated, so that heat input is less. The relaxed posture of most experimental animals under high temperature is familiar to all of us. Appleman and Delouche (1958) observed reduced fighting among goats when the temperature exceeded 35°C. In a group of four goats kept at 10°C, there were 13 attacks per hour by the dominant animal of the group. At 35°C there were two attacks per hour, and at 40°C there was only one attack. There is, therefore, a reduced metabolic requirement for work or behavioral display in hot environments, as well as reduced adrenal and thyroid activity in the resting animal. The grazing time of even well-adapted cattle (Bennie, 1956) is shorter at higher temperatures. At 20°C they were active 94 percent of the time, but at 29°C they grazed and ruminated only 63 percent of the day.

Future Research

Further study of the effect of temperature on feed-regulating mechanisms could well utilize trained animals. For example, Laties and Weiss (1960) observed that it is possible to train rats to press a bar to provide themselves with heat. In their experiments they observed that naive rats pressed the lever for heat earlier than did rats which had been acclimated to 20°C for a month. This difference was reflected in the rates at which body temperature fell in the acclimated and nonacclimated rats. Such a procedure could supplement our current research in the area of feed-regulating mechanisms under conditions of various temperature.

REFERENCES

Åkerman, B., B. Andersson, E. Fabricius, and L. Svensson, 1960. Observations on central regulation of body temperature and of food and water intake in the pigeon (*Columba livia*). *Acta Physiol. Scand., 50:* 328–336.

Appleman, R. D., and J. C. Delouche, 1958. Behavioral, physiological and biochemical responses of goats to temperature 0° to 40°C. *J. Animal Sci., 17:* 326–335.

Armstrong, D. G., K. L. Blaxter, N. McC. Graham, and F. W. Wainman, 1959. The effect of environmental condition on food utilization by sheep. *Animal Prod., 1:* 1.

Bennie, J. G. S., 1956. The Mauritius Creole breed of milch cattle. *Empire J. Exp. Agr., 24:* 192–204.

Brobeck, J. R., 1960. Food and temperature. *Recent Progr. Hormone Res., 16:* 439–466.

Findlay, J. D., 1950. The effect of temperature, humidity, air movement and solar radiation on the behaviour and physiology of cattle and other farm animals. *Hannah Dairy Res. Inst. Bull. No. 9:* 1–178.

Findlay, J. D., and D. L. Ingram, 1961. Brain temperature as a factor in the control of thermal polypnoea in the ox (*Bos taurus*). *J. Physiol., 155:* 72–85.

Graham, N. McC., F. W. Wainman, K. L. Blaxter, and D. G. Armstrong, 1959. Environmental temperature, energy metabolism and heat regulation in sheep. I. Energy metabolism in closely clipped sheep. *J. Agr. Sci., 52:* 13–24.

Harrison, G. A., 1963. Temperature adaptation as evidenced by growth of mice. *Federation Proc., 22:* 691–697.

Heitman, H., Jr., and E. H. Hughes, 1949. The effects of air temperature and relative humidity on the physiological well being of swine. *J. Animal Sci., 8(2):* 171–181.

Henschel, A., 1964. Laboratory facilities for adaptation research: high and low temperatures. In *Handbook of Physiology,* edited by D. B. Dill; Section 4, Ch. 18. Am. Physiol. Soc., Washington, D.C.

Heywang, B. W., and M. G. Vavich, 1962. Energy level of a 16% protein diet for layers in a semi-arid sub-tropical climate. *Poultry Sci., 41:* 1389–1393.

Hill, F. W., 1962. Meeting nutrient requirements for poultry. In *Introduction to Livestock Production,* edited by H. H. Cole; pp. 502–524. W. H. Freeman and Co., San Francisco.

Jensen, L. S., L. H. Merrill, C. V. Reddy, and J. McGinnis, 1962. Observations on eating patterns and rate of feed passage of birds fed pelleted and unpelleted diets. *Poultry Sci. 41:* 1414–1419.

Johnson, H. D., A. C. Ragsdale, and C. S. Cheng, 1957. Environmental physiology and shelter engineering XLV. Comparisons of the effects of environment on rabbits and cattle. 1. Influence of constant environmental temperature (50° and 80°F.) on the growth responses and physiological reactions of rabbits and cattle. *Missouri Univ. Agr. Exp. Sta. Res. Bull., 646:* 1–57.

Johnson, H. D., and H. H. Kibler, 1963. Temperature-humidity effects on thyroxine I^{131} disappearance rates in cattle. *J. Appl. Physiol., 18:* 73–76.

Kennedy, G. C., 1953. The role of depot fat in the hypothalamic control of food intake in the rat. *Proc. Roy. Soc. London Ser. B, 140:* 578–592.

Kennedy, G. C., and R. A. McCance, 1958. Endocrine aspects of overnutrition and undernutrition. In *Modern Trends in Endocrinology*, edited by H. Gardiner-Hill; pp. 79–95. Butterworth, London.

Kleiber, M., 1961. *The Fire of Life*. John Wiley and Sons, New York.

Laties, V. G., and B. Weiss, 1960. Behavior in the cold after acclimatization. *Science, 131:* 1891.

Lepkovsky, S., S. Feldman, and I. Sharon, 1962. Some basic mechanisms of hunger and satiety. *Proc. Nutr. Soc., 21:* 65–73.

Macfarlane, W. V., 1961. Endocrine functions in hot environments. Environmental physiology and psychology in arid countries. In *Review of Research;* pp. 153–222. UNESCO, Paris.

Ota, H., and E. H. McNally, 1961. Poultry respiration-calorimetric studies of laying hens. *U.S. Dept. Agr., ARS 42–43:* 1–34.

Ota, H., and E. H. McNally, 1965. *Preliminary Broiler Heat and Moisture Data for Designing Poultry Houses and Ventilating Systems.* Paper No. 65-411, Am. Soc. Agr. Eng. Summer Meeting.

Payne, W. J. A., and J. Hancock, 1957. The direct effect of tropical climate on the performance of European-type cattle. *Empire J. Exp. Agr., 25:* 321–338.

Pennycuik, P. R., 1961. *Functional Adaptations of Rats Living at 34°C.* Ph.D. Thesis, Univ. Queensland, Brisbane, Australia.

Rampone, A. J., and M. E. Shirasu, 1964. Temperature changes in the rat in response to feeding. *Science, 144:* 317–319.

Romijn, C., and W. Lokhorst, 1961. Climate and poultry. Heat regulation in the fowl. *Tijdschr. Diergeneesk., 86:* 153–175.

Schmid, W. D., 1965. Energy intake in the mourning dove (*Zenaidura macroura marginella*). *Science, 150:* 1171–1172.

Sellers, E. A., R. W. You, and N. M. Moffat, 1954. Regulation of food consumption by caloric value of the ration in rats exposed to cold. *Am. J. Physiol., 177:* 367–371.

Stewart, R. E., E. E. Pickett, and S. Brody, 1951. Environmental physiology with special reference to domestic animals. *XVI Missouri Univ. Agr. Exp. Sta. Res. Bull.,* 484.

Swift, R. W., and C. E. French, 1957. *Energy Metabolism and Nutrition.* Scarecrow Press, Washington, D.C.

Wayman, O., H. D. Johnson, C. P. Merilan, and I. L. Berry, 1962. Effect of *ad libitum* or force-feeding of two rations on lactating dairy cows subjected to temperature stress. *J. Dairy Sci., 45:* 1472–1478.

Wilson, W. O., 1948. Some effects of increasing environmental temperatures on pullets. *Poultry Sci., 27:* 813–817.

Wilson, W. O., E. H. McNally, and H. Ota, 1957. Temperature and calorimetric studies on hens in individual cages. *Poultry Sci., 36:* 1254–1261.

Wilson, W. O., F. R. Sampson, A. L. Moxon, and T. M. Paulsen, 1945. Vitamin A intake of chickens fed mash and grain free choice. *Poultry Sci., 24:* 237–240.

Yousef, M. K., and H. D. Johnson, 1965. Time course of thyroxine I^{131} disappearance rates in cattle during exposure to hot and cold environment. *Life Sciences, 4:* 1531–1543.

Effects of Macro- and Microenvironment on the Biology of Mammalian Reproduction

L. C. ULBERG, *Animal Science Department, North Carolina Agricultural Experiment Station, Raleigh, North Carolina*

INVESTIGATIONS INTO ASPECTS of the relationship between environment and physiological function are immediately faced with certain challenges. The mere act of observing the animal may change its "environment" and consequently may affect the response which is being used as a measure of physiological function. The inability to determine and measure precisely either the environment or the animal's response to that environment adds to the challenge, and one is forced to work with uncontrolled variations which fluctuate within set limits. For example, "biological variations", which are a part of most biological data, may simply be the unexplained differences in response which result from inability to characterize precisely the relationship between the animal and its environment.

The instability of both the biological system and the environmental system further complicates the problem. Regardless of how animals are treated the aging process continues. When the change owing to aging is superimposed upon changes owing to diurnal and seasonal variations existing in both systems, the experimental results can often be described only in nebulous terms. Environmental control chambers are simply engineering attempts to stabilize and thereby control certain ambient conditions. At best these attempts can result only in gross control of the situation. But it must be recognized that it is the best that can be accomplished with the use of our present knowledge.

The multitude of factors which go to make up the environment may interact so as to influence the physiological functions of the animal (Findley, 1963; Tromp, 1963). This interaction can lead to misinterpretation and even confusion as to the exact relationship between a particular physiological response and a set of gross environmental circumstances. This situation exists especially when the physiological response under study is mammalian fertility or reproduction (Boyd, 1965; Hafez, 1964a), because reproduction is the result of a series of precisely timed physiological events that occur in a specific sequence. A breakdown in any one of the events completely terminates the process. When this happens the whole process must be reinitiated (Dutt, 1964).

Climatic Factors Alter Mammalian Reproduction

Many excellent reviews concerned with the effect of various climatic factors on mammalian reproduction are available and more are being published. Therefore, this discussion is not intended to be another catalog of observations, but rather an attempt to summarize and thereby establish the current state of knowledge on the subject. Published reviews have documented the fact that the pattern of mammalian reproduction is intimately associated with changes in climatic conditions (Hafez, 1964b). The seasonal mating patterns of most wild animals provide well-known examples of this association. The process of spermatogenesis can be interfered with during periods of high air temperature. Fertility in the mammalian female can also often be lowered by high air temperatures, especially when combined with high humidity. The pattern of reproductive failure in the female can occur in many forms. Under conditions of severe thermal stress ovarian function may cease so that the female will not exhibit estrus and consequently will not mate. But cessation of estrus is normal for some species during certain periods of the year. Sheep, for instance, become anestrous as the number of daylight hours increases, although in other species the breeding season starts with the increase in the amount of daylight. The obvious implications of these changes are that environment controls the hormonal systems of animals which, in turn, bring about a radical change in physiological function. In this example light is the environmental factor most often discussed as directly responsible for the physiological change.

There are other examples of environment being responsible for changes in reproductive physiology. A 30 percent decrease in human conception rate during summer months in Hong Kong was reported by Chang *et al.* (1963), who suggested that at least part of this decrease in conception rate could be the result of high ambient temperature. Tromp (1963) reported that sex ratios at birth vary by season. Others have reported that fetal birth weight is drastically reduced by subjecting the mother to conditions of high air temperature during the gestation period (Shelton, 1964).

Observations made on dairy cows in Arizona suggest that a high air temperature causes early embryo death, but only when associated with high humidity (Stott and Williams, 1962). Physical exercise or activity augments the harmful effects of climate on reproduction in sheep (Spies *et al.*, 1965). The listing of similar reported examples could continue, but these should suffice to demonstrate the intimate relationship which exists between factors which make up environment and physiological mechanisms which control the reproductive process.

Reports from which these examples were taken dealt mostly with macroenvironment, that is, those climatic forces acting on the potential parent which in some way influence the reproductive pattern. Only measurements of gross responses have generally been reported; these include failure of sperm production, absence of ovarian function, embryo death, or light birth weight of fetuses. The literature lacks biological explanations for changes in these responses to climatic forces. With the documentation of the fact that climate does influence reproductive function, efforts should now be directed toward the development of an understanding of the physiological processes involved. Only with this knowledge will it become possible to develop the most efficient systems, engineering or otherwise, which can be used to remove the reproductive process from the control of climate.

The macroenvironment, as used in this discussion, includes those factors which act on the potential parent, either directly or indirectly. They include light, humidity, radiation, and so forth. Microenvironment, on the other hand, is that environment which immediately surrounds and directly controls some physiological event associated with reproduction. Figure 1 provides a simple example to demonstrate how these definitions are used in this discussion. The microenvironment, when severe enough, will cause a stress on the animal which will interfere with some normal physiological function. One might be interested in the effects of changes in air temperature upon the growth rate of an embryo during a particular stage of its development. The temperature around the embryo (the microtemperature), which in turn affects growth, can be increased by increasing the ambient temperature (the macrotemperature). It must be acknowledged that knowing the exact macroenvironmental condition, no matter how precisely it has been measured, does not necessarily tell us the conditions surrounding the physiological

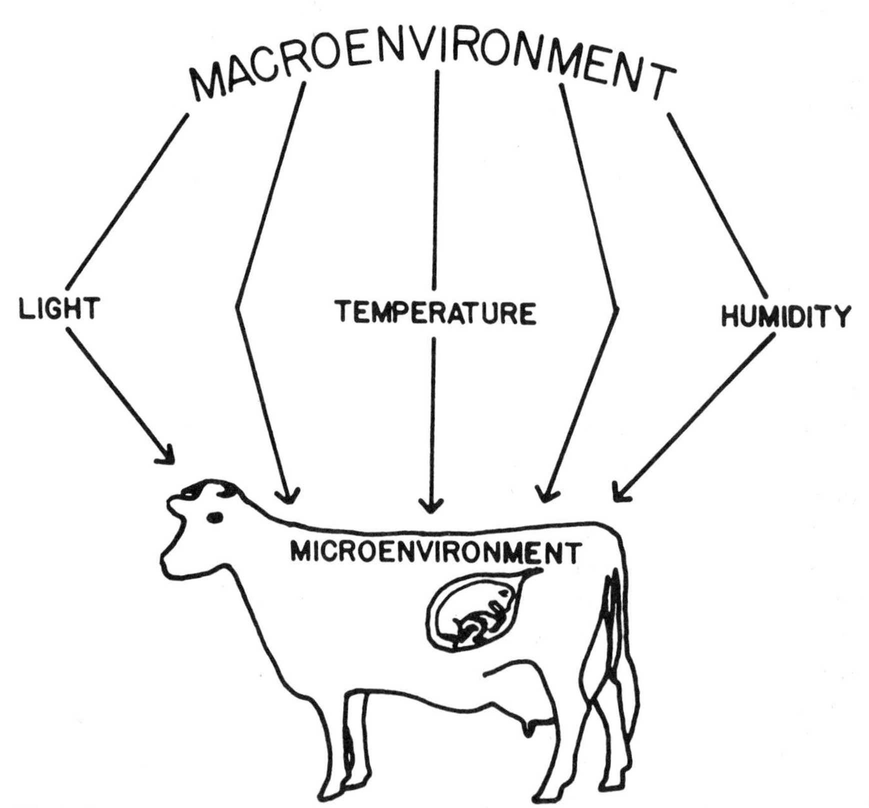

Fig. 1. The total macroenvironment acts on the animal to produce a microenvironment within the animal.

event or even what physiological event is involved in the response which is under investigation.

The microtemperature can be increased in other ways, such as by exercise, mild systemic infection in the potential mother, time of day, or many other possibilities. Thus the microtemperature may be the result of the whole macroenvironment. Perhaps more important in the development of a biological explanation for the change in response is that high air temperature may be acting through an entirely different physiological mechanism from the one postulated, so that the microtemperature, therefore, may not be important in that change.

Macroenvironmental factors, such as light, air temperature, and humidity, influence microenvironmental conditions, such as body secretions or temperatures. Before either can elicit some biological response, in this case fertility, each must act through one or more physiological events. The point is diagrammed schematically in Figure 2. To control better the relationships between environment and physiological response there has to be a better understanding of the links which connect them.

When the physiological response is mammalian reproduction, attempts to understand the mechanisms involved may be accomplished in one of three ways: A particular event, such as early cell division of an embryo, can be removed from the influence of the animal and studied *in vitro*. The embryo is then subjected to a specific set of controlled conditions by bypassing those factors which cannot be standardized. Biochemists use this method when they determine chemical reactions. Another method is to attempt to standardize the microenvironment as nearly as possible. This makes the measurement and control of such factors as body temperature more important than the control of air temperature. If neither of these two

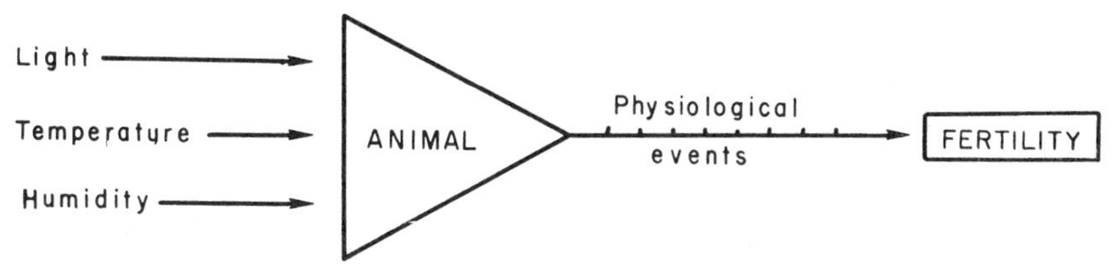

Fig. 2. Environment influences fertility by acting through one or more physiological events within the animal.

methods is possible, then the presence of uncontrolled factors has to be reckoned with when changes in responses are interpreted. Often this is the best that can be done because of the limitations of present knowledge and technique.

High Ambient Temperature Reduces Reproductive Rate

Examples of the delicate balance which exists in the relationship between environment and response can be drawn from observations made in our laboratory. Air temperatures of 32°C, with relative humidity readings of about 65 percent, would drastically lower the reproductive rate in sheep, and it has been further observed that under these conditions many embryos enter the uterus appearing morphologically normal. The return to estrus of the potential mother at a normal time, however, suggests early embryonic death. There are many physiological events associated with reproduction which occur in a precise sequence during this period of the embryo's development. The sperm, immediately after mating, are subjected to the environment of the female reproductive tract; the ova leave the ovary and come under the control of the environment of the oviduct; final maturation of the egg occurs at the time of the union of sperm and ovum. The first development of the new individual begins before it finally reaches the uterus. These observations are simply descriptive and yield no clue as to the physiological mechanisms which may be involved in the failure of the embryo to survive.

Delayed Embryonic Death

Observations on ova from heat-stressed females suggested that they were morphologically normal after going through all these physiological events, but their true viability at this point in development had to be determined (Alliston and Ulberg, 1961). This was accomplished simply by recovering ova from donor females maintained under environmental conditions, either 32° or 21°C, with a relative humidity of 65 percent. At the higher air temperature there was a 1° to 2° increase in the rectal temperature and a very marked increase in respiration rate. Females in both temperatures were mated and their embryos recovered from their oviducts at about the time the embryos were to enter the uterus. Embryos were classified for morphological normality, and those which were judged normal were placed in the uterus of a synchronized recipient animal. There was a decrease in the fertilization rate (88 percent vs. 59 percent) in animals maintained at the higher air temperature (Fig. 3). But, by 30 days after mating there was also a decrease in embryo survival rate in those recipients which had received embryos started in the oviducts of the females (56 percent vs. 10 percent) maintained at the higher temperature. This indicated to us that death was not the result of an abnormal physiological function at the time of death, but rather the result of something which had happened to that embryo before it entered the uterus.

Resistance of Unfertilized Ova

Next, ova were recovered shortly after ovulation from donor females kept in the two different air temperatures and transferred to mated recipients (Woody and Ulberg, 1964). Ova were then fertilized in the recipient, so that the effect of high temperature could be only upon the ovum and not the sperm. The results of this study showed that there were just as many embryos 30 days post-mating (35 percent vs. 47 percent) in those recipients which received ova from animals maintained at 32°C as there were in

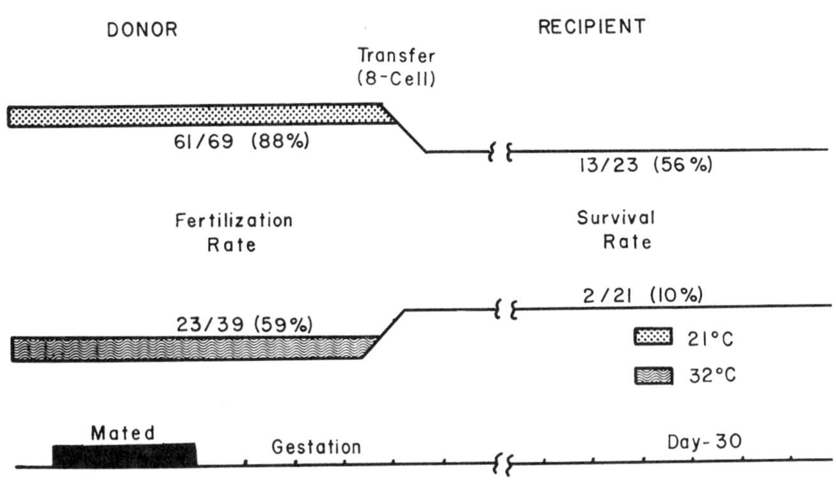

Fig. 3. Subsequent survival rate ratio and percentage of transferred sheep ova which originated in the reproductive system of females maintained at two different air temperatures.

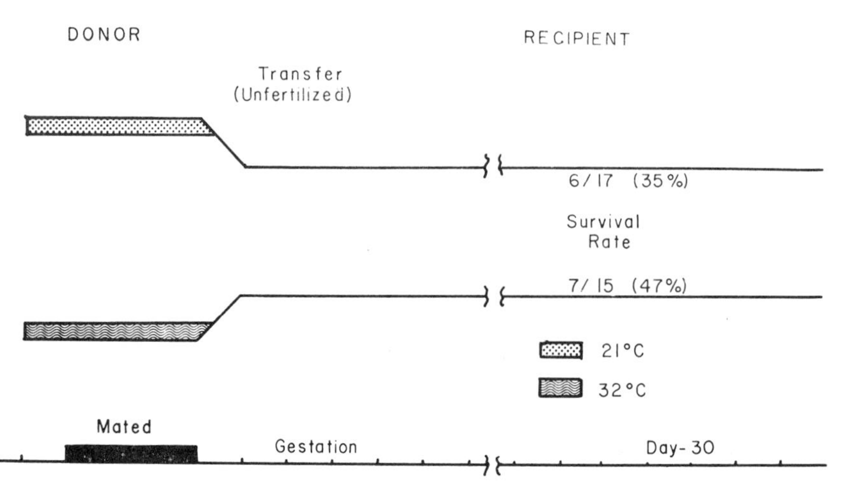

Fig. 4. Influence of high air temperature on sheep ova prior to fertilization as determined by percentage of subsequent embryo survival of ova transferred to mated recipients.

those which received ova from animals maintained at 21°C (Fig. 4). In this study the ovum had been isolated from the sperm during thermal stress and no damage was apparent. This suggested that the high air temperature had not altered the ovum prior to fertilization. The stress was acting through some physiological event which normally occurs between the time of ovulation and the time the egg enters the uterus, although the actual cessation of development occurs much later.

Response of Sperm to Stress

The next step in the investigation was to isolate and stress the sperm. The uterus could influence the sperm on their way up to the fertilization site in such a way as to bring about delayed embryonic death. In an attempt to study this possibility, highly fertile males were mated to females kept in the two air temperatures (Howarth *et al.*, 1965). Since embryonic death occurred in rabbits subjected to thermal stress (Phase G, Fig. 6) as it did in sheep, rabbits were used in this study. Six hours after mating the sperm were recovered and used to inseminate recipients which were near the time of ovulation. Fertilization was determined, the eggs which had cleaved were redeposited and allowed to go to 12 days post-

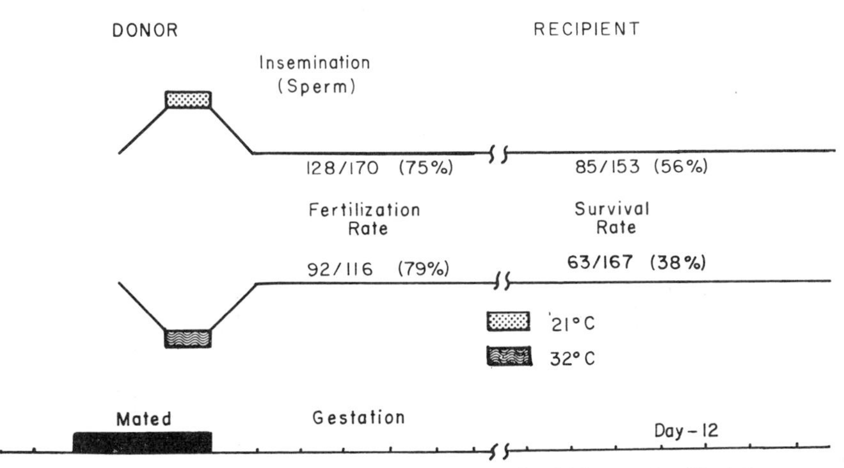

Fig. 5. Percentage of subsequent embryo survival of rabbit ova fertilized by sperm from heat-stressed females.

mating. There was no difference in the fertilization rates of eggs from recipients fertilized by the two types of sperm (75 percent vs. 79 percent, Fig. 5) ; however, again the survival rate of embryos was affected. Sperm which had spent six hours in the reproductive tract of a doe maintained at 32°C caused a significant decrease in the survival of recipient eggs (56 percent vs. 38 percent). This observation suggested that either the sperm or something brought in with the sperm was, at least in part, responsible for the death of the resulting embryo. These results are still descriptive because a physiological explanation for these observations is not readily apparent. They do, however, pull out of the total sequence certain possible events which could be involved in the response observed. This should make it easier to postulate a possible malfunctioning physiological mechanism.

Direct Effect of Temperature on Gametes

Sperm. Further elucidation was attempted by subjecting, *in vitro,* either the sperm or the fertilized ova at precise stages of development to temperatures comparable to those observed as rectal temperatures in thermal-stressed females. These observations are summarized in Figure 6. Sperm subjected, *in vitro,* for three hours to a temperature increase of 2°C (40° vs. 38°C) resulted in no significant effect on fertilization rate but did result in a significant decrease

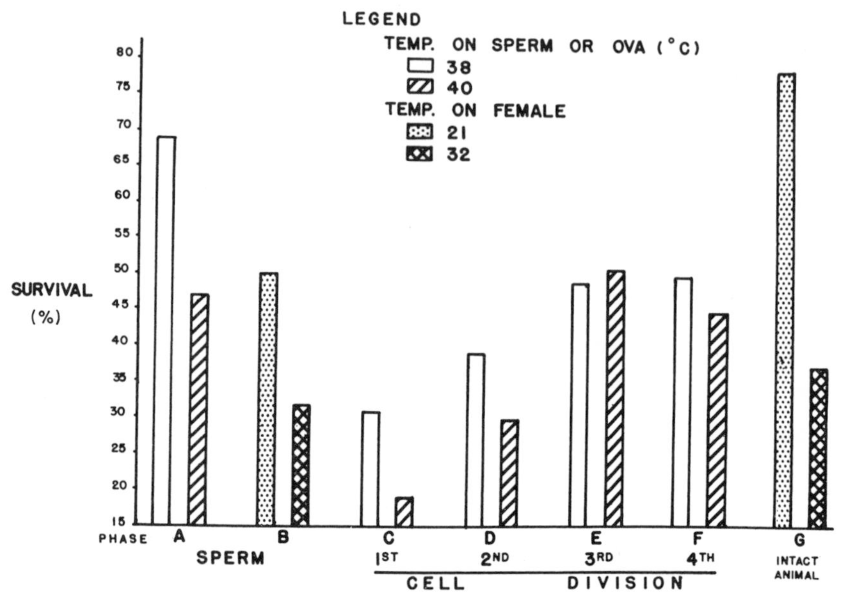

Fig. 6. Summary of experiments investigating the effect of temperature on specific phases of early development as determined by embryo survival at 12 days post-mating in the rabbit.

Phase of development investigated:

A. Sperm were subjected to either of two temperatures for three hours *in vitro* prior to insemination of normal females.

B. Sperm were recovered after six hours *in utero* from females maintained at either of two temperatures, then used to inseminate normal females.

C. Embryos grown at either of two temperatures for six hours *in vitro* through first cell division, then redeposited in normal reproductive systems.

D. Same as C except *in vitro* growth was during second cell division.

E. Same as C except *in vitro* growth was about the time of the third cell division.

F. Same as C except *in vitro* growth occurred when the number of blastomeres was increasing from about 8 to 16.

G. Difference in embryo survival in intact females subjected to two different air temperatures during the first 12 days of gestation.

in the rate of survival of the subsequent embryos (Phase A, Fig. 6; Burfening, unpublished data). This is the same response pattern observed for sperm subjected to the higher body temperature of the female (Phase B, Fig. 6) and simply suggests that, in part, it is the temperature acting directly on the sperm rather than some physiological mechanism mediated through the female which is responsible for lowered fertility.

Fertilized Ova. In an attempt to determine the direct effect of high temperature upon the fertilized ova, they were subjected, *in vitro,* to 38° or 40°C during the period of the first cell division (Alliston *et al.,* 1965). Embryos were grown for six hours *in vitro* and then replaced in the reproductive system of a recipient and allowed to remain for 12 days. In rabbits there are implant sites formed so that at 12 days post-mating the number of sites can be counted and the number of sites with living embryos determined. An embryo may live long enough (nine days) to cause a site to be formed but be dead at 12 days. In this experiment there was a significant decrease in the percentage of the sites which contained live embryos for those eggs grown during the first cell division in the higher temperature (Phase C, Fig. 6). This suggests that, as in sperm, the temperature acts directly upon the embryo during the first cell division to influence survival rate later in the period of development. The importance of critical timing of stress can be further realized by comparing these results with those obtained from the same type of study except that the culture period was during the second cell division rather than the first (Phase D, Fig. 6). At the second cell stage in development the effect of culture temperature was less than at the earlier stage but more than at the later stages (Phases E or F, Fig. 6). This points out the drastic changes which occur in an embryo's response to environmental stress over a short period of developmental time (Alliston and Ulberg, 1965).

Conclusions

These observations are in accord with reports suggesting that extreme air temperature is harmful to reproduction. But they demonstrate further the futility of attempting to develop a biological explanation for the relationship between some broad environmental conditions and some rather general animal performance, such as reproduction, in terms of response units. Without extreme precision in the measurement of both the environmental conditions and the physiological response involved, usually all that can be hoped for is to observe and describe trends.

Author's Note: Published with the approval of the Director of Research of the North Carolina Agricultural Experiment Station as Paper No. 2201 of the Journal Series.

REFERENCES

Alliston, C. W., B. Howarth, Jr., and L. C. Ulberg, 1965. Embryonic mortality following culture *in vitro* of one- and two-cell rabbit eggs at elevated temperatures. *J. Reprod. Fertility, 9:* 337–341.

Alliston, C. W., and L. C. Ulberg, 1961. Early pregnancy loss in sheep at ambient temperatures of 70° and 90°F. as determined by embryo transfer. *J. Animal Sci., 20:* 608–613.

Alliston, C. W., and L. C. Ulberg, 1965. *In vitro* culture temperatures and subsequent viability of rabbit ova. *J. Animal Sci., 24:* 912.

Boyd, H., 1965. Embryonic death in cattle, sheep and swine. *Vet. Bull., 35:* 251–266.

Chang, K. S. F., S. T. Chan, W. D. Low, and C. K. Ng, 1963. Climate and conception rates in Hong Kong. *Human Biol., 35:* 366–376.

Dutt, R. H., 1964. Detrimental effect of high ambient temperature on fertility and early embryo survival in sheep. *Intern. J. Bioclimatol. Biometeorol., 8:* 47–56.

Findley, J. D., 1963. Veterinary biometeorology. *Intern. J. Bioclimatol. Biometeorol., 7:* 137–143.

Hafez, E. S. E., 1964a. Effects of high temperature on reproduction. *Intern. J. Bioclimatol. Biometeorol., 7:* 223–230.

Hafez, E. S. E., 1964b. Ecology and fertility. *Proc. 5th Intern. Congr. Animal Reprod. Artif. Insem., 2:* 7–26.

Howarth, B., Jr., C. W. Alliston, and L. C. Ulberg, 1965. Importance of uterine environment on rabbit sperm prior to fertilization. *J. Animal Sci., 24:* 1027–1032.

Shelton, M., 1964. Relationship of environment temperature during gestation to birth weight and mortality of lambs. *J. Animal Sci., 23:* 360–364.

Spies, H. C., C. S. Menzies, S. P. Scott, L. L. Coon, and G. H. Kiracofe, 1965. Effects of forced exercise and cooling on reproductive performance of fine wool ewes bred during the summer. *J. Animal Sci., 24:* 9–12.

Stott, G. H., and R. J. Williams, 1962. Causes of low breeding efficiency in dairy cattle associated with seasonal high temperature. *J. Dairy Sci., 45:* 1369–1375.

Tromp, S. W., 1963. *Medical Biometeorology.* Elsevier Publishing Co., New York.

Woody, C. O., and L. C. Ulberg, 1964. Viability of one-cell sheep ova as affected by high environmental temperature. *J. Reprod. Fertility, 7:* 275–280.

Factors in Reducing the Adverse Effects of Climate on Animal Performance

R. E. McDOWELL, *Animal Husbandry Research Division, Agricultural Research Service, U. S. Department of Agriculture, Beltsville, Maryland*[1]

SEVERAL OF THE PRECEDING papers have dealt with experiments involving the effects of various climatic elements on the physiological responses of animals. Although the results indicate important influences of temperature on the comfort and well-being of animals, caution must be exercised in applying the results to actual situations. Several other factors must be considered in developing satisfactory procedures to reduce the adverse effects of a thermal environment.

In extreme climates nature places a premium on fitness and, by consistent pressures, develops strains or species fitted for survival under existing conditions. Variation of circumstances and demands in the natural habitat does not permit the forthright development of a new species, but the inevitable trend molds and reshapes the animal until it either adapts to the local environment or perishes. This is a slow process. With increasing pressures for higher total output and efficiency to meet demands from his animals, man is giving increased attention to providing environments, even under extreme conditions, which he thinks will permit animals to express as near their genetic potential as possible and give maximum economic return.

Elements of the Environment

Since man's physiological processes are very sensitive to changes in temperature and air movement, and to a somewhat lesser degree

[1] Present address: Department of Animal Science, Cornell University, Ithaca, New York.

to the humidity of the air and the solar radiation of his surrounding environment, he has looked primarily at these elements in relation to the performance of his animals. An extensive volume of literature is devoted to studies of the direct effects of various climatic elements on animals. The problems of adaptability and what environments make for high output would in most situations be simplified if it were necessary to consider only the direct actions of the climate on the animals. Under most circumstances this would be an oversimplification of the problem, because the indirect effects confound the solutions and many times far overshadow the direct effects. Hence, as we attempt to modify conditions for satisfactory animal functioning, we must consider the environment in a broader sense.

A modification of Bonsma's concept of the environment (Bonsma, 1958), the "wagon wheel" (Fig. 1), is used to depict the complexity of the problems usually encountered. In this illustration, man is the axle and the animal the hub. The lubricant is management which facilitates rotation of the hub around the axle. The running surface of the wheel represents the total environment and each spoke denotes a particular environmental factor. The concentric arrows represent interactions between the various components. If any particular element acts so drastically on the animal that it succumbs or degenerates, the leverage of the particular spoke will be so great that the hub will be broken and the delicate balance between the environment and the animal will be upset. Thus, the direct actions as well as the interactions must be coped with in most cases. A further complication is that traditional husbandry practices often prevent appropriate judging of the direct effects and their interactions.

It is readily evident from this illustration that a knowledge of local environmental conditions and the attitude of the livestock producers are the initial requisites in making rational decisions regarding effective changes. For example, if the direct effects of climate are to be alleviated, the extent of the extremes in temperature (frequency of occurrence and duration), the correlated humidity, solar radiation (both direct and reflected), and rate of air movement must be known. A knowledge of the interactions of the elements at various temperature levels is also required, because, under

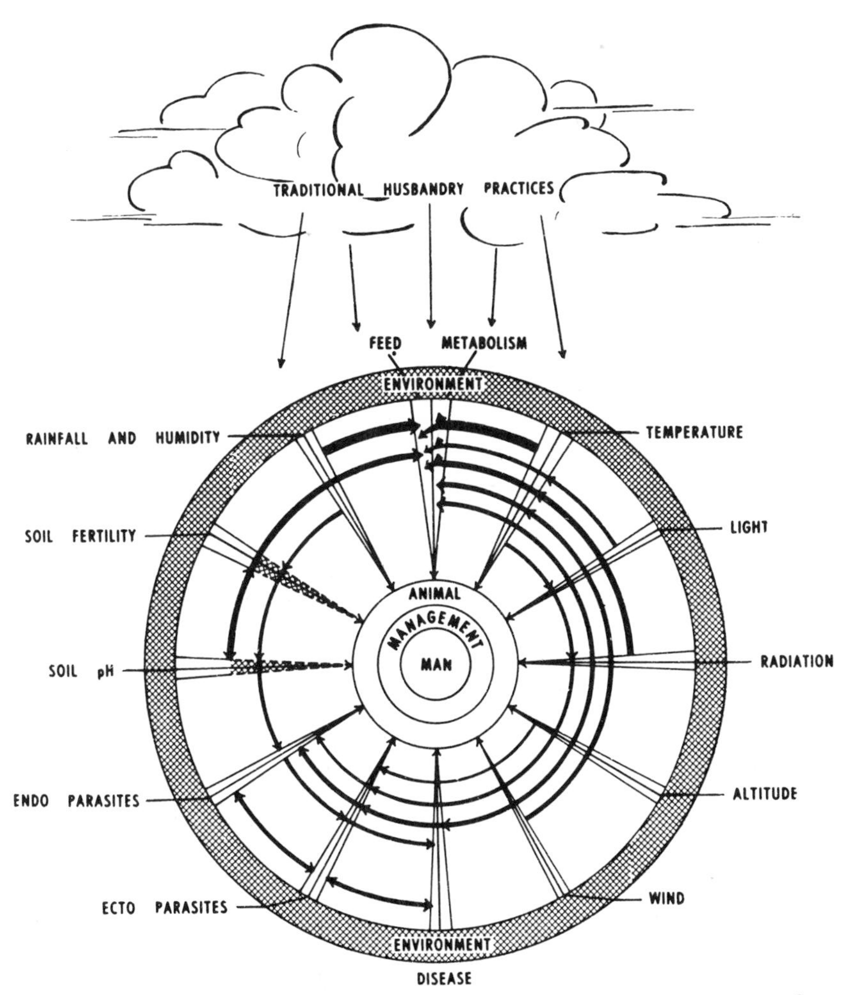

Fig. 1. Elements of the environment which directly or indirectly influence the performance of animals (Adapted from Bonsma, 1958).

field conditions, the interactions, as they operate through the feed supply and create conditions which promulgate disease, often become primary.

Characterizing the Animal Response

The second requisite is how the animal response to an adverse environment is to be characterized. This is important in determining the effectiveness of measures employed. For instance, if changes in body temperature or respiration rate are used as criteria for measuring the animal's responses, they may identify the animal which has the least shift in its heat balance as a result of hyperthermia or one that has a low basal metabolic rate and low maintenance requirements, but this may prove antagonistic to the level of performance desired.

In studies of the effect of heat stress (40°C and 34 mm mercury (Hg) vapor pressure) on crosses of Red Sindhi, a Zebu breed from India, it was found that crosses with 50 percent or more Red Sindhi breeding showed less rise in rectal temperature and respiration rate—the measures used to characterize "physiological adaptability"—than did purebred Jerseys, Holsteins, and Brown Swiss. In all breed groups, however, the level of rise was negatively associated with milk yield and growth rate—the measures of "productive adaptability". It was also found that the level of metabolic heat production had a high positive relationship to the changes in respiration rate and rectal temperature. From these observations, it was concluded that selection for the traits of physiological adaptability would be largely incompatible with the improvement of milking performance and consequently undesirable in usual circumstances (McDowell, 1966a). Since milk yield or some other commodity is usually the desired end product, most of the ensuing discussion will center on measures of productive adaptability.

The state of acclimatization of the animals to the habitat before they are subjected to the stresses of high temperature and/or humidity is also an important consideration in interpretation of the response of animals to adverse climatic conditions. This aspect has many times been ignored and the causative relationships have thus been confounded. Studies of the response of animals to thermal stress showed that the conditions to which the animal was subjected before the test largely determined the degree of reaction. This applies to changes in body temperature, endocrine functions such as thyroid activity, rumen activity, efficiency of energy utilization, changes in blood constituents, milk production, and growth rate. By way of illustration, Figure 2 shows the average response of six yearling Shorthorn heifers exposed to a constant air temperature of 32°C and 22 mm Hg vapor pressure (60 percent relative humidity) for 200 days (Weldy *et al.*, 1964). The test was begun in late

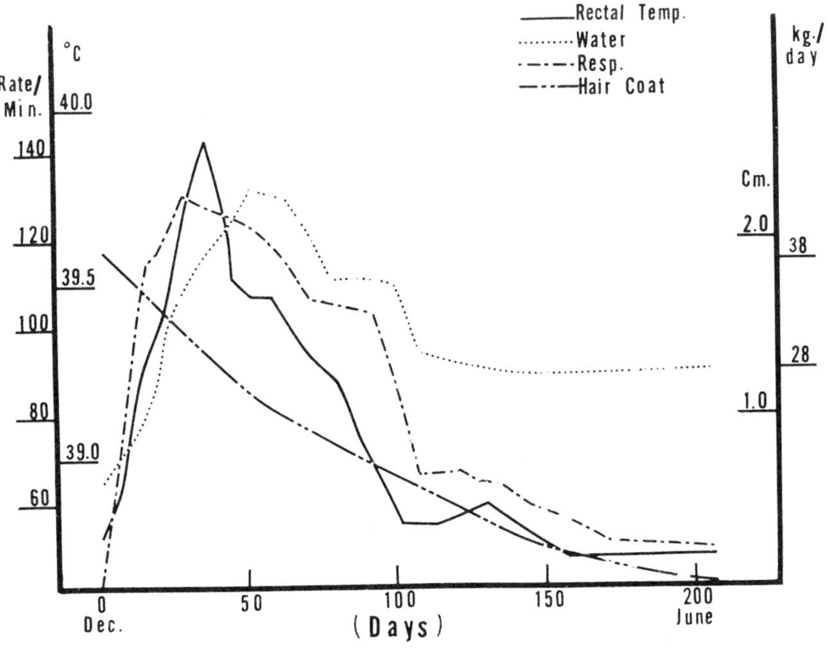

Fig. 2. Average responses of six winter-acclimated yearling Shorthorn heifers subjected to a constant air temperature of 32.2°C and 22 mm Hg vapor pressure for 200 days (Data from Weldy *et al.*, 1964).

December after the animals had become accustomed to cold weather. The heat stress caused a significant change in all the physiological responses measured, but by the 95th day all had either plateaued at a level different from the preliminary period or had returned to near normal levels. In most cases, adjustment to the heat stress was evident by the 40th day.

The most pronounced change observed in their physical appearance was the shedding of the hair coat twice; first at about five weeks, then at eight to ten weeks. At the beginning of the experiment the coats were about 2.0 cm in depth and at the close about 0.5 cm. With the onset of heat stress, the average daily body weight gains declined from 0.81 kg to 0.27 kg by the end of three weeks and to 0.08 kg by the end of the sixth week. By the 12th week, however, gains had returned to near normal. The reason for the decline is not clear since the feed offered was constant at 4.10 kg of total digestible nutrients (TDN) per 45.3 kg of body weight.

There was little or no depression in feed intake and no significant change in the digestibility of dry matter or in the total bacterial counts of rumen ingesta. It seems, therefore, that the energy was partially used in combating the effects of the thermal heat load, such as the energy expended in increased respiration rate.

Figure 3 shows the responses of another group of yearling heifers that had been exposed to summer conditions at Beltsville, Maryland, before they were subjected to a constant temperature of 32°C for 14 weeks, beginning in September (Bond *et al.*, 1961). As in the case of the animals acclimated to winter conditions, rectal temperatures rose rapidly, but instead of gradually returning to a fixed level the summer-acclimated heifers showed a rapid decline followed by marked fluctuations. The feeding regime for this group was similar, but the depression of body weight gains was less (0.41 kg a day at three weeks) and they were back to normal by the fifth week. The hair coats continued to grow for the first four weeks but remained stable thereafter. There was some thinning as the test progressed, but no distinct shedding as in the winter test.

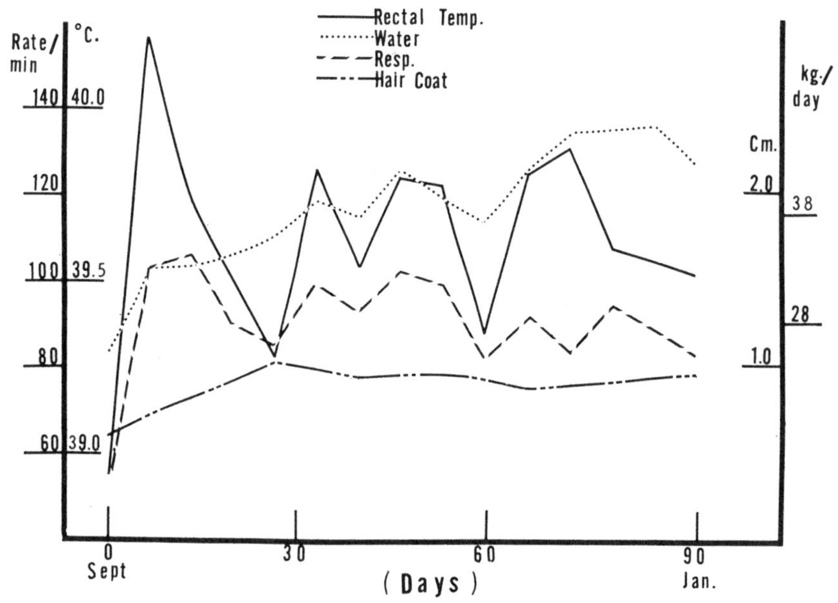

Fig. 3. Average responses of summer-conditioned yearling heifers subjected to prolonged thermal stress (Data from Bond *et al.*, 1961).

The results from the two experiments indicate several important points regarding judgment about modulating the effects of hyperthermia: (1) the stage of acclimatization of the animal is important in discerning the response to high temperature conditions; (2) given time, cattle can adjust in both physiological and productive adaptability to rather severe heat stress; and (3) the use of gradual exposure to changes in environment should be used to promote acclimatization. Although somewhat less striking in comparison, similar observations have been made under field conditions with lactating Jersey cows in Georgia and Holsteins in Louisiana (Branton *et al.*, 1953; Johnson *et al.*, 1962; Johnston *et al.*, 1966; and Shrode *et al.*, 1956).

Importance of Breeds

Much has been written about the potential of different breeds or types of cattle to withstand the effects of adverse climatic conditions. Figure 4 shows the relative relationships of energy input to milk yield for three major groups. The curve extending from the far right to left (H) is for Holsteins; the intermediate curve is for Zebu-European first generation crosses (X); and the shortest line is for pure Zebu and crosses with ⅞ or more Zebu breeding (Z). The peaks of the curves represent the average milk yields of herds of 100 or more cattle of each type kept under good feeding and management conditions. The input-output ratios are based on a constant proportion of therms of energy for maintenance (8.0 kcal a day for a 590 kg Holstein and 4.1 kcal a day for a 295 kg Zebu) plus the best data available for the proportion of energy consumed in milk production (0.13–0.19 kcal/kg milk, depending on the level of production). If we assume that the curves in Figure 4 reasonably describe the input-output relations at various levels of energy input, what happens when air temperature, humidity, and thermal radiation levels are raised?

Figure 5 shows the effect of various levels of temperature, humidity, and radiation on yields. The data used represent a compilation of results from the University of Missouri, Louisiana State University, and the Agricultural Research Service, Beltsville (Branton *et al.*, 1953, 1966; Johnson *et al.*, 1960; Johnston *et al.*, 1966; McDowell and Weldy, 1963; McDowell *et al.*, 1955; Ragsdale *et al.*, 1950).

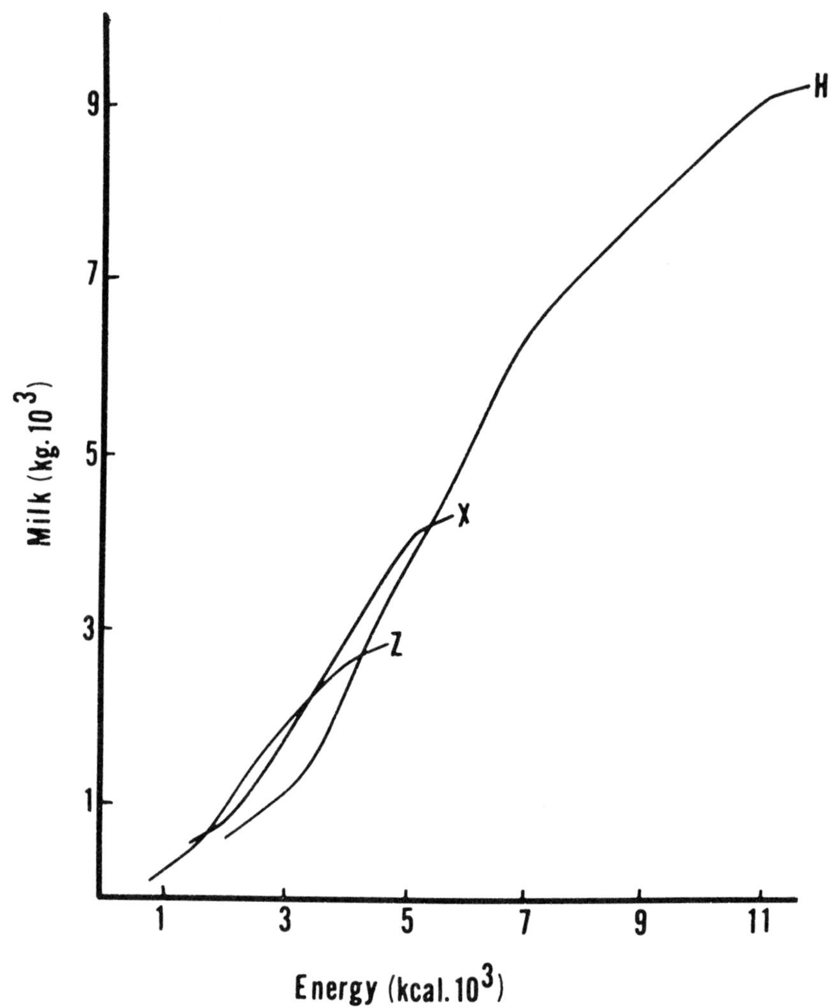

Fig. 4. Input-output ratios for milk yield of Zebu (Z), Zebu-European first generation crossbreds (X), and Holstein cows (H).

The 24.0°, 27.0°, 29.4°, 32.2°, and 35.0°C lines represent the expected depressions in lactation yields at these temperatures when relative humidities are 50 percent or less. The TH lines represent humidity of 60 percent or above at the five temperatures. The ET, or effective temperature, lines include an estimate of the additional impact of average daily thermal radiation at the various temperature levels. To illustrate the point, the 29.4° line shows lactation

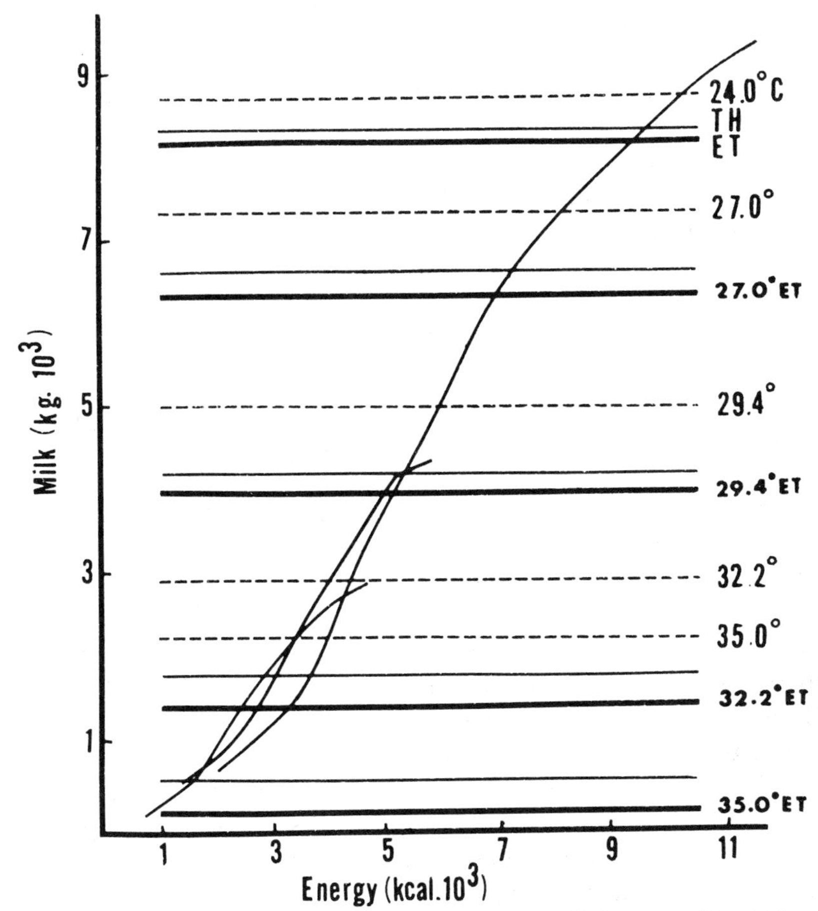

Fig. 5. Influence of temperature, humidity, and solar radiation on milk yield and energy intake of Zebu, Zebu-European crossbreds, and Holstein cows. (Milk production curves the same as in Figure 4.) °C represent temperature effects with humidity < 50 percent; TH, humidity > 60 percent; and ET, the additional estimated effect of radiation.

milk yield is depressed to 5,000 kg for Holsteins. The TH line for this temperature is 4,227 kg and the ET is 4,045 kg. Thus, under hot, humid conditions it would be expected that the lactation milk yield of Holsteins would be depressed about 50 percent, but the performance of Zebu crosses and pure Zebus would not be seriously impaired.

This graph depicts striking results but suggests only what could happen since the estimates are based largely on psychrometric laboratory experiments of relatively short duration. Its other major shortcoming is that the temperature and humidity conditions were, for the most part, constant and, therefore, do not adequately characterize conditions which occur in natural environments. This is not to say that high temperatures, humidity, and exposure to the radiant heat load of a summer day are not hazards to performance; but in warm climates these are largely confounded by other factors.

For instance, the persistency of high temperatures and the pattern of rainfall largely control the quantity and quality of feed that will be available. These two elements are also primary factors in determining the disease and parasite conditions in hot climates. Figure 6 shows how essential it is to alleviate or reduce the indirect effects of the climatic elements to obtain efficient performance. Availability of energy is the primary limiting factor. The hatched area in the lower left-hand corner gives the minimum energy requirements to sustain a Zebu animal weighing 275–310 kg in a "survival-type environment", meaning that animals in situations like this gradually mature and eventually manage to produce enough female offspring to replace themselves but provide little milk (McDowell, 1966b). If the level of energy is increased, performance may be improved but it reaches a point of diminishing returns because of still other limiting factors. The remainder of the lines for levels of production are not based on direct experiments to test the various hypotheses, but are compilations of observations from allied studies made in warm to hot climates (Branton *et al.,* 1953; Johnston *et al.,* 1966; McDowell, 1966a; Shrode *et al.,* 1956). These data show that if energy can be made available, milk output will increase as other constraints of the natural environment are reduced.

In a climate characteristic of the Gulf Coast area in the United States, when animals are kept in drylot and fed mostly silage and concentrates, the performance per cow reaches 6,300 kg or more, a level readily acceptable for temperate conditions. The area between the 6,300 and 8,600 kg lines, labeled "Feed and Mgt.", involves a number of additional techniques of husbandry as applied by an individual, such as zero pasture, frequent feeding—up to six times per day—and the use of green chopped forages along with stored forages. The 8,600 kg level represents a herd of Holsteins in an area

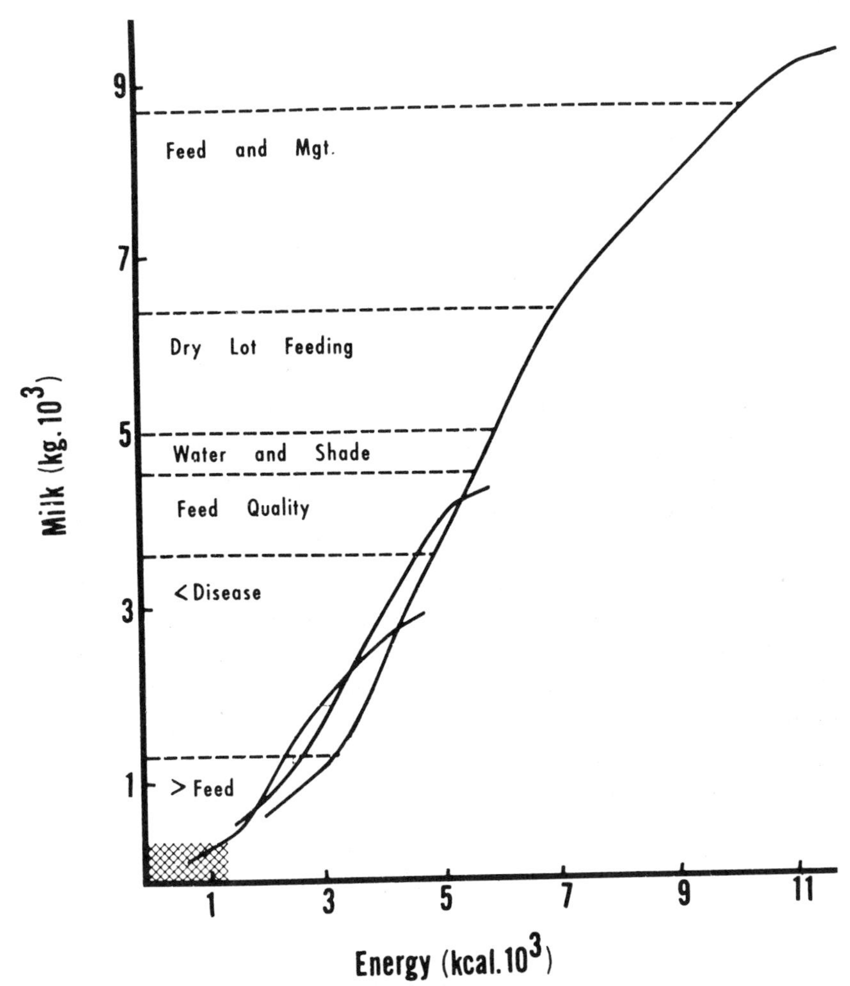

Fig. 6. Environmental factors which influence milk yield-energy intake efficiency ratios for Zebu, Zebu-European crossbreds, and Holstein cows. (Milk production curves the same as in Figure 4.)

where the mean daily temperature exceeds 24.0°C for more than 130 days a year. It seems, therefore, that the level of environment which can be provided will in a large measure dictate the type of cattle that will perform most satisfactorily. It is also evident that as efforts are made to overcome the indirect effects of climate, the measures usually recommended to relieve the stress of direct influences—shade, a good water supply, and high quality feed—become a part of the system. Thus, in making decisions on means of alleviating the effects of adverse environments, attention must be given to (1) all elements of the local environment and (2) the genetic potential of the breeds which may be used. Since means of preventing or reducing stress require investment of capital, the capability of the animal to provide a return should be contemplated. Present findings also show that unless the breeds have many similarities, such as size and internal and external characteristics, direct comparisons are not valid.

Feed Supply in Adverse Environments

In most warm climates, the availability of an adequate supply of energy in quantity and quality is the major limiting factor, and often a defeatist approach has been taken toward remedial measures. Recent studies made in Louisiana and Georgia indicate that the situation can be greatly improved by changing the systems used in handling the forages which can be produced locally. If the pasture recommendations for southern Louisiana are followed, grazing can be made available 350 or more days per year (Table 1), but it is sufficient in quality and quantity to support good levels of milk production for only 133 days, or 38 percent of the time, with 41 days of this being in the period June to October (Gross, 1963). With the onset of high temperature, there is a concomitant increase

Table 1. Days of grazing per year available for all forages used for dairy cattle at Louisiana State University (Adapted from Gross, 1963).

Forage evaluations		Months												Total days	Percent of total
Quantity	Quality[a]	J	F	M	A	M	J	J	A	S	O	N	D		
Surplus	Excellent			24				17				23	31	95	27
Adequate	Good		14		9	15								38	11
Adequate	Fair[b]	25	14	7	21		15	14	31					127	36
Deficient	Fair						15							15	4
Deficient	Poor					16				30	31			77	22
Total		25	28	31	30	31	30	31	31	30	31	23	31	352	

[a] Based on daily evaluations of quantity and quality of grazing available using standard scoring systems.

[b] Level of quantity and quality beyond which forages from other sources would be required to provide the desired kcal per day from forage.

in lignification and decrease in digestible energy of forages; thus, the animal is placed in double jeopardy by the climatic conditions. The Louisiana and Georgia studies showed that by reducing the grazing time to a few hours per day for about 100 days per year and supplementing with silages, the milk yield was increased about 21 percent, efficiency of gain in young stock 27 percent, and reproductive efficiency 11 percent. Similarly, striking results have been obtained with beef cattle—calf crops increased 30 percent per year and the length of the breeding season decreased 35 percent. Although the evidence is far from conclusive, it is apparent that changes in traditional systems of managing the feeds available may be used to improve both physiological and productive adaptability.

Other Considerations

The availability of water and means of stimulating its use, and air conditioning should also be considered to improve performance. It has been found, for example, that under high temperatures, cattle will increase their water intake as much as 400 percent. Some of this goes for increased urine output (+25 percent), free salivation, and respiratory vaporization (+54 percent); but most is excreted by evaporation from the body surface (+117 percent), as shown in Table 2 (McDowell and Weldy, 1963). Since evaporation from the body surface is the most efficient means of dissipating heat, means to promote this capability should be employed, namely, controlled ventilation or refrigerant cooling and increased water supply. Limited data imply wide variation among individuals in their ability to secrete water to the body surface. Therefore, much more attention

Table 2. Mean water loss (kg/24 hrs) by non-lactating Holstein cows at 20.1°C and one and two weeks at 32.2°C (Data from McDowell and Weldy, 1963).

Air temperature °C	Time (wk)	Feces (kg)	Urine (kg)	Saliva (kg)	Respiratory (kg)	Surface (kg)
20.1	1	13.0	11.7	0.0	7.6	10.6
32.2	1st	13.4	13.8	2.1	11.1	26.3
32.2	2nd	9.8	14.7	2.4	11.7	29.4

should be given to understanding the processes involved as well as the genetic relationships.

Although refrigerant cooling would aid in reducing the stress of thermal environments, it is usually not economically feasible for large animals in areas where it is most needed. Therefore, the use of less expensive devices, such as shades, fans, and sprinklers, and the relegation of peak performance to cooler seasons appear most practicable for improving efficiency of performance.

Although the evidence discussed deals with cattle, the basic principles apply toward decisions concerning other kinds of livestock.

Conclusions

The relationship of climate to efficient livestock performance is a complex problem. Although much more knowledge is required before satisfactory solutions can be recommended for field use in adverse climatic conditions, present results suggest that modification of many of the generally accepted practices offers promise for improvement of both efficiency and total production. The degree of application of existing as well as future research findings will be dictated by economics, but it seems that in most situations some means of alleviating the direct and indirect effects of climate are already economically feasible.

In the more developed areas, the evidence seems to favor the establishment of stabilized environments. On the surface, this may appear to be a satisfactory solution, but there is the possibility of another set of problems associated with confined environments, such as air pollution and the buildup of toxic materials from animal waste.

REFERENCES

Bonsma, J. C., 1958. *Livestock Philosophy.* Bull. No. 5, Publ. Univ. Pretoria, Johannesburg, South Africa.

Bond, J., J. R. Weldy, R. E. McDowell, and E. J. Warwick, 1961. Responses of summer-conditioned heifers to 90°F. *J. Animal Sci., 20:* 966.

Branton, C., J. E. Johnston, and G. D. Miller, 1953. Physiological and hereditary responses of lactating Holstein-Friesian and Jersey cows to natural environmental temperature and humidity. *J. Dairy Sci., 31(5):* 585.

Branton, C., R. E. McDowell, and M. A. Brown, 1966. *Zebu-European*

Cross-breeding as a Basis of Dairy Cattle Improvement in the U.S.A. Southern Cooperative Series Bull. No. 114.

Gross, L. V., 1963. *Dairy Cattle and Climate in Southern United States.* M. S. Thesis, Univ. Maryland, College Park, Maryland.

Johnson, H. D., H. H. Kibler, A. C. Ragsdale, and M. D. Shanklin, 1960. Effects of various combinations of temperature and humidities on milk production. *J. Dairy Sci., 34(6):* 871.

Johnson, J. C., Jr., B. L. Southwell, R. L. Givens, and R. E. McDowell, 1962. Interrelationships of certain climatic conditions and productive responses of lactating dairy cows. *J. Dairy Sci., 45(5):* 695.

Johnston, J. E., E. J. Stone, and J. B. Frye, Jr., 1966. *Effects of Hot Weather on the Productive Function of Dairy Cows. I. Temperature Control during Hot Weather.* La. Agr. Exp. Sta. Bull. No. 608.

McDowell, R. E., D. H. K. Lee, M. H. Fohrman, J. F. Sykes, and R. A. Anderson, 1955. Rectal temperature and respiratory responses of Jersey and Sindhi-Jersey crossbred females to a standard hot atmosphere. *J. Dairy Sci., 38(9):* 1037–1045.

McDowell, R. E., and J. R. Weldy, 1963. Water exchange of cattle under heat stress. *Proc. Third Biometeorol. Congr.,* Pau, France.

McDowell, R. E., 1966a. The role of physiology in animal production for tropical and sub-tropical areas. *World Rev. Animal Prod., 1:* 39–46.

McDowell, R. E., 1966b. *Problems of Cattle Production in Tropical Countries.* Cornell Intern. Agr. Develop., Mimeo 17.

Ragsdale, A. C., H. J. Thompson, D. M. Worstell, and S. Brody, 1950. *Milk Production and Feed and Water Consumption Responses of Brahman, Jersey and Holstein Cows to Changes in Temperature, 50 to 105°F and 50 to 8°F.* Mo. Agr. Exp. Sta. Res. Bull. No. 460.

Shrode, R. R., T. B. Patterson, and E. N. Vega, 1956. A study of factors associated with individual range in rectal temperature of milking Holstein and Jersey cows. *J. Animal Sci., 15:* 1220.

Weldy, J. R., R. E. McDowell, J. Bond, and P. J. Van Soest, 1964. Responses of winter-conditioned heifers under prolonged heat stress. *J. Dairy Sci., 47(6):* 691.

IV. Ground Level Climate and Weather Modification

The Effect of Weather Modification on Physical Processes in the Microclimate

WILLIAM E. MARLATT, *Department of Atmospheric Science, Colorado State University, Fort Collins, Colorado*

THE DEVELOPMENT OF ANY SCIENCE, whether it be botany, physics, meteorology, or chemistry has progressed from mythology through observation, measurement, understanding, prediction, and control. Unfortunately, in meteorology, probably more than in any other science, development had only touched on understanding before emphasis was placed on prediction. This is not surprising because of the great economic need for weather forecast information. Not until the last two decades, with the advent of the weather satellite which provided the first truly worldwide atmospheric measurements, and of the high-speed, large-volume computer which permitted analysis of these measurements on a real time basis, has there been a rapid advance in the area of understanding.

Our understanding of the atmosphere is still meager, but it has progressed to the extent that control of certain aspects of the weather and climate now appear possible. The purpose of this paper is not to explain what will happen in the microclimate by weather and climate control, but to point out some of the possibilities, limitations, and ramifications that certain techniques of weather modification will have directly and indirectly on microclimate.

The fact that little or no basic research has been done is of particular concern. This research is vitally needed to gain the understanding required for predicting what will happen to physical and ecological processes resulting from weather and climate modification.

Smith (1958) has classified the climate according to a scale suitable for our discussion:

Large scale (macroclimate): areas encompassing thousands of square miles, continents, or hemispheres.

Mesoscale (mesoclimate): areas encompassing hundreds of square miles, several counties, or a state.

Microscale (microclimate): areas encompassing a few acres, a field, or a garden.

Ecoscale (ecoclimate): areas encompassing a leaf, a bush, or a tree.

Direct Weather Modification

Modification of the microscale and ecoscale has been important to our culture since man first planted a garden. Measurable ecological effects resulting from various techniques practiced on a local scale have been known for a long time. Textbooks have been written on the subject, although many ways by which the microclimate may be modified for man's benefit have not been exploited. On the other hand, many techniques of microclimate modification have been used without any knowledge of possible results. As an example, defoliation has been used to speed ripening and simplify harvesting of cotton, yet, to the author's knowledge, no studies have been conducted to attempt to understand the effects of this severe modification on the temperature and moisture balances of the soil and plant. The adverse effects on the birds and animals when chemical sprays are used to kill unwanted insects have been widely discussed as a result of Rachael Carson's book, *Silent Spring* (1962), but there has been little thorough research.

One example of insufficient research in microclimate modification on a field-size scale was the federally sponsored planting of tree shelterbelts across the high plains area of the United States. These shelterbelts have resulted in a significant protection for crops against wind damage, but this benefit has often been offset by an upsetting of the water balance, resulting from the competition of the shelterbelt for the limited supply of soil moisture.

A few theoretical studies have been conducted on the possibilities of changing the dynamics and thermodynamics of global climate, but many scientists are not optimistic about man's ability to accomplish beneficial, practical, large-scale modifications; inadvertent climate modification seems more probable.

Precipitation Modification

The major emphasis is now on purposeful weather modification, and has been restricted to the mesoscale. During the past two decades the primary emphasis has been on attempts to increase the amount of precipitation falling from a cloud. Nearly everyone who has taken part in a field weather-modification experiment agrees that convective cloud modification is possible, but the proof of an increase in rainfall at a level of statistical significance is a most difficult problem (Grant and Mielke, 1965). The prospect of modifying winter clouds to increase snowfall appears more promising, particularly in mountain areas. From a microclimatic-ecological standpoint, the effects of increasing snowpack depth are quite different from those of modifying summer thunderstorms.

According to Gilman *et al.* (1965), it will probably be possible to increase precipitation over certain mountainous regions by 10 to 20 percent. Howell (1960) suggested that precipitation from cumulus—or at least from tropical cumulus clouds—may possibly be increased by 20 percent.

Let us assume that these estimates are not overly optimistic. The first problem would be to determine what this 20 percent additional precipitation would do to the growth and the species composition of the natural population of plants. One might also suggest a study of the effect of this increase in precipitation on the soils of the region under consideration. There are obvious plant and soil changes from an arid hilltop to a moist glen or soggy marsh, and increasing the precipitation could, conceivably, move plant communities uphill.

A recent study of this type was reported in 1965 by Waggoner (unpublished) in which Thornthwaite's 1946 climatic index was used to estimate ecological changes (Thornthwaite and Mather, 1955). Waggoner concluded that each 1 cm of surplus rainfall added or 1.7 cm deficiency removed will add 2 to the index in humid regions and 1.2 in dry areas. If, by modifying the weather, we can add 20 percent to areas receiving 20 and 40 inches, respectively, the corresponding indexes would move the classification by one category; theoretically this would change an oak-hickory forest to a beech-maple or a birch-beech-maple-hemlock forest to a spruce-fir forest in the northern United States.

Results from this sort of study have academic interest, but their value is questionable. Any modification of weather using our present techniques of cloud seeding to the extent that regions now receiving an annual average of 40 inches would receive 48 inches would undoubtedly be economically prohibitive. It is a common rule in agriculture that 20 inches of annual rainfall, assuming reasonably uniform distribution, is sufficient to maintain a stable farming economy. Because of economic considerations, most cloud-seeding efforts will be spent in regions where precipitation is only marginal for agriculture. Rather than speculate on the possible effects of a 20 percent increase in annual precipitation, it would seem more practical to consider the results of increasing precipitation during selected periods of the growing season. Even in areas with annual precipitation in excess of 40 inches with a reasonably uniform distribution, as is the case in the Middle Atlantic States, the effect of changing precipitation totals for individual months may influence crop development significantly. Figure 1 shows the mean effect of a one-inch increase in monthly rainfall totals on the yield of corn in the

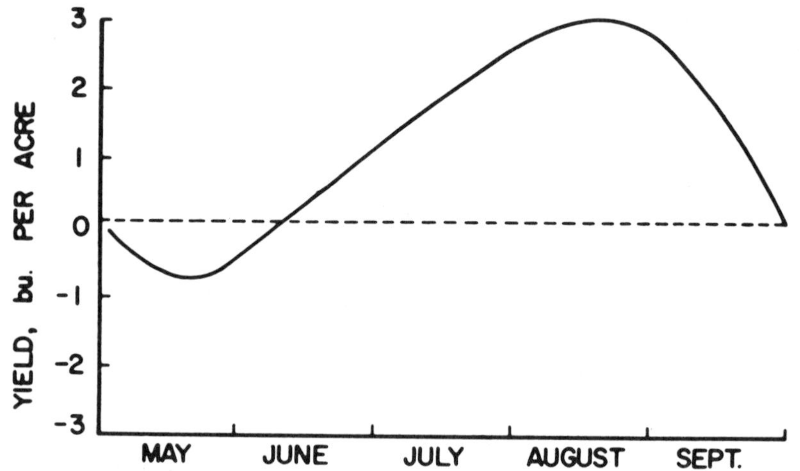

Fig. 1. Average change in corn yield in Middle Atlantic States as a result of a one-inch monthly increase in rainfall (After Davis and Harrell, 1942).

Middle Atlantic States. Maximum influence occurs in August, which at New Brunswick, New Jersey, has a mean precipitation total of 4.62 inches. One inch of additional precipitation here is equivalent to an increase of 22 percent.

Precipitation deficiency is the difference between actual and potential evapotranspiration, that is, the difference between the amount which a crop used and that which it would have used if there had been sufficient soil moisture. Precipitation surplus is the difference between actual precipitation and that needed for soil moisture recharge, assuming that the former is larger than the latter. The area under the surplus curve, multiplied by a drainage basin factor and a soil type factor, is an index of the rainfall available for reservoir storage. Figures 2 and 3 show the mean seasonal march of deficiency and surplus at New Brunswick, New Jersey (40°28′N, annual precipitation 43.67 inches), and at Lincoln, Nebraska (40° 49′N, annual precipitation 25.73 inches). While annual precipitation at New Brunswick is nearly twice that at Lincoln, the growing season precipitation is nearly equal and the mean maximum monthly total deficiency at Lincoln is only 0.25 inches less than that at New Brunswick. One important difference between the figures provided by these two stations is that by the end of the average growing season the soil moisture at New Jersey has been replenished and surpluses of rainfall exceed deficiencies; at the same time, deficiencies

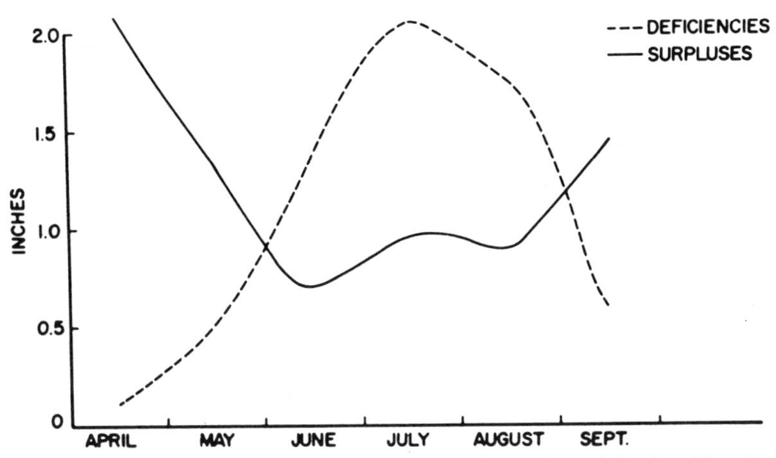

Fig. 2. Mean seasonal march of deficiencies and surpluses of precipitation, New Brunswick, New Jersey.

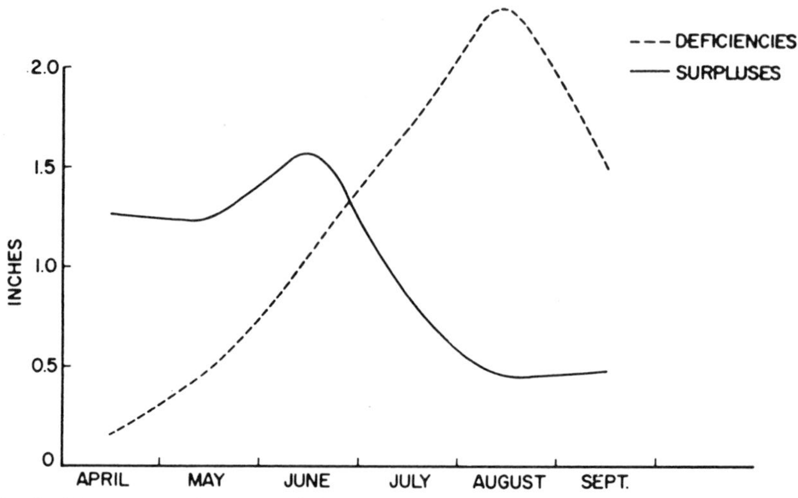

Fig. 3. Mean seasonal march of deficiencies and surpluses of precipitation, Lincoln, Nebraska.

exceed surpluses by an inch in Nebraska. Table 1 gives a comparison of averages of water balance components during growing seasons. From this table it is seen that both deficiencies and surpluses at Lincoln are approximately the same as those at New Brunswick. The distribution of these deficiencies and surpluses shown in Figures 4 and 5, however, are markedly dissimilar. It is evident that weather modification at the two locations would need quite different engineering and manpower requirements.

Techniques to increase precipitation would probably not be employed at either station during the years of minimum deficiencies

Table 1. A comparison of water balances (April–Sept.) for New Brunswick, New Jersey, and Lincoln, Nebraska.

	New Brunswick (inches)	Lincoln (inches)
Precipitation	23.92	22.11
Potential evapotranspiration*	24.25	24.30
Computed actual evapotranspiration*	17.34	17.57
Deficiency	6.90	7.17
Surplus	7.49	6.45

* Using the Thornthwaite-Mather water balance (Thornthwaite and Mather, 1955).

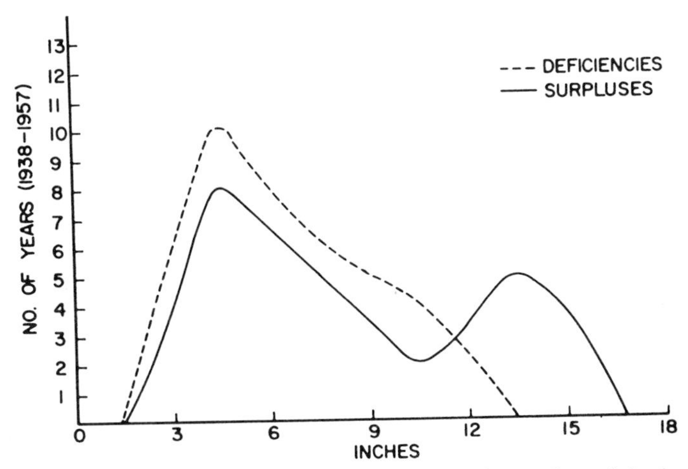

Fig. 4. Frequency of occurrence of deficiencies and surpluses of precipitation during the growing season (April–September), New Brunswick, New Jersey.

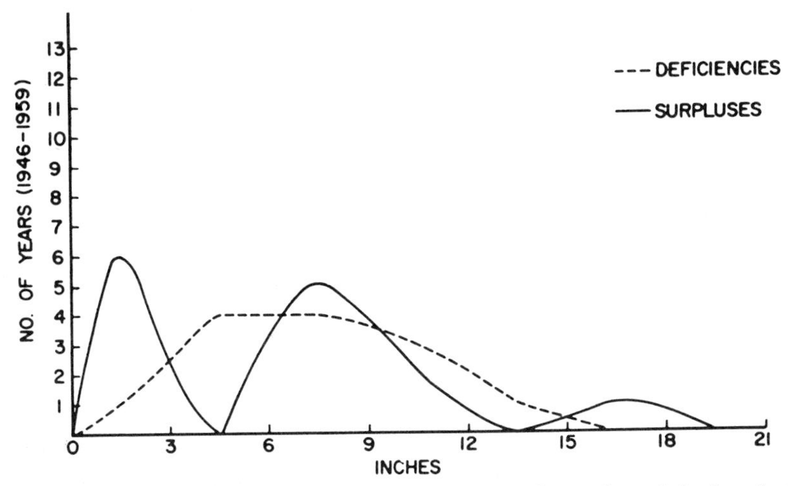

Fig. 5. Frequency of occurrence of deficiencies and surpluses of precipitation during the growing season (April–September), Lincoln, Nebraska.

and large surpluses. The years of large deficiencies, unfortunately, are years with only a limited number of opportunities for cloud seeding. From a realistic viewpoint, one would have to conclude that few permanent ecological changes would occur as the result of a capability for increasing precipitation by 20 percent.

Another facet of the effect of weather modification on the physical processes in the microclimate is the possibility of artificial changes in the character of rainfall. For example, during the growing season of the years 1951–1953, the Raton Pass area along the Colorado-New Mexico border was the target area of a major cloud-seeding operation. Discussions with a rancher living in the target area revealed that, during the three generations his family had lived at that location, the years of the cloud-seeding experiment were the only years that drinking water had to be brought in for the livestock. The rains in those summers were, in his words, "grass rains", that is, rains of low intensity, small drops, and little or no runoff. Such effects of character modification of precipitation are important in microclimate modification.

Hurricane Modification

From Figure 4, it may be seen that the distribution of precipitation surpluses at New Brunswick is strongly bimodal with a second mode between 12 and 15 inches. Examination of individual precipitation records showed that these large surpluses were exclusively the result of hurricane rainfall. Until now, the only serious program for hurricane modification has been Project Stormfury which has been directed toward modification of the structure of the hurricane cloud wall. Photographs and other measurements indicate that a change in the cloud structure takes place during massive seeding, but that the magnitude of the change is within the limits of those observed in nature. The recent discovery that much of the water vapor producing hurricane clouds is a result of evaporation from the ocean surface indicates that surface modification of the ocean may possibly provide a more direct hurricane-modification technique.

Let us assume that someday it will be possible to modify hurricanes sufficiently to steer them away from coastlines. From Figure 4 it is seen that this could result in a 40 percent reduction in seasonal runoff. But, by so doing, we would remove a major source of precipitation for reservoir recharge, and reduction of this amount of reservoir storage water would produce water shortages comparable to those of the recent droughts in the northeastern states. Insufficient reservoir water supplies often result in restriction of lawn irrigation which in turn produces marked ecological changes in the microclimate: the grass becomes dry and dormant, surface temperatures are elevated, relative humidity in the lowest layers is depressed, insect eggs fail to hatch, etc.

Energy Balance Modification

Another area of weather modification on the mesoscale, which has shown practical possibilities although little or no research has been done on its effect on the microclimate, is that of modifying the energy exchange at the earth-atmosphere interface. Let us assume hypothetically that large supplies of fresh water were brought into the desert of the Great Basin of North America. (Several scientists have recently suggested that we now have the engineering capability for cutting a channel for water vapor transport through the Sierras.) Studies have shown that alfalfa and other agricultural crops can be grown in this area provided ample water is available. Several microclimatic effects are immediately envisioned. First, albedo of the surface would decrease from the perhaps 0.4 of sand to the less than 0.1 of plants. The effect of increasing plant cover on net radiation is shown in Figure 6. Second, much of the available radiant energy is now used in latent heat of evaporation rather than in heating the surface soil. Figure 7 shows the effect of plant cover on evapotranspiration. Third, the water vapor content of the lowest layers of the atmosphere will be increased locally due to the increased transpiration.

If we carry this hypothesis to its extreme, one might ask if this increased water vapor content in the atmosphere over the Great Basin would, in turn, change the local precipitation regime. Under the present natural environment, in which orographic lifting is a primary prerequisite for most precipitation in this area, any increase in precipitation would occur along the western slope of the Rocky Mountains to the east of the Great Basin. Black and Tarmy (1963) have suggested, however, that it may be possible to change the surface albedo to provide a thermal mountain and thus change the areal distribution of precipitation.

Indirect Weather and Climate Modification

Within the past few years it has become apparent to many persons that, by the nature of his activities, man is indirectly modifying his climate possibly more than he ever would be able to by purposeful

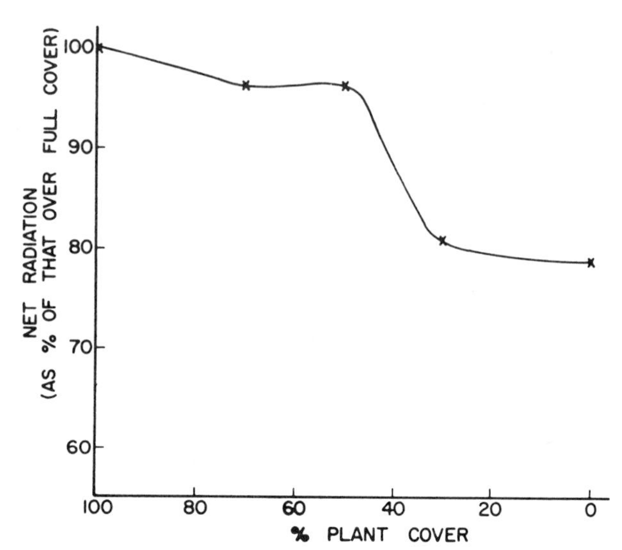

Fig. 6. Effect of plant cover on net radiation (average of 35 midday observations), Marboro, New Jersey.

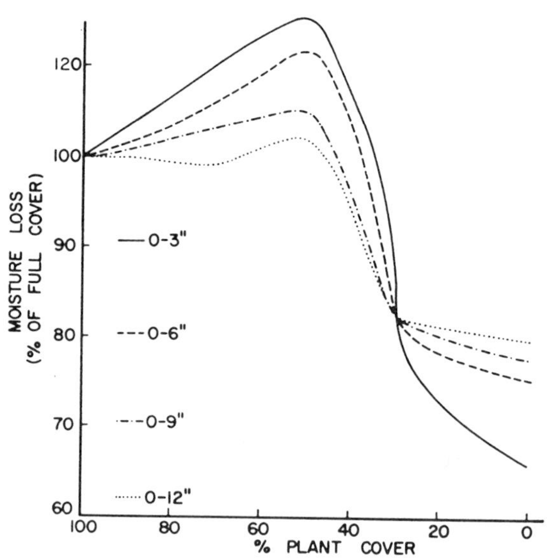

Fig. 7. Effect of plant cover on evapotranspiration (average of 35 midday observations), Marboro, New Jersey.

modification, and in most cases in a manner which results in creation of an adverse environment.

The most serious indirect modifications of the microclimate are results of man's polluting the atmosphere. It has long been known that the "dust dome" over cities produces a marked greenhouse effect, with the incoming ultraviolet rays of the sun being filtered out and the outgoing infrared radiation being trapped within the dome. In addition, the asphalt, brick, and concrete surfaces of the cities are large absorbers of heat. The first frost of autumn occurs later and the last frost of spring occurs earlier. During World War II this fact was used as an argument to convince urban dwellers that it was their patriotic duty to convert their lawns to victory gardens. The results were disappointing. Because of the nature of these pollutions, the growth and quality of vegetation in urban areas is much poorer than in clean air. Fruit trees, for example, grown in normal city air are 10 percent smaller and produce proportionately less fruit than the same trees grown in unpolluted areas. Man-made atmospheric pollution, unfortunately, is not confined to the immediate urban environs. Smog from the Los Angeles basin has been tracked to northern Idaho. Vegetable damage in the southern part of New Jersey has resulted from the spread of pollution from the metropolitan areas of New York and Philadelphia. Studies by the U. S. Public Health Service have shown that from Boston to Washington and for 100 miles inland there is not a square mile that does not have damage to vegetation from air pollution.

While the effects of air pollution are plainly evident in the microclimate, there are other ways in which our activities result in the indirect modification of the climate, as in the spreading of condensation trails from jet aircraft (Fig. 8). Results of a field study of radiation transfer reduction by cirrus are shown in Table 2. In this study outgoing radiation was measured by satellite-, aircraft-, and ground-based instruments. In the case of Orbit 1567, under clear skys, the difference between actual surface temperature and blackbody equivalent temperature measured by a radiometer aboard a light aircraft was only 3.2°C and between the aircraft and satellite was 2.0°C. In the case of Orbit 1596, the sky was covered by an overcast of cirrostratus so thin that the stars were easily visible. The outgoing surface radiation was screened off and replaced by radiation

Fig. 8. Cirriform clouds formed by the spreading of aircraft condensation.

at cloud temperature to such an extent that the difference between aircraft and satellite measurements of surface temperature was 18°C.

Research to understand the total effect of man-made clouds has not been undertaken. Results shown in Table 2 indicate that the effect has a direct relationship to the physical properties of the microclimate.

Conclusion

Each activity of man may be considered a weather modification of the microscale environment. Research in cloud physics on the mesoscale indicates that weather modification to increase precipitation may become practical and economically feasible. There is no doubt

Table 2. Comparison of surface, aircraft, and satellite measurements over the Pawnee National Grassland, Colorado.

Orbit No.	1567	1596
Date	10/3/63	10/5/63
Local time (M.S.T.)	0322	0226
Satellite zenith angle	47°	57°
H_2O mass (cm)	1.99	1.95
O_3 mass (atmos. cm)	0.397	0.499
T_e (°A)	278.5	282.9
T_a (°A)	275.3	279.3
Altitude above ground (ft)	14,000	12,000
T_{BB} (°A)	272.0	276.0
Sensor degredation	3.3	3.5
T_s (°A)	273.3	261.5
$T_e - T_a$ (°A)	3.2	3.4
$T_e - T_{BB}$ (°A)	6.5	6.9
$T_e - T_s$ (°A)	5.2	21.4
$T_a - T_{BB}$ (°A)	3.3	3.5
$T_a - T_s$ (°A)	2.0	18.0
Sky condition	Clear	Thin cirrostratus

T_e is the earth surface temperature of the Pawnee National Grassland as measured by thermistors.

T_a is the equivalent blackbody temperature measured by a Barnes IT-2 radiometer on a light aircraft.

T_{BB} is the theoretically computed temperature that would be observed by an undegraded radiometer at the 0.1 mb level at the indicated satellite zenith angle.

T_s is the equivalent blackbody temperature measured by TIROS VII (channel 2) corrected for sensor degradation. Measurements by Marlatt (1964) (Analysis by Reap, 1965).

that either modifying amounts of precipitation received or modifying the distribution of rainfall will affect the microclimate of a region, but to what extent is unknown. Whether it will be possible to change radically the ecology of a region by cloud seeding, however, is questionable. Indirect modification by man's activities is more probable. The increasing air-pollution menace may have more far-reaching ramifications on the microclimate than anything man could do to the weather on purpose. To quote Rachael Carson: "In biological history, no organism has survived long if its environment became in some way unfit for it, but no organism before man has deliberately polluted its own environment."

Because the microclimate is easily modified by many types of activities on many scales, immediate and concentrated research is essential, so that we may know in advance how our purposeful or accidental weather modification will change the microclimate.

REFERENCES

Black, J. F., and B. L. Tarmy, 1963. The use of asphalt coatings to increase rainfall. *J. Appl. Meteorol., 2:* 557–564.

Carson, R., 1962. *Silent Spring.* Houghton, Mifflin Co., Boston, Massachusetts.

Davis, F. E., and G. D. Harrell, 1942. Relation of weather and its distribution to corn yield. *U. S. Dept. Agr. Tech. Bull., 806.*

Gilman, D. L., J. R. Hibbs, and P. L. Laskin, 1965. *Weather and Climate Modification.* A report to the Chief, U.S.W.B., U. S. Dept. Commerce, Washington, D. C.

Grant, L. O., and P. W. Mielke, Jr., 1965. *A Randomized Cloud Seeding Experiment at Climax, Colorado, 1960–65.* Presented at the Weather Modification Section, Fifth Berkeley Symposium on Mathematical Statistics and Probability, Berkeley, California, December. Research supported by the Atmospheric Sciences Section, National Science Foundation, Washington, D. C.

Howell, W. E., 1960. Cloud seeding in the American tropics. *AGU, Geophysical Monograph, No. 5:* 412–423.

Marlatt, W. E., 1964. *Investigations of the Temperature and Spectral Emissivity Characteristics of Cloud Tops and of the Earth's Surface.* Atmos. Sci. Tech. Paper #51. Colorado State Univ., Fort Collins, Colorado.

Reap, R. M., 1965. *Comparison of Grassland Surface Temperatures Measured by TIROS VII and Airborne Radiometers Under Clear Skies and Cirriform Cloud Condition.* SMRP, Research paper #44, Univ. Chicago, Chicago.

Smith, L. P., 1958. *Farming Weather.* Thomas Nelson and Sons, Ltd., London.

Thornthwaite, C. S., and J. R. Mather, 1955. The water balance. *Drexel Inst. Tech., Publ. in Climatology, 8(1):* 1–104.

Weather Modification and Forest Fires

DONALD M. FUQUAY, *Northern Forest Fire Laboratory, Intermountain Forest and Range Experiment Station, Forest Service, U. S. Department of Agriculture, Missoula, Montana*

WEATHER MODIFICATION might have a beneficial effect in many ways on the problem of the ignition and control of forest fires, particularly if we use the term "weather modification" to mean man's ability to change some undesirable condition in the environment. The practical problem remains, however, of how to change the physical processes without introducing undesirable side effects. The fundamental processes involving exchanges between the surface and the atmosphere have not been well described. Finding ways to alter these processes in a desirable manner and to predict adequately the effect of these changes on interrelated processes is a formidable problem.

Forest Fire Conditions

A forest fire is a free-burning fire in a natural fuel complex. In general terms, the fuel may be standing timber augmented by a collection of fallen branches and needles on the surface, brush cover, or the debris left from logging operations. Three general conditions under which the meteorological conditions may affect the forest fire are:

1. The pre-fire situation during which the fuel is conditioned by its exposure to the environment.
2. The ignition phase during which fuel condition is very important.
3. The free-burning phase during which the rate of fire spread and rate of energy release are influenced by the condition of the fuel, the wind flow, humidity, and precipitation.

Many other non-meteorological factors, such as fuel type, quantity, distribution and compactness, and the slope, influence the rate of fire spread. In all phases, the meteorological factors most directly affecting the occurrence and behavior of the forest fire are temperature, precipitation, humidity, wind, and the potential for ignition by lightning.

The conditions most suitable for ignition and spread of fires come after a long period of hot, dry weather. Low humidities and drying winds condition the fuel to the point where it can be readily ignited and the spread is rapid. Any form of weather modification that would produce rain, increase ambient relative humidities, and decrease the drying effects of direct solar radiation and wind could be beneficial. Light, flash fuels are very sensitive to even a small increase in relative humidity which causes an increase in fuel moisture. Probability of ignition and initial spread are reduced by a small increase in humidity. For example, raising ambient relative humidity by only 15 percent may change the fire situation from "dangerous" to "easy". Thus, initiating even a very light rain during critical fire conditions could be beneficial. Unfortunately, the most severe forest fire conditions occur during extremely dry, subsiding air conditions marked by a total absence of clouds—conditions not amenable to initiating rain according to our present knowledge.

Wind influences forest fires by increasing the drying rate of fuels, by fanning the point of ignition, by aspirating going fires and increasing the burning rate, by mechanically increasing the rate of spread by carrying burning embers ahead of the fire front causing spot fires, and by other ways. Little information is available on possible mechanisms for altering the surface wind pattern, but elimination of strong downdraft winds is an appealing possibility. These downdrafts, originating from thunderstorms or shower clouds with high bases, flow radially away from the location of the rainfall and, deflected by surface obstructions, can result in erratic and unpredictable fire behavior without normal regard for topography. Downdrafts, with measured gusts between 60 and 70 miles per hour, have been observed to drive fires down steep slopes, and frequently there is no rain at the ground surface before or after such occurrences.

These downdrafts commonly accompany "dry" thunderstorms over the plateau and Rocky Mountain regions. Downdrafts from dry thunderstorms are more violent than those from clouds with low bases. Byers and Braham (1949) indicated that the downward movement of air is initiated within the cloud by frictional drag of the falling raindrops. Additional impetus is given below the cloud base as rapid evaporation cools the descending air current. Thus, a high cloud base and a deep dry adiabatic environment from the cloud base to the surface contribute to the violence of these winds.

It is possible that seeding clouds to increase rain might deter the development of downdrafts by saturating the air between the cloud base and the surface. It can also be argued that, at least in the initial stages, this seeding could also intensify downdrafts. Intense seeding, such as that used in hail modification experiments, could alter the pattern of storm development and possibly prevent or emolliate downdrafts. No research efforts aimed at modification of downdraft winds have been reported. However, reports are available from a commercial operation in Panama (Weather Engineers, Inc., 1961) aimed at reducing blowdown damage in banana plantations. Here, where damage from a single blowdown situation can result in losses of several million dollars, limited success was claimed.

Lightning Research

Lightning is the greatest single cause of forest fires in the western United States. More than 9,000 reported fires are started by lightning each summer in America's forests and grasslands (Barrows, 1966). The problem exists in many other parts of the world. From 1946 to 1962, the United States experienced more than 140,000 lightning-caused fires. Eighty-five percent of them occurred in the western United States and caused severe losses of timber, wildlife, watershed, and recreation resources.

Control of lightning fires is difficult and complex because many fires may start from a single storm in a rough, mountainous, and heavily forested area. During a ten-day period in July, 1940, the National Forests in western Montana and northern Idaho reported 1,488 lightning fires. In this period, 335 lightning-caused fires occurred in 24 hours. Such outbreaks severely overload the fire control organizations. Any method of reducing the number of lightning-caused fires would yield great economic benefits. A method of reducing peak numbers of fires started by a single storm system would be of special importance. Because of the magnitude of the lightning-fire problem, the Forest Service developed a program of lightning research with two broad objectives:

1. To obtain a better understanding of the occurrence and characteristics of lightning storms and lightning fires in the northern Rocky Mountain region.

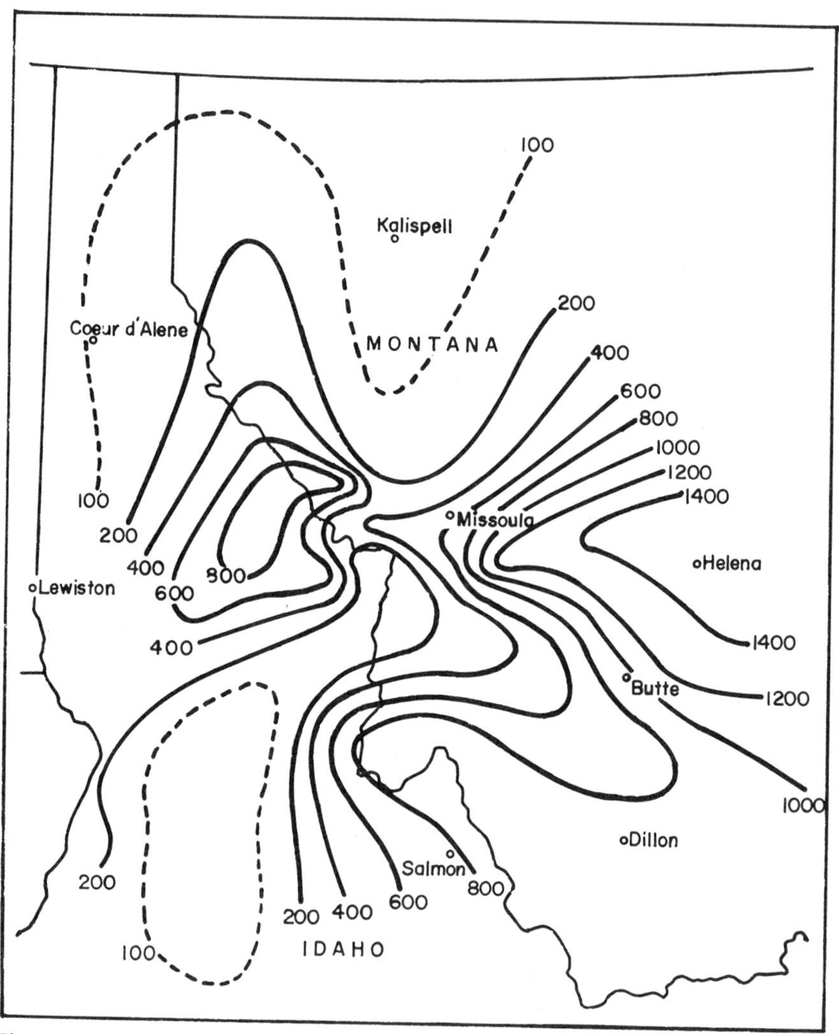

Fig. 1. Observed cloud-to-ground discharges per 1,000 square miles for July and August, 1960.

2. To investigate the possibility of preventing or reducing the number of lightning fires by applying techniques of weather modification.

The first step in this lightning research program was to learn where and when lightning storms occur over the northern Rocky Mountain region. Since 1955, we have received special thunderstorm reports from a network of forest fire lookouts located throughout the northern Rocky Mountain States. These observations tell when and where thunderstorms occur, how long they last, and how much cloud-to-ground lightning they produce.

A specific example of these data (Fig. 1) shows how observed lightning discharges were distributed throughout the region in the summer of 1960. Note the zones of frequent lightning occurrence near the Idaho-Montana border and in southwestern Montana where observers reported 800 or more cloud-to-ground discharges per 1,000 square miles per year. These patterns of lightning occurrence are being compared with the numbers of reported lightning fires and the surface weather and fuels in seeking answers to many questions. Are there similar patterns for fire occurrence? Our preliminary studies indicate that such patterns do exist, and that, in some areas, high fire zones coincide with relatively low lightning zones. This suggests that lightning is a more efficient fire starter in some areas. If this is so, what combinations of meteorological, topographical, and fuel conditions account for this? Can we develop a "natural risk factor", based on storm character and existing meteorological conditions, that will help predict peak loads of lightning-fire occurrence? We expect to find answers to some of these questions as we analyze several years' data recorded from this lookout network.

Characteristics of Mountain Thunderstorms

The character of individual lightning storms over a test site in western Montana was observed to determine the relation between the physical development of the thunderstorm and its electrical development. This study required search and vertical-scan radar, time-lapse cameras, and electrical field sensors. Vertical soundings were made by instrumented aircraft. The same system records data on storms treated with silver iodide.

A stylized diagram of a typical mountain thunderstorm has been

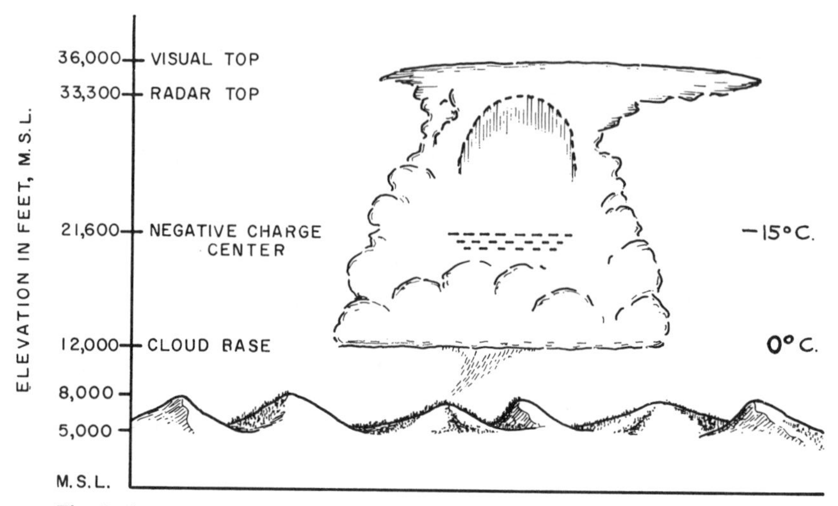

Fig. 2. An average summer thunderstorm in the northern Rocky Mountains.

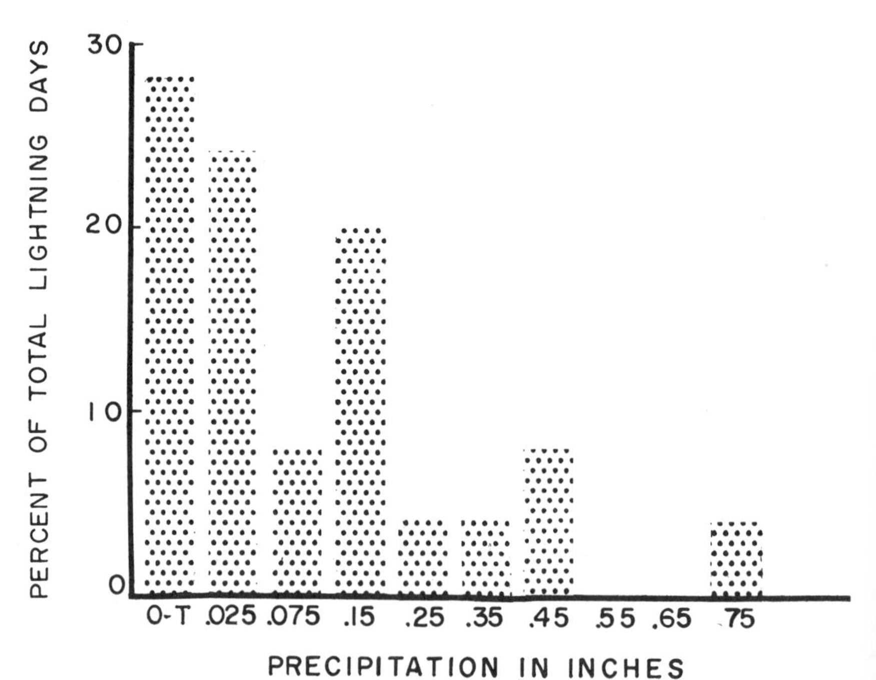

Fig. 3. Distribution of precipitation from mountain thunderstorms.

drawn from observations made in the research area and from data from the observation network. This representation, a composite of many individual storms, is shown in Figure 2. The cloud base in this typical storm is 12,000 feet above mean sea level (msl), and the average visual top extends to 36,000 feet. A given storm might have a base between 6,000 and 17,000 feet and a top as high as 45,000 feet. The average base temperature is very near the freezing level. The mountain thunderstorm is relatively shallow when compared with storms occurring over the plains both west and east of the Rockies, where radar tops from 50,000 to 60,000 feet are common.

The distribution of precipitation from mountain thunderstorms is shown in Figure 3. The precipitation is less from storms having higher bases; approximately 80 percent of all storms yield less than 0.2 inch, and 50 percent yield less than 0.05 inch of rain.

Some examples of relationships within these storms are shown in Figure 4. A strong association is indicated between maximum radar tops and the frequency of lightning discharges. The minimum echo height for lightning to be present is about 21,000 feet above msl. As the average maximum radar height of the cells increases, the total number of lightning discharges increases. The highest radar echoes, near 43,000 feet, were accompanied by 500 to 600 lightning discharges; about 150 of these were flashes to the ground.

A relationship exists between hail occurrence and the frequency of lightning discharges, the flash rate, and duration of the storm. The cumulative frequency of lightning discharges is plotted for storms with and without hail in Figure 5. More than twice as much lightning was recorded during lightning storms with hail as during those with no hail. Fifty percent of the hailstorms had more than 200 lightning discharges whereas 50 percent of the storms without hail had only 80 or more discharges. The total number of cloud-to-ground and intracloud discharges was greater in hailstorms than in storms without hail.

The difference in total lightning might be due to a difference in storm duration, because the duration of storms with hail is longer than for storms without hail. Therefore, an intensity ratio, defined as the ratio of total lightning to storm duration, was computed for all storm periods (Fig. 6). At all points the lightning intensity, in discharges per hour, is greater for storms with hail than for storms without hail. Thus, lightning storms with hail generally produce more lightning and produce it faster than those without hail. Further, the storm that produced the largest hailstones also produced the most lightning. These results suggest that if cloud-seeding reduces the size and volume of hail, it may also reduce the amount of lightning produced by the storm.

Lightning Modification

The present lightning research program is based on the belief that, with increased knowledge of thunderstorms and lightning, we can cope better with the lightning-fire problem. There is always the hope, as stated earlier, that man may someday be able to influence lightning occurrence. It is imperative that we know if, and in what way, weather modification efforts affect the fire-starting capabilities

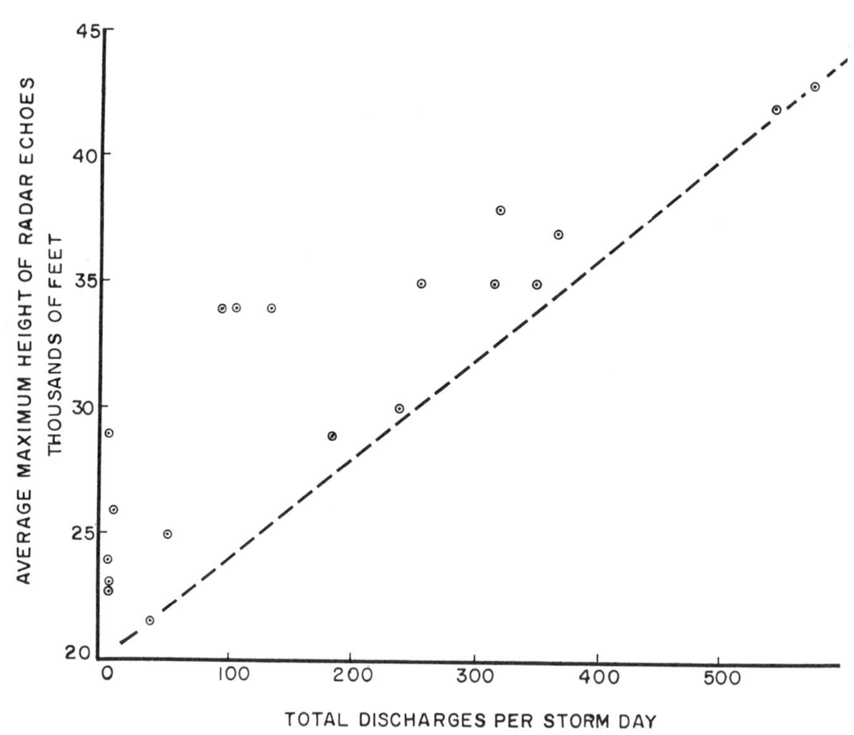

Fig. 4. Maximum radar echo height and number of lightning discharges. Dots indicate height related to discharges; dashed line indicates relationship between height and lightning frequency.

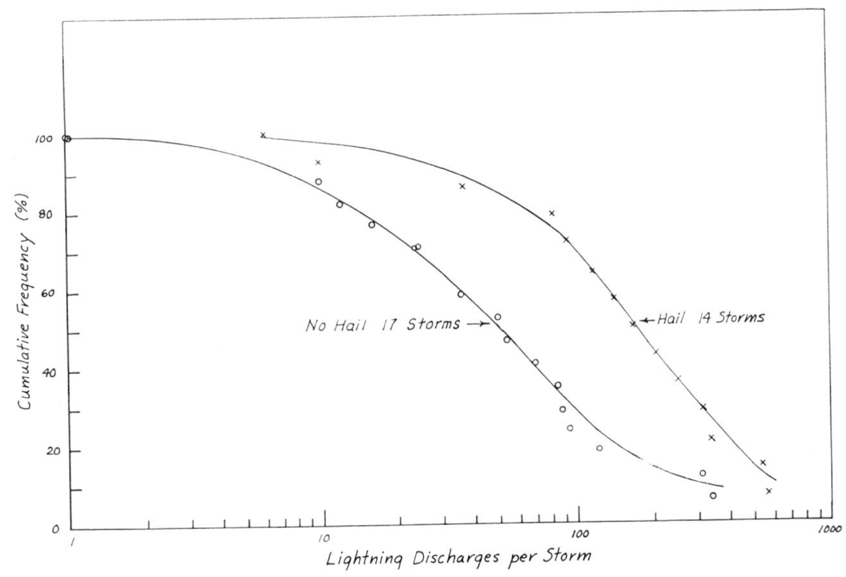

Fig. 5. Cumulative frequency distributions of lightning discharges from thunderstorms with hail and no hail.

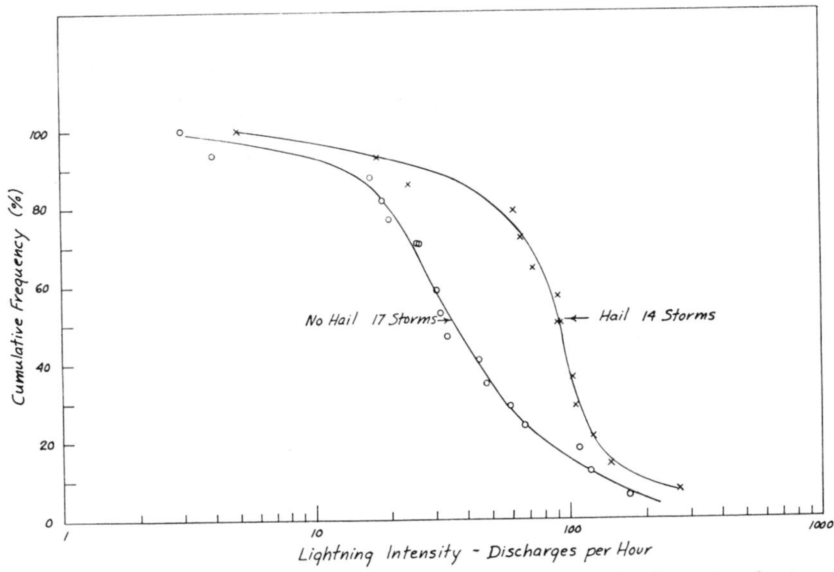

Fig. 6. Cumulative frequency distributions of lightning intensity from thunderstorms with hail and no hail.

of lightning. Currently, cloud-seeding projects are carried out over forested areas, and more are proposed. Lightning counts associated with rain—projects to increase rain in Arizona (Battan, 1965) and cloud seeding in California—suggest that this degree of seeding may increase lightning activity. Contradictory, but not conclusive, evidence from a two-year study in Montana suggests that seeding with a much higher number of active silver iodide (AgI) freezing nuclei may reduce the number of cloud-to-ground lightning discharges.

A two-year pilot experiment was conducted during the summers of 1960 and 1961 in western Montana. Seeding was done from aircraft and ground-based generators. Lightning within the selected test area was recorded by a network of five electric field meters. We found that there were 38 percent fewer ground discharges on treatment days than on days when clouds were not treated. Intracloud and total lightning discharges showed decreases of 8 and 21 percent,

Fig. 7. Project Skyfire airborne silver iodide smoke generator (U.S. Forest Service photograph).

respectively, on treated days during the two-year period. Analysis of these data by a statistical test showed that the probability of this distribution occurring by chance is about 1 in 4.

Further analysis of the pilot experiment showed two serious limitations to this approach. First, based on the physical models used, insufficient freezing nuclei were dispensed in the test area. Second, the field meter system available could not resolve details of the lightning discharge. Subsequently, new cloud-seeding generators were developed and calibrated, and a continuous lightning recording system was developed.

Equipment and Seeding Methods

Two dual-burner generators are normally carried on each aircraft (Fig. 7). Each burner produces about 10^{14} nuclei per second effective at $-20°C$ and has a seeding time of about 90 minutes.

Ground-based generators mounted on trailers are also used (Fig. 8). These generators have four forced-draft burners. Each burner produces about 5×10^{13} nuclei per second effective at $-20°C$.

In a typical seeding operation, three ground-based units are operated on the upwind side of the test area. Two aircraft, each with two generators, fly near the cloud base on the upwind side of the

Fig. 8. Ground-based silver iodide smoke generator (U.S. Forest Service photograph).

test area. The normal flight follows a racetrack pattern about five miles long.

With this seeding plan, from five to ten kilograms of silver iodide per hour are released into the test area. Assuming reasonable values for updrafts and cell dimension, we calculate the concentration of AgI nuclei effective at $-15°C$ introduced into small cumulus to be about 10^4 per liter and, in a typical thunderstorm, to be about 5×10^3 nuclei per liter. There is strong evidence that nuclei released in updrafts at a cloud base form ice crystals at the expected temperature level within the cloud.

Identification of Lightning Discharges

We record and identify lightning discharges occurring within a designated test area on both seeded and unseeded days. Figure 9 is a schematic drawing of the lightning recording system. There are three electrostatic field change sensors, two with time constants of five milliseconds and one of five seconds; a photocell device for sensing luminosity; a microphone to indicate thunder transit time; and voice channel recording. All sensors record on a seven-channel magnetic tape recorder. Not shown is an automatically triggered

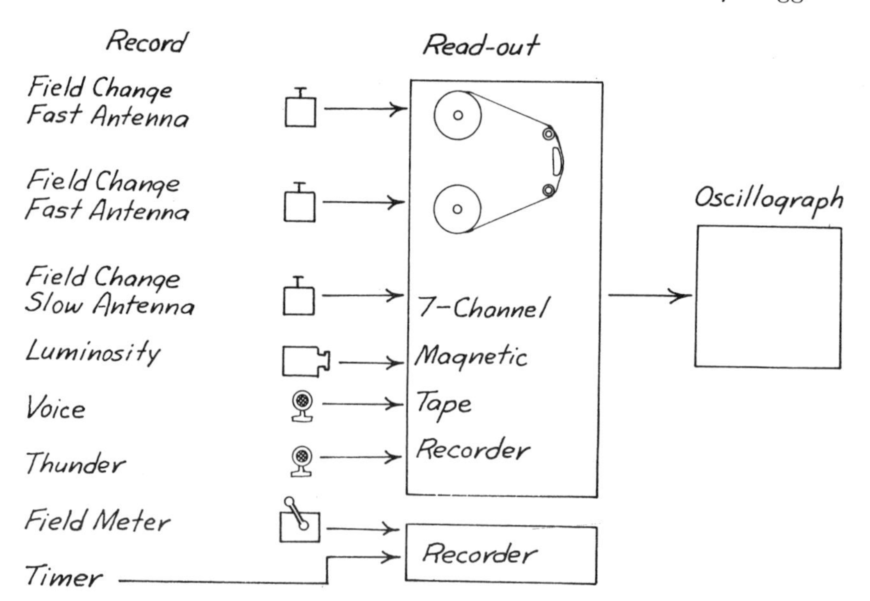

Fig. 9. Diagram of a lightning recording system.

camera to photograph the discharge and a rotating optical system that indicates the direction to the discharge.

Usually two complete time-synchronized stations are located about five kilometers apart. From the simultaneous recordings, we can calculate information on each cloud-to-ground discharge with a known terminal point.

A tracing from an actual oscillograph pattern and a photograph of a typical discrete cloud-to-ground discharge is shown in Figure 10. The upper trace is from the luminosity from the discharge. The middle trace is from an antenna with a five-second time constant and the lower trace from a fast antenna with a five-millisecond time constant. The cloud-to-ground discharge begins as a predischarge breakdown within the cloud, leading to a stepped leader to ground, followed immediately by the first return stroke. At succeeding intervals of 40 and 50 milliseconds two additional return strokes are shown.

A typical intracloud discharge (Fig. 11) is characterized by a high rate of pulsing lasting throughout most of the discharge. An oscillo-

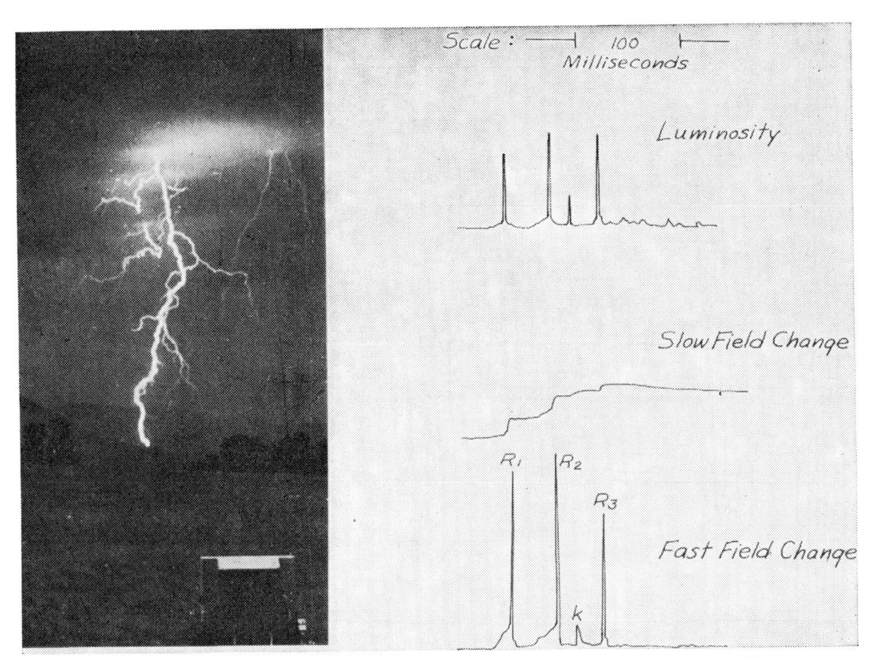

Fig. 10. Photograph and oscillograph trace of a discrete cloud-to-ground discharge.

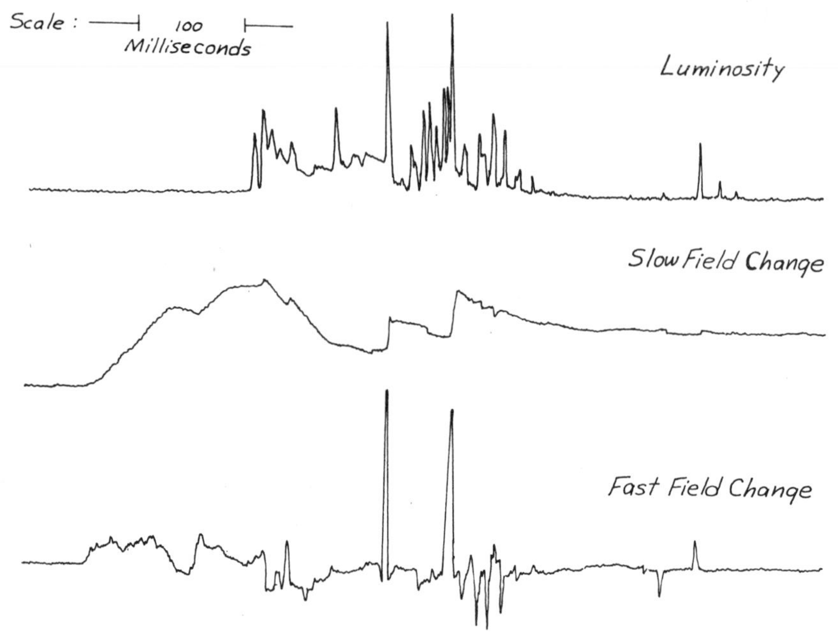

Fig. 11. Oscillograph trace of an intracloud discharge.

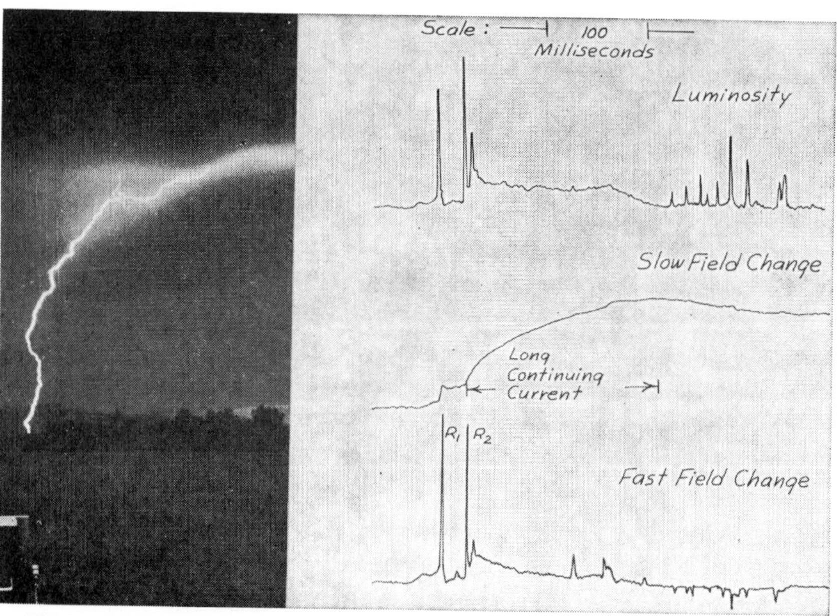

Fig. 12. Photograph and oscillograph trace of a hybrid cloud-to-ground discharge.

gram of a cloud-to-ground discharge with a long-continuing current portion is shown in Figure 12. This hybrid discharge starts out as a typical cloud-to-ground discharge with two return strokes. After the second return stroke, however, continuous charge transfer takes place for the next 200 milliseconds. This is caused by continuing current with accompanying luminosity in the lightning channel. About 15 percent of all the cloud-to-ground discharges observed in 1965 appear to be of this hybrid type. In some storms half of the ground discharges were hybrid. We suspect that these hybrid discharges, with long-continuing currents, may be the major igniters of forest fuels. Although the current is relatively low, a few hundred amperes, this current is sustained over a long period. This could result in forest fuels being heated to the ignition temperature. We are investigating the possibility that the frequency and duration of these hybrid discharges may be altered by cloud seeding.

Theoretical Consideration for Lightning Suppression

We do not yet have good working hypotheses for lightning modification, chiefly because the mechanism of charge generation and separation within thunderstorms is essentially unknown. For the development of working hypotheses, currently accepted theories on thunderstorm electrification are being examined from the standpoint of the effect of ice nucleation on the charging processes and the beginning of the lightning discharge. For example, a theory of Mason and Latham (1961) states that the charging rate in a thunderstorm should be proportional to the number of solid precipitation/ice crystal collisions. Since seeding increases the number of ice crystals within a cloud, the result of seeding could be an increase in lightning frequency.

An alternate hypothesis based on an entirely different mechanism could result in less lightning. Our measurements indicate that ground discharges originate in the region of maximum potential gradient between the negative and lower positive charge centers, corresponding to the −10° to −15°C temperature zones. This is also the region in which we could expect to make the greatest change in the ice crystal concentration by AgI seeding. The change in particulate population from liquid drops to ice crystals may increase the leakage current between the charge centers, decrease the potential gradient, and inhibit the start of the leader process to ground.

We have just completed a laboratory study of the effect of liquid and solid water particles on the sparking potential of air at pressures and temperatures similar to conditions within thunderstorms. The results of the study are summarized in Figure 13. Drops of water larger than 0.2 mm in diameter lower the sparking potential in the gap. Irregular ice crystals 0.1 mm to 3.0 mm in length reduce the sparking potential by about 35 percent at 675 mm pressure, but this potential does not vary with the size of the particle. Lowering the surrounding air pressure to 250 mm of mercury (Hg) changes the potential reduction factor to about 30 percent. Thus, for small particles, changing drops to ice crystals may lower the sparking potential in that region. This, in turn, could limit the maximum potential gradient that can exist in this region and inhibit the start of a cloud-

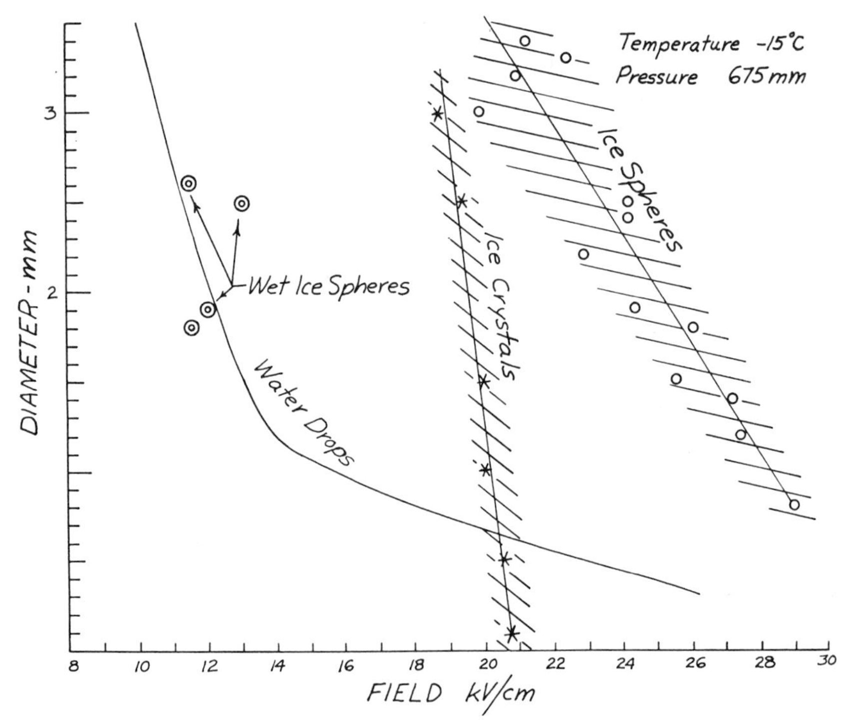

Fig. 13. Breakdown electric field in an airgap with ice particles and water drops of varying size.

to-ground discharge. It is much too soon, however, to attempt extrapolation from these laboratory results to conditions within a thunderstorm.

Conclusion

Information from studies on mountain thunderstorms and fire-starting lightning discharges has been used to develop a three-year program to evaluate what effect seeding with silver iodide will have on the frequency and character of lightning discharges from mountain thunderstorms. This program, started in the summer of 1965, involves the seeding of thunderstorms occurring within a test area in western Montana. About 2,000 lightning discharges were recorded within the test area during June, July, and August, 1965. About 40 percent of these discharges occurred during periods established for the statistical evaluation of seeding effects. Data from additional seasons hopefully will provide definite information on whether and how cloud seeding affects the frequency and character of lightning discharges. If there are effects from seeding, the next step will be to determine how these changes will influence the ignition of forest fires caused by lightning.

Author's Note: This research was supported by the Atmospheric Sciences Section, National Science Foundation, NSF Grant No. GP-2617.

REFERENCES

Barrows, J. S., 1966. Weather modification and the prevention of lightning-caused forest fires. In *Human Dimensions of Weather Modification,* edited by W. R. Sewell; pp. 169–182. Dept. Geog., Research Paper 105, Univ. Chicago, Chicago, Illinois.

Battan, L. J., 1965. Some factors governing precipitation and lightning from convective clouds. *J. Atmos. Sci., 22:* 79–84.

Byers, H. R., and R. R. Braham, Jr., 1949. *The Thunderstorm.* U. S. Govt. Printing Office, Washington, D. C.

Latham, J., and B. J. Mason, 1961. Electric charge transfer associated with temperature gradients in ice. *Royal Soc. Proc., A(260):* 523–536.

Weather Engineers, Inc., 1961. *A Pictorial Report of Project Wind Control.* Weather Engineers, Inc., Soquel, California.

The Influence and Implications of Windbreaks on Agriculture in Dry Regions

NORMAN J. ROSENBERG, *Department of Horticulture and Forestry, University of Nebraska, Lincoln, Nebraska*

THE PIONEERS to the Great Plains of the United States and Canada planted windbreaks primarily to guard their comfort and that of their animals. Possibly aesthetic considerations or homesickness for the forested regions of Europe and the eastern United States prompted these plantings as well. We know less about the motives of the Russian plainsman and the settled agriculturist of Western Europe. It appears that in their case, too, planting preceded recognition that windbreaks influence other than wind speed reduction and protection of the crop from mechanical injury.

La Cour in the late nineteenth century (Van der Linde, 1962), prompted by his observations that plant growth was generally improved in sheltered areas, made the first scientific study of shelter effect in Denmark. He observed that shelter caused higher daytime and lower nighttime temperatures than occurred in the open. Since that time literally hundreds of researchers have attempted studies of shelter effect on microclimate and on plant growth.

During the last 15 years reviews have been undertaken of a vast literature which stems from the United States and Canada, Soviet Russia, Western Europe, Scandinavia, the Mediterranean countries, and Japan. Important, but limited, reviews preface books on their own original research by Jensen in Denmark (1954) and Caborn in England (1957). More ambitious reviews have recently been completed under the auspices of the United Nations' Food and Agriculture Organization (F.A.O.) by Van der Linde (1962) and World Meteorological Organization (W.M.O.) by Van Eimern (1964). The most comprehensive by far is that of Van Eimern.

When a large quantity of literature exists, particularly on research in such complex and puzzling areas as crop production and micrometeorology, some contradictory statements are to be expected. The wealth of conflicting material in shelter-effect research, however, exceeds all expectation. On matters of radiation balance, air temperature, atmospheric humidity, soil heat flux, carbon dioxide exchange, and even water use by sheltered plants, sharply divergent findings are reported. Van der Linde (1962), Van Eimern (1964), and, most recently and perhaps most methodically, Guyot (1963) have attempted to rationalize these differences by examination of climatic and experimental circumstances under which conflicting reports and interpretations were developed.

The author has noted (Rosenberg, 1966a) that at least a part of the documented disagreement on the nature and magnitude of shelter effect may be due to the fact that sensors are often improperly exposed. The practice of sheltering temperature and humidity sensors in standard meteorological screens leads to exaggerated reports of nocturnal temperature depression in shelter. True daytime temperature increases in shelter are minimized as are daytime and nocturnal vapor pressure increases.

The Nebraska Windbreak Studies

Studies of shelter effect were conducted in the subhumid eastern and semiarid western parts of Nebraska by my associates and me during the years 1962–1965 and are continuing at this writing. Snap beans, dry beans, and sugar beets were grown in shelter under irrigation regulated to maintain mean soil moisture stress at less than two bars in the root zone. The microclimatic conditions and plant responses resulting from shelter were compared with conditions in open sites treated identically in all other ways. We measured net radiation, soil heat flux, solar radiation, temperature, humidity, and gradients of these. Most recently CO_2 content and gradient in sheltered and open sites were measured.

In order to generate shelter effect we constructed four-sided shelters of two tiers of snow fence (210 cm high). Parallel rows of snow fence (120 cm high) and barriers composed of two rows of corn, reaching 240 cm in height, have been tested as a means of sheltering sugar beet plants. Views of a four-sided and of a parallel snow fence shelter are shown in Figures 1 and 2.

Long-term and almost continuous observations of macro- and microclimatic conditions in the sheltered and open zones have been made in conjunction with each of the studies. During our first study all sensors were recorded on a strip-chart multipoint potentiometer. Data reduction was manual (Rosenberg and Allington, 1964). Through the following years data recording has been fully automated by use of the Meteorological Data Handling System designed by Fritschen and Van Bavel (1963). Recently we have coupled a Beckman CO_2 analyzer to the data-handling system in order to measure CO_2 quantity and gradient in sheltered and open sites.

Fig. 1. A four-sided shelter 15 meters on a side, built of 2 tiers of snow fence 210 cm high. Dry beans growing at Scotts Bluff, Nebraska, 1963.

Fig. 2. A two-sided shelter spaced at 15 meters, built of a single tier of snow fence 120 cm high. Sugar beets emerging at Scotts Bluff, Nebraska, 1964.

Influences of Windbreaks

Wind Reduction in the Sheltered Zone

A good deal of information is available concerning the influence of windbreaks on wind speed to the lee and to the windward. Experience has shown that windbreak efficiency is increased by increasing permeability. The area effectively sheltered is increased and the gross turbulent motions which result from winds overtopping the windbreak are somewhat reduced.

A permeable windbreak permits more laminar flow as overtopping air rejoins that penetrating the belt. Effective shelter is maintained for a greater distance downwind and large-scale turbulent eddying is minimized. Wind speed is reduced less near a permeable windbreak but the effect persists for a greater distance downwind. A great deal of experimental evidence indicating the above to be a realistic evaluation of the influence of windbreak permeability is presented by Van Eimern (1964).

Effects of growth of the sheltered crop and of alteration in permeability of the windbreak on its efficiency are illustrated in Figure 3 (Rosenberg, 1966c). Single-tier snow fence and double rows of corn with crops in the intervening 15 meters were studied at Scotts Bluff, Nebraska, during the summer of 1964. The efficiency of the snow fence (shown by the lines Y_{SF}) decreased through the growing season (April to July to August) as the beets grew and the effective height of the snow fence over the beets decreased. At first the snow fence sheltered an area of about 12 times its height (12H). By the end of the season its effective height was such that it would have had to shelter an area nearly twice as great. The efficiency of the double corn rows as a wind barrier (shown by the lines Y_{CN}) increased from July to August because the rows which had grown into an almost impermeable barrier were thinned to about 50 percent permeability.

The shelterbelts planted in the Great Plains during the dust bowl years of the 1930's and early 1940's were of the dense type. Although monuments to the art of the silviculturist, these belts were, for the reasons I have mentioned, rather poor agricultural windbreaks. Remedial action in the 1930's could not await the completion of a research program. Today foresters are studying ways and means of renovating and altering windbreaks planted during the dust bowl years to increase their effectiveness (Van Haverbeke, 1965).

Shelter Effect on Radiation

Windbreaks influence the radiation balance in adjacent fields chiefly by the shadows they cast. The barrier also intercepts, reflects, and reradiates some fractions of the solar or terrestrial radiant streams. Long shadows are cast when the sun is low, but these occur at times of day when intensity of solar radiation is low, and the effect may be unimportant.

It is interesting here to speculate on the sapping effect often attributed to windbreaks—that is, the reduction in yield of plants growing near living shelterbelts. Competition for nutrients and water is most often considered the dominant cause of sapping. Felch (1964) has found, however, that the total yield of dry beans harvested from strips adjoining north-south snow fence windbreaks at

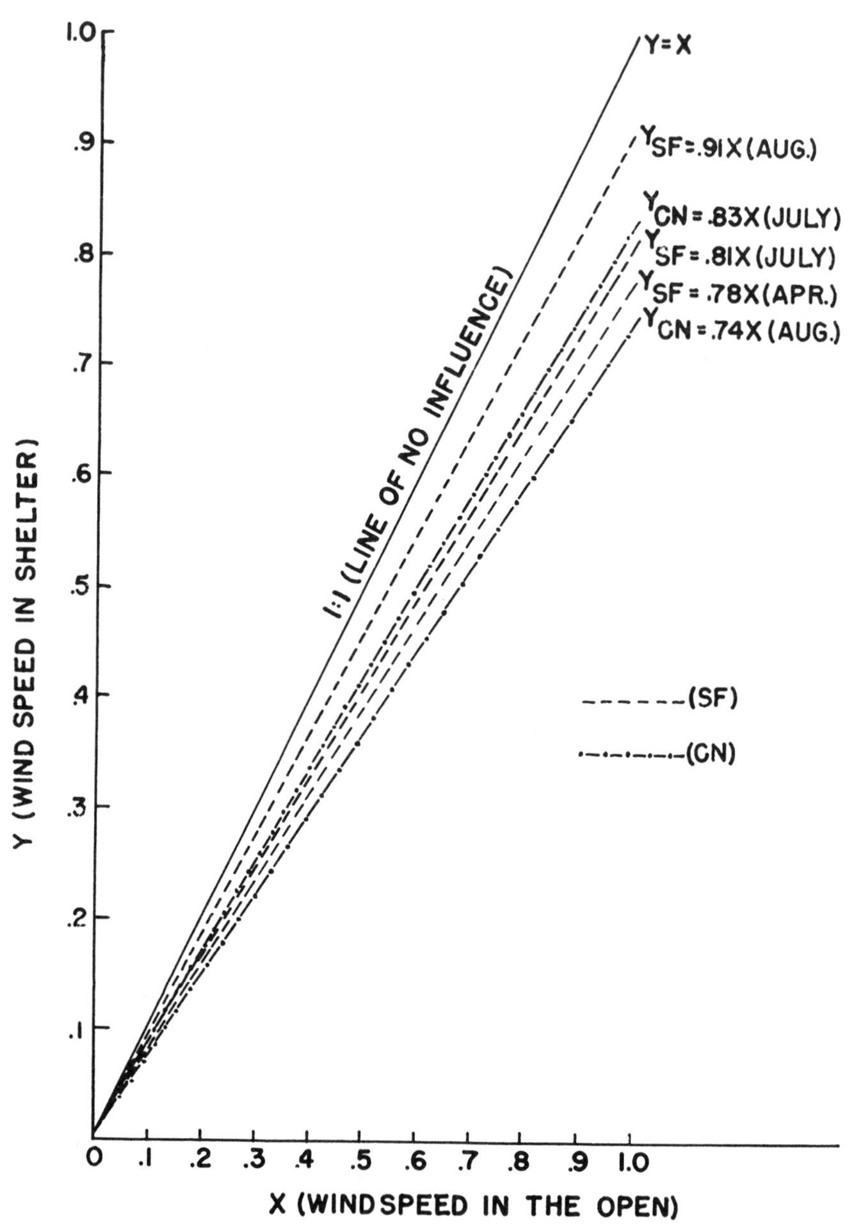

Fig. 3. Wind speed reduction efficiency of snow fence (Y_{SF}) and corn wind barriers (Y_{CN}) sheltering sugar beets, Scotts Bluff, Nebraska, 1964.

Scotts Bluff is reduced, but the yield from strips adjoining east-west windbreaks is not affected. Sapping caused by the nonliving and noncompetitive snow fence is probably owing to shading by the fences. The effect is not found consistently, although the dry bean plant is apparently more sensitive than is the sugar beet.

Shelter Effect On Air Temperature

La Cour (Van der Linde, 1962) found higher day and lower night temperature in shelter in the maritime climate of Denmark. Bodrov (1937) found higher morning but lower afternoon temperatures in shelters in the semiarid Russian steppes. Many workers have reported, for localities ranging from the south to the north of Russia, daily mean temperature increases in shelter ranging from 0.5° to 3.0° C.

Gagarin (Van Eimern, 1964) suggested that shelterbelts increase the continentality of a region by increasing the amplitude between daily temperature maxima and minima. Bates (1911) suggested that the more clear the weather, the greater the shelter effect on temperature. Steubing (Van Eimern, 1964) suggested that after a night of rain no temperature effect due to shelter can be found, as latent heat consumption minimizes generation of sensible heat to warm the air.

Woodruff *et al.* (1959) found noon temperatures at 30 cm above the plowed surface of a Kansas wheat field to be as much as 6° C greater in the lee of a shelter than in the open. Zones of warmer and zones of cooler air were found as they traversed the sheltered field to a distance of 26H. Further, and of interest later in this discussion, air temperature observed in this field decreased more rapidly with elevation above the ground (greater lapse rate) during the day in shelter than in the open.

Daytime temperatures over irrigated crops at Scotts Bluff have been found to be greater in shelter (Rosenberg, 1966b). Nocturnal temperatures are usually a fraction of a degree lower in shelter. Cloudiness minimizes the differences in daytime temperature between sheltered and exposed sites. During humid seasons lesser differences in temperature are observed between sheltered and exposed sites than during dry years.

Van der Linde (1962) considered that shelter generally increases temperature during a large part of the day and that in temperate regions this increase favors plant growth and animal comfort, especially during spring and fall. A temperature increase in summer might favor a large number of crops although it could, of course, be harmful to crops in hot regions—particularly hot arid regions. Cereals, according to Gagarin (Van Eimern, 1964) are not favored by the temperature increase in shelter in Russia, but other workers in the U.S.S.R. and in our own Plains region disagree (Stoeckeler, 1962).

Guyot (1963) believed the effects of shelter on air temperature may be predicted on the basis of whether evapotranspiration is increased or decreased. When evapotranspiration uses a greater share of available energy, less energy remains for generation of sensible heat.

Shelter Effect on Soil Temperature

Jensen (1954) in Denmark, Steubing (Van Eimern, 1964) in Germany, and other Western European workers have consistently noted increased soil temperature in sheltered zones and a proportional increase in soil temperature with increasing wind protection. Burnacki (Van Eimern, 1964) found in the Kamannaja steppe of U.S.S.R. that bare soil was warmer in shelter. After a wheat crop became established the opposite held true.

Jensen (1954) has attempted to explain differences in soil temperature on the basis of a pure energy balance—by decreased evaporation in shelter and consequently greater availability of energy for soil heating. The matter is not likely to be this simple, however. Decreased evaporation leaves wetter soils which, while they transmit heat more readily, causing increased soil heat flux by day, also transmit heat outward more readily by night. Further, heat capacity of wet soils is greater than that of dry soils, requiring, therefore, more heat to raise the temperature of a unit volume of wet than of dry soil. Also, as will be seen, the fact that sheltered plants may transpire more water than unsheltered plants means that the assumption that soils are wetter in shelter may not necessarily be realistic.

In the windswept high insolation region of Scotts Bluff, Rosenberg (1966b) found soil temperature under irrigation to be from 1°–2° C higher by day and a fraction of a degree lower by night with higher average temperature in shelter than in the open. This has been true under the tight canopy closure of dry bean crops. Under the more open canopy of sugar beets, slightly higher daytime and slightly lower nighttime soil temperature has been observed in the open (Rosenberg, 1966c).

Shelter Effect on Atmospheric Humidity

Many, if not most, of the pertinent observations of humidity in sheltered and exposed plots have been reported in terms of relative humidity. Simultaneous temperature measurements are often lacking. The data are, therefore, difficult to evaluate.

Aslyng (Van Eimern, 1964) studied the deficit of vapor pressure over a clover field sheltered by a hedge in Denmark and found deficits to be slightly greater in shelter than in the open by day and slightly lower by night. This was owing to the higher daytime and lower nighttime temperatures in shelter. Matiakin (1937) confined his report to shelter effect on vapor pressure over crops in the semiarid steppes of Russia and found increases of about one millibar (mb) over sheltered crops.

The influence of a shelter on humidity is tempered by evaporation and transpiration rates. These are influenced by the soil moisture regime and by vapor transport mechanisms which, too, are influenced by the presence of a wind barrier. A consensus view would suggest that the absolute humidity is greater over a sheltered crop by day and by night. Relative humidity may be lower by day because of the higher air temperatures prevailing in shelter and higher by night because of the lower air temperatures. Vapor pressure deficit may follow the opposite pattern.

I have found (Rosenberg, 1966b) that the consensus view described the situation over and within irrigated dry beans sheltered in a square snow fence (Fig. 4) during the years 1962 and 1963. On the other hand parallel snow fence and corn barriers had little influence on atmospheric humidity over irrigated sugar beets in the same location but during a different year (Rosenberg, 1966c).

Moisture Conservation in Sheltered Areas

It is generally recognized and agreed that the major influence of windbreaks on plant growth, particularly under dryland conditions,

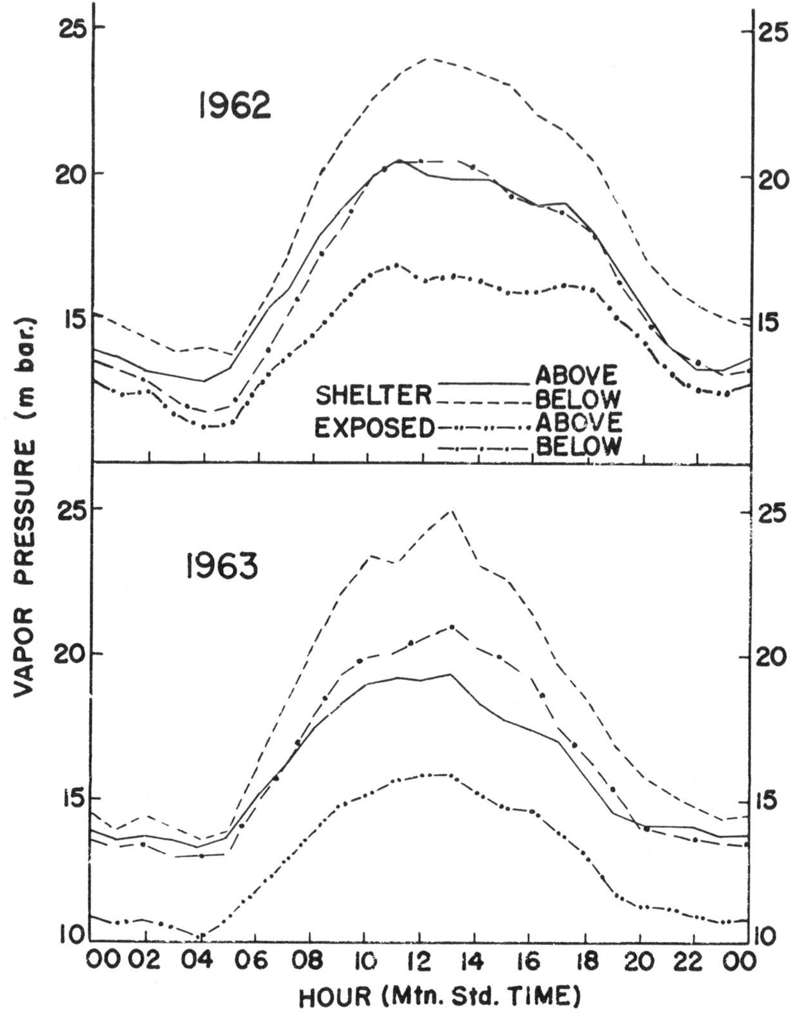

Fig. 4. Influence of a four-sided snow fence barrier on absolute humidity above and below the canopy of irrigated dry beans, Scotts Bluff, Nebraska, 1962, 1963.

is the redistribution and conservation of soil water. The windbreak when properly designed will, in northern latitudes, aid in uniform distribution of snow, thereby improving the supply of moisture to spring-grown crops. The windbreak is also expected to aid in reducing evaporation below that which is potentially possible in the region.

Evaporation is a function not only of the vapor pressure gradient between surface and air but also of the wind speed. Various empirical and semi-theoretical attempts at prediction of evaporation and transpiration dot the literature. Those which do not neglect the wind term are of greatest practical utility in estimating the effect of windbreaks on evaporation and transpiration in regions where wind speeds are not minor.

The effect of shelter on evaporation and transpiration has been studied primarily under conditions of potential evaporation (PE) — that is, where wetness of the evaporating surface approximates the free-water condition. Atmometers, evaporation pans, and wetted soils in isolated units have been used to measure shelter effect on PE with predictable results. Naegeli (Van Eimern, 1964) compared wind speed and evaporation from flat moist clay containers. An excellent relation of evaporation proportional to $u^{1/2}$ (square root of wind speed) was found. The applicability of such measurements to prediction of real evaporation where water supply to the surface does not approximate the free-water condition is in question.

Prediction of the water-conserving influence of windbreaks on bare soil under non-potential conditions is more difficult, but not unmanageable. The rate of drying in wet unsheltered soil will decrease after peak potential rates have persisted for a few days (Lemon, 1956). After some period of time, depending on the magnitude of the evaporative demand and on soil texture, structure, and capillary conductivity, evaporation will essentially cease. Some time later evaporation, proceeding at a rate in shelter lower than the external potential, will also cease and both soils will be equally dry. The slower rate of evaporation from sheltered bare soil may nonetheless constitute a very real advantage. Data on germination of sheltered sugar beet seeds (Rosenberg, 1966c) shown in Figure 5 illustrate this effect. Soils were moist at seeding, and soil temperature, the only other factor which might have influenced rate of beet seed germination, was not measurably different during the germination period.

It is shelter effect on the real evapotranspiration that is most difficult to predict. On dry land, for example, seeds which germinate rapidly because of beneficent shelter effect grow into larger plants and ramify roots more quickly into the soil. As these soils dry, crop cover decreases the relative importance of direct evapora-

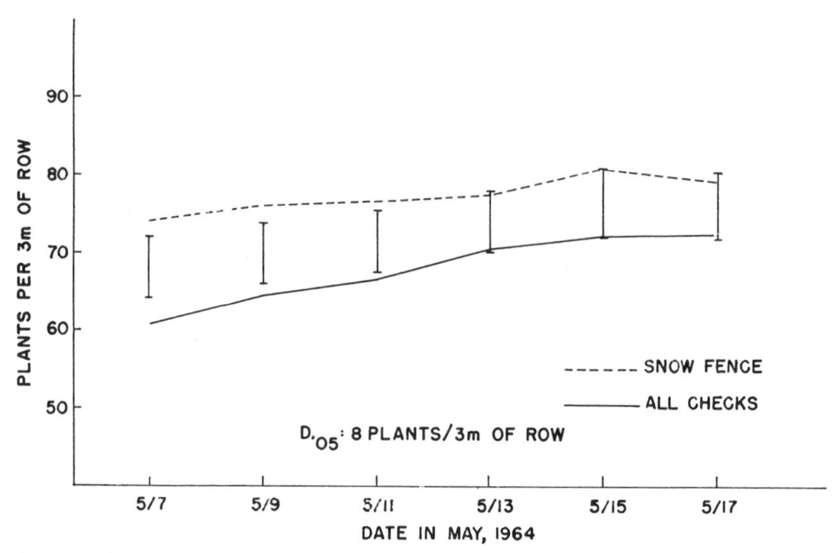

Fig. 5. Influence of snow fence barriers on rate of sugar beet stand establishment, Scotts Bluff, Nebraska, 1964. $D_{.05}$ indicates difference needed for significance at the 5% level of probability.

tion from the soil. Transpiration becomes the major mechanism of water withdrawal. In time, and assuming transpiration is a function of leaf area alone, water depletion will induce soil moisture stress in shelter. The development of the sheltered plants will be checked while the unsheltered plants grow in a less inhibited way. Jensen (1954) in Denmark and Mastinskaja (Van Eimern, 1964) in the East Volga region of U.S.S.R. have shown that the initial moisture advantage of sheltered plants is eventually dissipated in this way. Over a season during which some rain falls, however, the more luxuriant crops grown in shelter may actually use more water than do plants grown in the open. Interestingly, the efficiency of water use—the relative proportion transpired to that evaporated from the soil—may also be increased (Budyko, cited by Van Eimern, 1964).

As to whether an increase in the ratio of transpiration to evaporation results in greater dry matter or yield production per unit of water used has been much discussed. An indirect answer to this question is to be found in the data of Zukovsky (cited by Van Eimern, 1964). In one of the drier regions of the U.S.S.R., it was observed that during wet years significant increases in yields of grains, alfalfa, and pasture were obtained in shelter. During dry years, however, the magnitude of such increases was remarkably great. Utilization of the limited water available for transpiration during these dry years is evidently more efficient in shelter.

Pelton and Earl (1962) studied wheat yield and water use in a Saskatchewan field sheltered by 240-cm-high snow fencing. They demonstrated that shelter results in increases of as much as one bushel of wheat per acre inch of water consumed. Best results were obtained at 3H to the east (predominantly leeward) of the barrier.

Our studies at Scotts Bluff were undertaken on the assumption that in a broad irrigated region, such as the North Platte Valley of Nebraska, and under a liberal irrigation regime, the moisture variable could be effectively controlled. While microclimatic influences on phenological development have been found, we have found, no less, that even under ample irrigation the moisture variable cannot be removed in field studies of shelter effect. In fact it now seems likely that differential plant turgor, stomatal regulation, and transpiration rate are involved in improving plant growth in shelter.

Atmometers in shelter, both black and white Bellani plates, evaporated considerably less water during the 1962 studies than did similar instruments in the open (Table 1) (Rosenberg, 1966b). Since soil moisture removal under full plant canopy did not follow this pattern, the observations were repeated in 1963. Again atmometer evaporation was greater in the open over plant cover and also over bare soil. During both years, however, more soil water was extracted by plants growing in shelter. At the conclusion of the 1963 season all plant material was stripped from the plots. The pattern of soil moisture removal agreed with atmometer evaporation—that is, greater water use in the open. Evaporation from evaporimeters is indeed reduced by shelter in an irrigated region as is evaporation from a bare soil. Transpiration rate in bean plants is increased by shelter.

Physiological Regulation of Transpiration by Sheltered Plants

Further studies were made at Scotts Bluff during 1963 (Rosenberg, 1966b) and again at Mead during 1964 (Lecher, 1965; Rosen-

Table 1. Atmometer evaporation and soil moisture removal during periods of full and no plant cover in wind-sheltered and exposed sites, Scotts Bluff, Nebraska, 1962 and 1963.

Period	Plot condition	Atmometer type	Evaporation: Exposed plot (cm^3/day)	Evaporation: Sheltered plot (cm^3/day)	$D_{0.05}$[2] (cm^3/day)
1962 Aug. 8–Aug. 17	Full cover	Black	43.5	34.7	9.2
		White	24.6	18.5	5.8
1963 July 21–Aug. 4	Full cover	Black	42.5	28.7	3.6
		White	29.0	16.8	3.4
1963 Sept. 2–Sept. 7	Bare soil	Black	44.7	34.1	7.2
		White	30.3	23.4	5.2

Period	Plot condition	Soil moisture measure	Soil moisture removal: Exposed plot (bar)	Soil moisture removal: Sheltered plot (bar)	$D_{0.05}$ (bar)
1962 Aug. 8–Aug. 17	Full cover	Tensiometer	0.16	0.14	n.s.
		20–25 cm	0.75	0.84	0.07
1963 July 21–Aug. 4	Full cover	Gravimetric[1]	30.0	45.7	4.8
1963 Sept. 2–Sept. 7	Bare soil	Tensiometer	0.13	0.13	n.s.
		20–25 cm	0.21	0.16	0.01

[1] Unit of measurement for the period July 21–August 4, 1963, is one mm of water removed per 45 cm of soil depth.
[2] Difference needed for significance at the 5% level of probability.

berg *et al.*, 1967) to discover the mechanism for increased transpiration in shelter. Figure 6 illustrates the typical influence of shelter on the turgor and stomatal aperture of protected bean plants.

On August 9, 1963, at Scotts Bluff, four days after a thorough irrigation, air temperatures over dry bean plants in shelter were only slightly higher than in the open (Fig. 6). Dew point was significantly higher in shelter. Vapor pressure deficit was slightly lower over the canopy but considerably lower within the canopy of the sheltered plants. Black and white atmometers evaporated more water in the open than in shelter. Relative turgidity of the sheltered bean plant leaves remained considerably higher than in exposed plant leaves. Stomatal opening, when observations were begun at about 11:00 A.M., was markedly greater in leaves of the sheltered plants and midday stomatal closure was reduced in shelter.

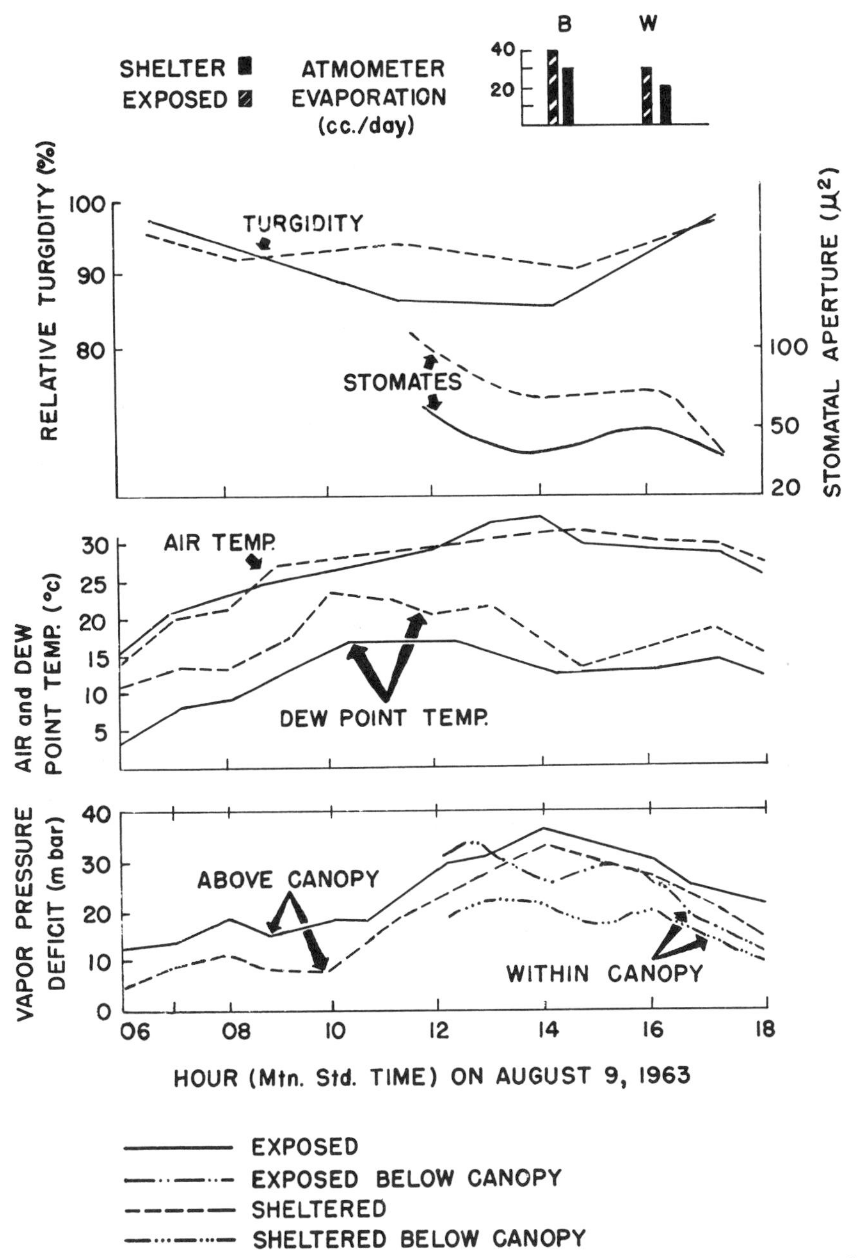

Fig. 6. Microclimatic conditions, atmometer evaporation, and leaf turgor and stomatal behavior of irrigated dry beans in a four-sided shelter and in the open at Scotts Bluff, Nebraska, August 9, 1963.

Even under good irrigation practice, then, in a large irrigated valley at 42°N latitude, where local oasis effects are likely to be small, major moisture stress occurs in unsheltered plants. These stresses are minimized by shelter. How much more important this effect may be in the truly arid regions of oasis-type irrigation can only be conjectured now. The biological implication of this wind-induced turgor loss and stomatal closure cannot be overemphasized. (This was also observed in British wind tunnel studies on vegetable crops by Winters, 1964.) Open stomates mean greater potential for photosynthesis by sheltered plants.

Aerodynamics and CO_2 Supply

Increased transpiration by sheltered plants is, in itself, no great benefit. It has been shown, however, that plant yield per unit of water used is generally increased in shelter. It must follow then that open stomates and higher plant turgor permit a greater photosynthetic potential to the sheltered plants. The potential, however, can be realized only if CO_2 is not limiting or in significantly shorter supply in shelter than in the open. It is here that the least definitive work has been done with the most contradictory results. The generally accepted scheme describing CO_2 relations in shelter is about like this: Because of still air in shelter at night, plant- and soil-respired CO_2 tends to accumulate more readily than in the open. With daylight this accumulation is rapidly consumed. Throughout the day relatively still air in shelter limits supply of CO_2 to the plants.

Data on CO_2 content of sheltered air are confounded by many factors. Among these factors are the more abundant vegetation in shelter and the possibility of more widely open stomates in leaves of sheltered plants which also may provide a stronger sink for CO_2. Measurement of CO_2 concentration alone does not provide a true measure of transport or flux of CO_2. Only if concentration and gradient of CO_2 are measured and accompanied by observation of turbulent transport can flux rates be established. Although it is probably true, as Lemon (1963) has stated, that air movement past a plant controls supply of CO_2 to the photosynthesizing organs, it may not be at all correct to equate the decrease of wind speed in shelter with decreased CO_2 supply.

Wind and temperature profiles in shelter and in nearby open sites have been recorded over many hours at Scotts Bluff and Mead in order to estimate transfer coefficients. We have observed that wind shear between two levels above the plant is considerably greater in shelter than in the open. Air temperatures at a fixed level are not greatly different, although slightly higher by day and slightly lower by night in shelter. Temperature gradients are more strongly lapse by day and more strongly inverted by night in shelter.

A distribution of Richardson numbers computed for 62 hours during July, 1963, at Scotts Bluff (Rosenberg, 1966b) showed that air in shelter of a 210-cm-high snow fence was considerably more unstable by day and considerably more stable by night. These facts taken together indicate, if current aerodynamic theory can be applied to this situation which deviates greatly from the ideal conditions and assumptions underlying the theory, that turbulent diffusion processes during the day are not reduced in proportion to the reduction of wind speed.

More detailed observations of atmospheric stability in shelter and open sites were made during 1964 at Mead (Rosenberg, 1965). Richardson number distributions were similar to those obtained earlier; there were more hours of instability by day and more hours of stability by night in shelter. Of the hundreds of hours studied only those during which neutral conditions prevailed were selected for wind profile analysis. The "log law" profile has been derived for conditions of neutral stability, and application to other conditions risks errors of a magnitude which may be great even in the open field. For that reason data shown here are confined to the neutral case.

Details are shown in Table 2 where zero plane (Z_0), drag coefficient (CD), shear stress (τ), friction velocity (u_*), and the eddy transfer coefficient for momentum (K), computed by the methods of Sutton (1953) for fully rough surfaces, in the open and in a four-sided snow fence shelter are reported as functions of wind speed in the open. Z_0 and CD decrease with increasing wind speed in shelter but are greater there than in the open. τ and u_* increase with increasing wind at about the same rate in shelter as in the open but are greater in shelter. K is estimated to be greater in shelter. The difference in K between sheltered and exposed sites

Table 2. Wind profile parameters under neutral stability in shelter and in open sites, Mead, Nebraska, 1964.

Wind speed (m sec^{-1})	Items	Plot	Parameter				
			Z_0 (cm)	CD	τ (dynes cm^{-2})	u_* (cm sec^{-1})	K (cm^2 sec^{-1})
1–2	5	Exposed	6.8	.03	.54	26.4	1425
		Sheltered	34.6	.13	.94	36.0	1945
2–3	22	Exposed	5.6	.03	1.29	32.3	1746
		Sheltered	30.9	.11	1.91	39.9	2153
3–4	33	Exposed	6.3	.03	2.38	44.1	2381
		Sheltered	29.4	.11	3.33	52.6	2838
4–5	36	Exposed	6.5	.04	4.19	58.4	3156
		Sheltered	28.9	.11	5.55	68.1	3676
5–6	12	Exposed	7.0	.04	6.12	71.7	3869
		Sheltered	26.8	.09	7.83	81.0	4374

decreases asymptotically with increasing wind speed. If the similarity principle that eddy transfer coefficients for heat, water vapor, and CO_2 are identical or linked with that for momentum holds in this case, then CO_2 flux in shelter should not be severely limited by the decrease in wind speed there.

Another interesting aspect of wind profile development is shown in Figure 7 (Rosenberg, 1966c). Snow fence and corn barriers differ greatly in their effects on the profile which develops over sugar beets. The corn barriers (CN) create a lesser shear than do snow fence barriers (SF) and consequently zero plane is projected more deeply into the canopy of the corn-sheltered beets. The differences diminish with increasing wind speed but remain real, nevertheless. As the beet plant maintains an upright and open leaf canopy into which light penetrates, the deeper or more normal penetration of wind is probably beneficial.

Table 3 summarizes our observations on shelter-induced microclimates. Wind speed is always reduced in shelter. Air temperature is higher by day but lower by night in shelter than in the open. Temperature lapse rates are more negative by day and more positive

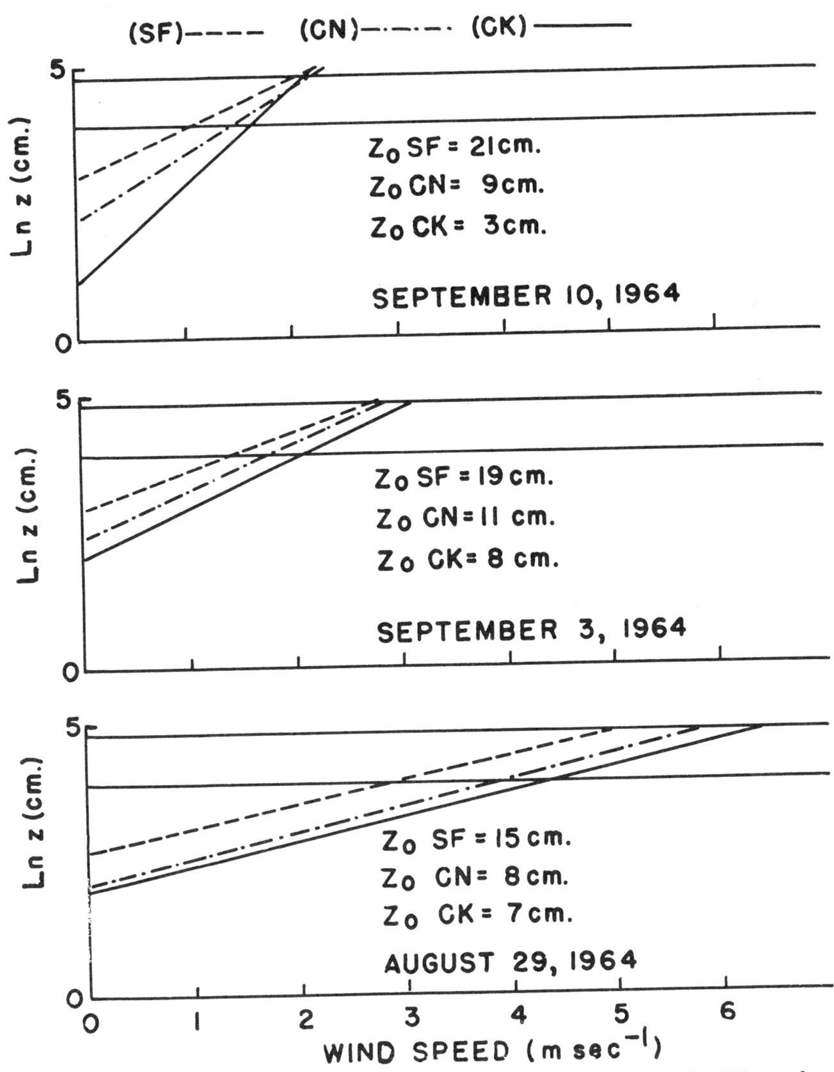

Fig. 7. Wind profiles over corn-sheltered (CN), snow fence sheltered (SF), and exposed (CK) sugar beets on days of calm, moderate, and strong wind, Scotts Bluff, Nebraska, 1964.

by night in shelter and wind shear is greater throughout the day and night. Together these factors lead to a situation where daytime air is more strongly unstable and nighttime air more strongly stable in shelter.

Table 3.—Summary of observed differences in microclimate, wind profile, and evapotranspiration in sheltered (S) and exposed (E) sites under irrigation.

Comparison	Day	Night
Wind speed	S < E	S < E
Air temperature	S > E	S < E
Lapse rates	(Neg.) S > E	(Pos.) S > E
Wind shear	S > E	S > E
Stability of air (Ri)	(Neg.) S > E	(Pos.) S > E
Zero plane	S > E	S > E
Drag coefficient	S > E	S > E
Shear stress	S > E	S > E
Friction velocity	S > E	S > E
Eddy transfer coefficient	S > E	S > E
Absolute humidity	S > E	S > E
Relative humidity	S ⩾ E	S ⩾ E
Vapor pressure deficit	S ⩽ E	
Potential evapotranspiration	S < E	
Actual evaporation	S < E	
Actual transpiration	S > E	

The greater wind shear in shelter suggests an elevation of zero plane, increased drag coefficient, shear stress, friction velocity, and eddy transfer coefficient, assuming the log profile holds in these circumstances. At the very least we may hope that reference to the log profile provides qualitative instruction.

Absolute humidity is higher by day and by night in shelter, but relative humidity varies according to whether temperatures are greater in shelter or in the open. Potential evapotranspiration is predicted, by all theories, to be greater in the open. Actual evaporation from evaporimeters and from bare soil agrees with these predictions. Actual transpiration on the other hand is, where irrigation keeps the plants well supplied with water, greater in shelter.

Conclusions

The value of windbreaks on dry land in subhumid and semiarid regions of the world is well documented. While all reasons for beneficial plant responses are not known, the favorable distribution of soil moisture and favorable influence on the internal water regime of sheltered plants is probably most important. Rapid seed germination and rapid plant and root development, favored by the increased temperatures during early growth, are also important factors.

In semiarid windswept regions where irrigation is practiced, much of the limitation of water supply to plant growth is removed. But evaporative demand may not be decreased sufficiently to remove all moisture stress on the plant. Windbreaks can be effective in reducing evaporative demand, minimizing plant water stress, and guarding against the loss of photosynthetic potential which accompanies turgor loss and stomatal closure.

Less well understood today is the matter of CO_2 supply to sheltered plants. Indications are that the reduction in CO_2 supply predicted on the basis of reduced horizontal wind passage may have been overstressed. Available experimental data are questionable. Modern analytical techniques for CO_2 content and gradient measurement and improvements in wind-sensing systems should make this problem solvable in the near future.

There is every reason to believe that windbreaks increase efficiency of water use—that is, greater food or fiber production for each unit of water expended. This may be true not only in subhumid and semiarid regions, but also in the true deserts where oasis-type irrigation is practiced.

The foresters tell us that trees can be grown anywhere, even in the desert. Tree planting should not be excluded from consideration as a means of improving plant growth in arid regions. Tall plants—corn, sorghums, even elephant grass where adapted—might also serve well as windbreaks in arid regions and be included in the irrigation rotation. If properly spaced and managed, windbreaks such as these can be used to reduce wind speed and evaporative demand with little effect on air temperature. Wind profiles of almost normal shape but lower than normal speed can be generated with such barriers. The small area lost to production of the major crop can be compensated by the grain or forage harvested from the windbreak itself.

Windbreaks are among the most practical means of beneficially modifying climate in agricultural regions. I have not attempted here to document yield responses observed by the many workers who have contributed to the literature of shelter effect. Yield increases have ranged from the insignificant to the spectacular. The vast majority of reports including our own indicate beneficial effects due to windbreaks. For detailed information the reader is referred to the excellent review articles cited earlier.

Author's Note: The author is indebted to his colleagues W. T. Bagley, R. E. Neild, D. P. Coyne, and Lionel Harris, and to his students R. E. Felch and D. W. Lecher who have aided, advised, and participated in the Nebraska studies of shelter effect discussed here. These studies have been supported by grants from the U. S. Department of Commerce; ESSA (Contract CWB-10428) ; Great Western Sugar Company; and Nebraska Resources Division, State Department of Agriculture.

REFERENCES

Bates, C. G., 1911. Windbreaks: Their influence and value. *U. S. Dept. Agr., Forest Serv. Bull., 86:* 1–100.

Bodrov, V. A., 1937. Methods of observation on the microclimate and agricultural yield in a territory protected by shelterbelts (Trans. from Russian. U.S.D.A. Library, Trans. No. 7308, typewritten). *Forest Serv., U. S. Dept. Agr.* Washington, D. C.

Caborn, J. M., 1957. Shelterbelts and microclimate. *Forestry Comm. Bull., No. 29:* 1–135, H. M. Stationery Office, Edinburgh, Scotland.

Felch, R. E., 1964. *Growth and Phenological Responses of Irrigated Dry Beans to Changes in Microclimate Induced by a Wind Barrier.* M.S. thesis, Univ. Nebraska, Lincoln, Nebraska.

Fritschen, L. J., and C. H. M. Van Bavel, 1963. Micrometeorological data handling system. *J. Appl. Meteorol., 2:* 151–155.

Guyot, G., 1963. Les Brise-Vent: Modification des microclimats et amelioration de la production agricole. *Ann. Agron., 14:* 429–488.

Jensen, M., 1954. *Shelter Effect Investigations into the Aerodynamics of Shelter and its Effects on Climate and Crops.* Danish Tech. Press, Copenhagen, Denmark.

Lecher, D. W., 1965. *Growth Responses of Two Irrigated Varieties of the Snap Bean to Microclimatic Changes Induced by a Wind Barrier.* M.S. thesis. Univ. Nebraska, Lincoln, Nebraska.

Lemon, E. R., 1956. The potentialties of decreasing soil moisture evaporation loss. *Soil Sci. Soc. Am. Proc., 20:* 120–125.

Lemon, E. R., 1963. Energy and water balance of plant communities. In *Environmental Control of Plant Growth,* edited by L. T. Evans; p. 55–78. Academic Press, New York.

Matiakin, G. I., 1937. Shelterbelts protecting farmland in the semidesert and their influence on the microclimate of the intermediate spaces (Trans. from Russian. U.S.D.A. Library, Trans. No. 7312, typewritten). *Forest Serv. U. S. Dept. Agr.,* Washington, D. C.

Pelton, W. L., and A. U. Earl, 1962. *The Influence of Field Shelterbelts on Wind Velocity and Evapotranspiration.* Annual Report, Can. Dept. Agr. Exp. Farm, Swift Current, Saskatchewan, Canada. (Mimeograph)

Rosenberg, N. J., 1965. *Relationship between Wind Barrier Induced Microclimate and Plant Growth Response.* U. S. Weather Bureau, Washington, D. C. (Mimeograph)

Rosenberg, N. J., 1966a. On the study of shelter effect with sheltered (screened) meteorological sensors. *Agr. Meteorol., 3:* 167–177.

Rosenberg, N. J., 1966b. Microclimate, air mixing and physiological regulation of transpiration as influenced by wind shelter in an irrigated bean field. *Agr. Meteorol., 3:* 197–224.

Rosenberg, N. J., 1966c. Influence of snow fence and corn windbreaks on microclimate and growth of irrigated sugar beets. *Agron. J., 58:* 469–475.

Rosenberg, N. J., and R. W. Allington, 1964. A microclimate sampling system for field plot and ecological research. *Ecology, 45:* 650–655.

Rosenberg, N. J., D. W. Lecher, and R. E. Neild, 1967. Wind shelter induced growth and physiological responses in irrigated snap beans. *Proc. Am. Soc. Hort. Sci.* (In press)

Stoeckeler, J. H., 1962. Shelterbelt influence on Great Plains field environment and crops: A guide for determining design and orientation. *U. S. Dept. Agr. Prod. Res. Rept. No. 62:* 1–25.

Sutton, O. G., 1953. *Micrometeorology;* pp. 229–272. McGraw-Hill, New York.

Van der Linde, J., 1962. Trees outside the forest. In *Forest Influences. FAO Forestry Forest Prod. Studies, No. 15:* 141–208, Rome.

Van Eimern, J., 1964. Windbreaks and shelterbelts. *WMO Tech. Note No. 59.* World Meteorol. Org., Geneva, Switzerland.

Van Haverbeke, D. F., 1965. "First-aid" for your shelterbelt. *Nebraska Exp. Sta. Quart., 2(2):* 17–18.

Winters, E. J., 1964. Some effects of wind upon vegetable crop plants. *Proc. Brit. Ecological Soc. and Hort. Education Assoc., Sci. Horticulture, 17:* 53–60.

Woodruff, N. P., R. A. Read, and W. S. Chepil, 1959. Influence of a field windbreak on summer wind movement and air temperature. *Kansas Agr. Exp. Sta. Tech. Bull. 100.*

Microclimate Before and After Irrigation

LEO J. FRITSCHEN, *College of Forest Resources, University of Washington, Seattle, Washington*

PAUL R. NIXON, *Soil and Water Conservation, Research Division Field Station, U. S. Department of Agriculture, Lompoc, California*

THE MICROCLIMATE is the detailed climate of a small area, ranging in size from a small crevice to several acres, over which small variations exist from place to place; it also includes the climatic structure of the air space which extends from the surface of the earth to a height where the effects of the immediate character of the underlying surface climate cannot be distinguished from the general local climate. The air space is generally four times the height of the surface growth or structures (A.M.S., 1959). The zone composes the environment of man, animals, insects, and plants. This discussion will be limited to the zone generally occupied by man and plants, with emphasis on water use by plant communities.

The influence of irrigation on the microclimate is relative to the area of irrigated lands compared with the area of arid lands. In the southwestern United States solar radiation is absorbed by vast acreages of arid land and is converted into sensible heat, which ultimately raises the temperature of the air mass. Solar radiation absorbed by irrigated areas is largely converted into latent heat, thus tending to lower the temperature of the air mass. Relatively small acreages of land, however, are irrigated because of limited water supply, topography, and other factors. One would not expect the microclimate of a region to be greatly modified by irrigation, because those areas are small compared to the area of arid land.

The influence of irrigation upon the microclimate can be discussed more adequately by first reviewing the physical processes involved. The sun is the ultimate source of energy for the earth. Energy reaches the earth either as direct solar radiation, diffuse solar radiation, or atmospheric radiation (Fig. 1). Of the energy reaching the earth's surface, part is absorbed and part is reflected. The amount reflected depends on the solar angle and the color of the reflecting surface. For irrigated crops in an arid environment, it varies from 14 to 27 percent (Fritschen, 1966).

Energy absorbed at the surface is used in various ways. Part of it is radiated back to the atmosphere as longwave radiation. This process continues day and night and is a function of the emissivity and absolute temperature of the surface; for example, a plant surface at 20°C would radiate approximately 0.6 cal/cm^2 min (ly/min). The remainder of the energy received at the earth's surface (net radiation) is used in heating the soil surface, in heating the air, in evaporation, and in plant growth. The amount of energy used in each of these processes depends on the condition of the surface; for example, with wet bare soil the largest heat sink is evaporation. As the soil surface dries, more and more energy is used in heating the air and the soil. When the surface is covered with a non-wilting plant canopy, the evaporation process is again the largest heat sink, and in many cases energy is extracted from the air mass to support this process.

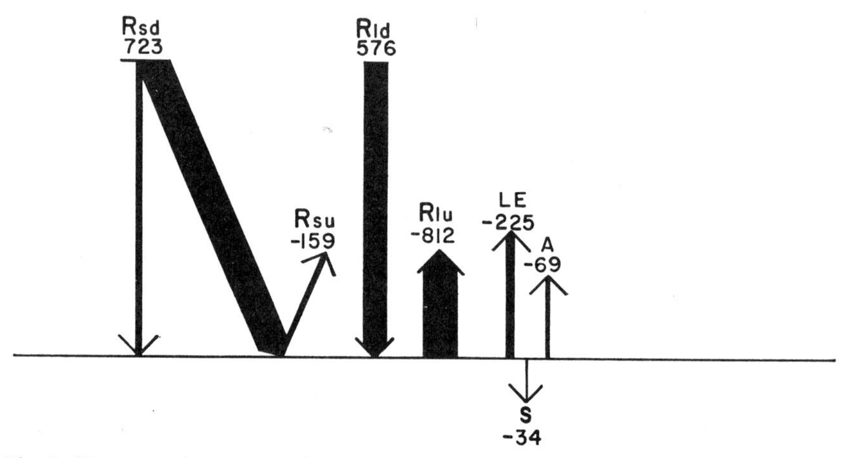

Fig. 1. Energy exchange over drying bare soil on May 2, 1961. Rsd is solar radiation down, direct plus diffuse; Rsu, solar radiation up; Rld and Rlu, longwave radiation down and up; LE, latent heat flux; A, sensible heat; and S, soil heat flux in ly/min.

Most of the processes described are considered to take place vertically. The horizontal component of the total flux is called advection and is generally smaller than the vertical fluxes, although in some circumstances the horizontal flux may be quite large.

Thus, irrigation would be expected to lower the air temperature, to increase the vapor pressure, to decrease the amount of energy used in heating the soil and the air, and, in some cases, to cause energy to be extracted from the air. Irrigation would also tend to reduce the amount of energy reflected and the amount of energy reradiated to the atmosphere as longwave radiation. The questions that remain to be answered are how large are these effects, and how far can they be detected from the evaporating surface? These factors will be discussed with respect to small oases, large oases, and a transect of an irrigated, arid valley.

Small Oases

On an experimental field, 73 × 92 m, located in the heterogeneously irrigated Salt River Valley of Arizona, energy balance components were measured over open water, then over wet and dry bare soil (Fritschen and Van Bavel, 1962). The results (Fig. 2) indicate that the days were quite similar with respect to solar radiation. However, air temperature and vapor pressure of the air mass gradually increased over the period (Tables 1 and 2).

The evaporation from wet bare soil was greater than that from open water, although the evaporation rate was greatly diminished after three days of drying. The difference in evaporation between open water and wet soil is largely due to the surface-to-air vapor-pressure gradient, which was greater over the wet bare soil during most of the day. The wet soil heated up more quickly in the morning and was warmer at night than the open water. The soil surface also had a larger aerodynamic roughness than the open water, thus increasing turbulent exchange. Lower evaporation on May 2, 1961, was due to the drying surface restricting the upward flow of water. As a result energy was used to heat the air and the soil.

There was lower net radiation on April 29, 1961, than on April 25, 1961, because of warmer surface temperature and high, thin cirrus which attenuated solar radiation. As the soil surface dried, increasing surface temperature and changing color decreased net radiation

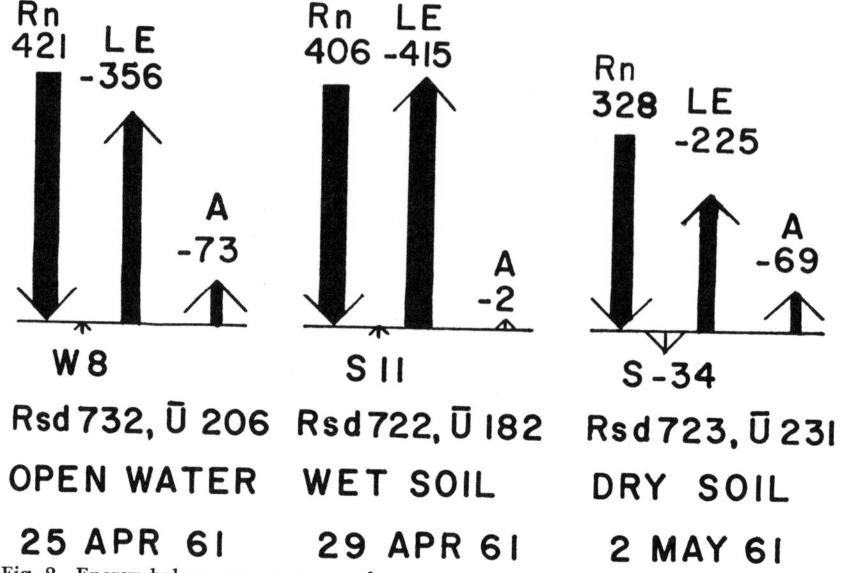

Fig. 2. Energy balance components of open water, wet soil, and dry soil. Rn is net radiation; LE, latent heat flux; A, sensible heat; W, change in energy in the water layer; S, soil heat flow; Rsd, solar radiation down; and Ū, average wind speed.

(May 2, 1961). The ratio of the amount of energy used in evaporation to net radiation was 0.85 for the open water, 1.02 for wet soil, and 0.84 for dry soil.

Air temperature and vapor pressure indicate that the influence of irrigation was limited to a very shallow layer. Difference in air temperatures between various heights at the experimental field and the U.S. Weather Bureau Airport Station located 3.9 km northwest are presented in Table 1. The temperature differences above 160 cm are consistent and probably reflect location, while the temperature differences below 160 cm changed during the period and appear to reflect the surface condition. Thus we conclude that the air temperature was modified up to 1.5 m, or a fetch-to-height ratio of about 30. Vapor-pressure difference at 160 cm between the experimental field and the Airport Station apparently does not reflect surface conditions (Table 2).

Irrigation of bare soil would produce a larger change in the microclimate than irrigation of a crop, provided the root-zone soil water is above wilting point. This is because the root system is able

Table 1. Air temperature (°C) at U. S. Weather Bureau Airport Station, Phoenix, Arizona, and at various heights in the experimental field, 1961.

	Surface		
Location	Open water April 25	Wet soil April 29	Dry soil May 2
Airport	17.1	23.9	25.9
40 cm	13.3	18.9	21.5
80 cm	13.3	19.2	21.6
160 cm	13.1	19.8	21.8
320 cm	13.8	20.2	22.6
640 cm	14.3	21.6	23.0

Table 2. Vapor pressure (mb) at U.S. Weather Bureau Airport Station, Phoenix, Arizona, and at 160 cm above the surface in the experimental field, 1961.

	Surface		
Location	Open water April 25	Wet soil April 29	Dry soil May 2
Airport	3.5	4.7	5.4
160 cm	3.8	4.1	5.2

to extract larger quantities of water at a faster rate than can be transported through the soil.

Energy balance components of sudan grass before and after irrigation are given in Table 3. The last irrigation prior to September 12 was on August 14, nearly 30 days earlier. The days presented cannot be compared directly because solar radiation was lower on the 12th, and air temperature and vapor pressure was 3°C and 2 mb greater on the 17th. Nevertheless, the evaporation/net radiation (LE/Rn) ratios compare favorably, being 1.23 and 1.28 on the 12th and 17th respectively, illustrating that irrigation did not greatly increase the evapotranspiration and, presumably, did not materially affect the air temperature and vapor pressure, although no data were available to substantiate this point. Ratios of LE/Rn greater than unity indicate that energy was extracted from the air mass.

Table 3. Positive net radiation of sudan grass at Phoenix, Arizona, before and after irrigation. Area irrigated after September 12, 1962. Net radiation (Rn), soil heat flow (S), evaporation (LE), sensible heat (A), solar radiation (Rsd), and average wind speed (U).

Date	Rn	S	LE	A	Rsd	U
	langleys					m/sec
Sept. 12	264	12	−324	47	494	0.7
Sept. 17	303	24	−388	60	519	1.4

A smaller LE/Rn ratio of 1.11 from alfalfa inundated to 18 cm than of 1.29 from the alfalfa after irrigation (Table 4) indicates that presence of free water did not increase evapotranspiration. To the contrary, the ratios indicate that a relatively larger amount of energy was extracted from the air mass for evapotranspiration. The larger ratio may have been enhanced by about a 5-cm growth and a slightly greater wind speed. The average air temperatures and dew points were the same for both days, 26° and 0°C, respectively.

The concept of energy extraction from the air mass by irrigated crops at considerable distance from the edge of irrigation in a desert is supported by data from the Salt River Valley in Arizona. Evapotranspiration from alfalfa and sudan grass measured with weighing lysimeters generally exceeded net radiation during the summer months (unpublished reports on file at the U.S. Water Conservation Laboratory, Phoenix, Arizona). Air-temperature differences measured at 5 and 40 cm above alfalfa, cotton, barley, wheat, oats, and grain sorghum also indicate a downward flux of energy (Fritschen,

Table 4. Net radiation (Rn), soil heat flow (S), evaporation (LE), sensible heat (A), solar radiation (Rsd), and average wind speed (U) for periods of positive net radiation during inundation of alfalfa, Mesa, Arizona, May 13, 1964, and two days after inundation, May 15, 1964.

Date	Rn	S	LE	A	Rsd	U
	langleys					m/sec
May 13	297	−39	−329	71	532	1.5
May 15	428	−45	−554	171	709	1.9

Table 5. Temperature (°C) and vapor pressure (mb) over wheat (From Arkhipova and Glebova, 1952).

Day after irrigation	Section of the field	Air temperature height (m) 0.2	0.6	Vapor pressure* height (m) 0.2	0.6
1st	irrigated	30.4	30.7	8.6	8.8
	nonirrigated	33.2	31.7	6.1	6.6
8th	irrigated	26.2	26.1	15.6	14.9
	nonirrigated	28.2	27.9	14.5	14.7

* Calculated from relative humidity.

1966). The fields on which these measurements were made are in a heterogeneous area, ranging from 4 to 10 km from the nearest desert. Lemon *et al.* (1957) reported advected energy 16 km downwind from the edge of an irrigated area of cotton. These facts tend to lead to the conclusion that in arid regions large acreages would have to be irrigated to modify the temperature regime significantly.

Observations on clear days over irrigated and nonirrigated wheat in the Voronezh Province of U.S.S.R., reported by Arkhipova and Glebova (1952), indicated that the irrigated area was cooler and more humid (Table 5). The difference between the irrigated and nonirrigated area decreased with elevation and days after irrigation. Maximum differences 20 cm above the crop were less than 3°C and 3 mb.

Alissow *et al.* (1956) presented data from a small oasis in Russia (Table 6). Again very little difference is noted at the 2-m level,

Table 6. Temperature (°C) and vapor pressure (mb) in a small oasis at 1:00 P.M., July 17, 1927 (From Alissow *et al.*, 1956).

Type of surface	Air temperature height (m) 0	0.5	2.0	Vapor pressure* height (m) 0	2.0
Unirrigated	42.2	37.0	35.8	18.2	14.1
Alfalfa	32.8	34.4	34.9	38.8	14.5
Rice	31.0	32.5	34.8	25.1	18.9

* Calculated from relative humidity.

indicating that the influence of the surface is restricted to the lower layers of air. They point out that the climatic differences resulting from irrigation are dependent on the size of the individual oasis and the intensity of irrigation.

Large Oases

Thornthwaite (1958), reviewing the ways man may influence the climate, stated that while man's influence on his environment can be great, it is generally of limited areal extent and duration and, in the main, does little to the climate. He cited Ribinsky Dam in Russia as an example. The construction of the dam produced almost no perceptible change in the monthly average air temperature on shore, perhaps a few tenths of a degree; the average wind speed along the shore was doubled, but the effect was local. He also cited examples in the United States of the Salton Sea and Lake Mead. These lakes scarcely change the climate, even in the immediate vicinity, despite the fact that both are located in an arid region. For instance, 600 m from the Salton Sea shoreline, the moisture content of the air is relatively unaffected.

To increase the July vapor flux over Arizona by 10 percent and, consequently, precipitation by the same amount, McDonald (1962) calculated that a reservoir as large as the combined areas of Lakes Erie and Ontario would have to be constructed along the southern boundary of the state. The artificial reservoir would cover 16 percent of the total area of Arizona.

Bennett and Nelson (1960) reported other Russian studies of oases:

> "Liakhov (1953) studied the influence of the Volga River, north of Astrakhan, on the microclimate of the adjoining desert. Microclimate stations were set up on the banks of the Volga and at distances ranging from 200 to 5,000 meters from the western bank to determine the degree to which the river ameliorated a hot, desiccating east wind, locally called a *sukhovei,* commonly experienced in this region in summer. Measurements of temperature, humidity, and wind were made at heights of 20 cm and 2 m above the ground. Modification of the humidity during daytime apparently was limited to within 500 meters of the river. At

Table 7. Relative humidity differences (percent) between the large Ami Darya oasis and adjacent desert at 2 m above the ground (From Alissow *et al.*, 1956).

Hour	Mar	Apr	May	Jun	Jul	Aug	Sep	Oct	Nov
7:00 A.M.	11	4	7	16	22	23	21	19	10
1:00 P.M.	5	2	5	7	8	8	8	4	1
9:00 P.M.	3	3	7	16	21	23	13	16	1

2 meters above the ground, the mean vapor pressure at 1300 was 11.9 mb on the west bank of the river, 11.0 mb at a distance of 500 meters, and 11.1 mb at 2,000 meters . . . ."

Alissow *et al.* (1956) presented mean monthly differences in relative humidity between the large Ami Darya oasis and the adjacent desert (Table 7). Differences are indeed small, even during the period of peak irrigation. The differences may be due, in part, to air temperatures which appeared to be 1° to 3°C cooler in the oasis (Table 8). The smaller differences during the day suggest rapid turbulent exchange.

Ohman and Pratt (1956) investigated the influence of the Yuma irrigation project upon desert humidity of southwestern Arizona. The results indicate that evapotranspiration increased the average vapor pressure 9 to 10 mb and decreased the air temperature 5°C at a height of 1.5 m above the ground surface within the irrigated area. The lateral extent of this effect was limited to 30 m or less into the desert. The almost complete absence of advected moisture in the desert was attributed to the convection resulting from intense surface heating, the effect being that the moisture was carried aloft before surface winds could transport it horizontally.

Table 8. Temperature differences (°C) between the large Ami Darya oasis and adjacent desert at 2 m above the ground (From Alissow *et al.*, 1956).

Time	Mar	Apr	May	Jun	Jul	Aug	Sep	Oct	Nov
Mean monthly temperature	−1.2	−0.6	−1.1	−2.2	−3.1	−2.8	−2.3	−1.7	−0.8
1:00 P.M.	−0.3	−0.2	−0.7	−1.5	−2.0	−2.1	−1.4	−1.3	−0.3

DeVries and Birch (1961) compared air temperature and vapor pressure between irrigated pastures, 6 × 7 km, and dryland pastures in Australia. At 125 cm the air temperature over the irrigated area was 1° to 2°C cooler in the summer, while the vapor pressure was 0.7 to 2.0 mb greater.

A theoretical analysis by De Vries (1959) suggests that the horizontal influence of the irrigated area to its lee extends over about the same distance as the area's width measured in the wind direction and to a height equal to 0.01 of the horizontal distance.

Traverse of Irrigated and Desert Lands

The foregoing data are point samples and may be somewhat biased by location. Further indications of the influence of irrigation upon the microclimate are presented in the form of a transect. The transect across the lower San Joaquin Valley in southern California started 39 km west of Bakersfield at the western edge of an irrigated area, and proceeded 16 km east, 16 km south, and 24 km east. The route traversed large irrigated areas, desert areas, and mixed areas. The irrigated areas were determined from aerial photographs, land-use maps, and visual observations.

Measurements consisted of air temperature and vapor pressure at 65, 100, 365, and 400 cm above the surface, net and solar radiation, wind speed at 365 cm, and direction. Air-temperature and vapor-pressure sensors were mounted on a tower attached to the right side of the front bumper of a pickup truck, so that the intakes were 120 cm in front of the truck. A mobile micrometeorological laboratory housing an automatic data-logging system was hitched to the rear of the truck. Data were recorded every minute. The air-temperature and vapor-pressure sensors had a time constant of 4 to 5 minutes. The traverse speed was 4.6 m/sec; thus the time constant amounted to 1.2 km, or 0.7 mile.

With the exception of cloud cover, the weather remained uniform during the period. Air temperature at Bakersfield Airport increased from 33° to 36°C. Vapor pressure was 13 to 14 mb, and the wind was northeast at 3 to 4 m/sec. The sky was clear when the traverse started; however, scattered to broken altocumulus at 4,570 m, originating from thunderstorms in the mountains to the south, marred the last 24 km.

Air temperature at 1 m and temperature differences along the traverse are shown in Figures 3 and 4. The overall temperature increase with time was similar to that at Bakersfield. Temperature depressions along the route are correlated with the trajectory of the air from irrigated and cropped fields. The most pronounced depressions at 11:15 to 11:20 A.M. and 2:36 to 2:45 P.M. PST varied between 1° and 2°C.

The 4-m temperature averaged 1°C cooler than the 1-m temperature, and approached 0.5°C cooler in irrigated areas and 1.5°C cooler in desert areas.

Air vapor pressure at 1 m along the traverse is shown in the upper portion of Figures 3 and 4. The vapor pressure is strongly correlated with air trajectory from irrigated areas. Large changes in vapor pressures were encountered, and these do not represent the extremes because of the distance constants of the sensors. Vapor pressure measured in the desert region, 12:53 and 2:35 P.M., ranged from 13 to

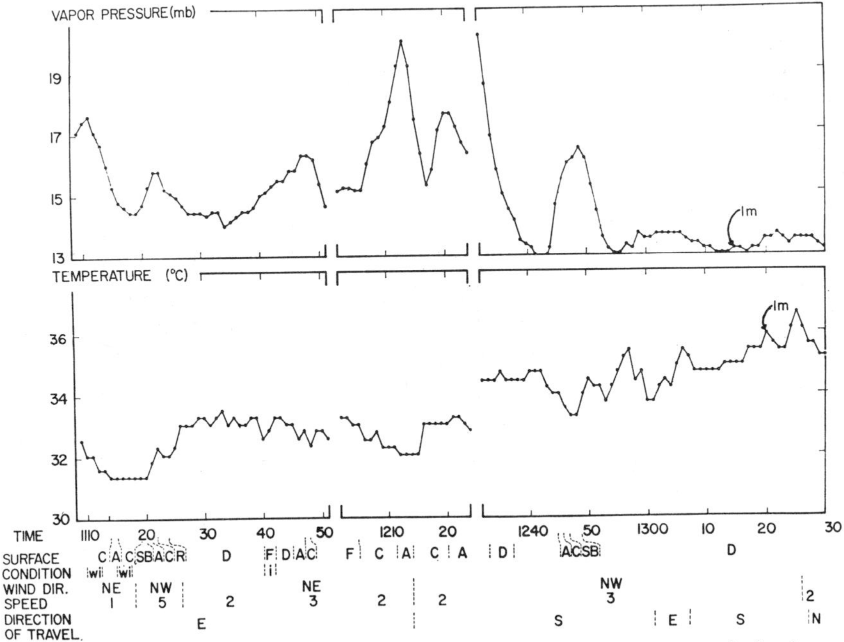

Fig. 3. Vapor pressure and temperature measured during the transect of the lower San Joaquin Valley. Surface condition: C is cotton upwind; A, alfalfa; SB, sugar beets; R, rice; D, desert; F, fallow; W, recently irrigated; and i, being irrigated.

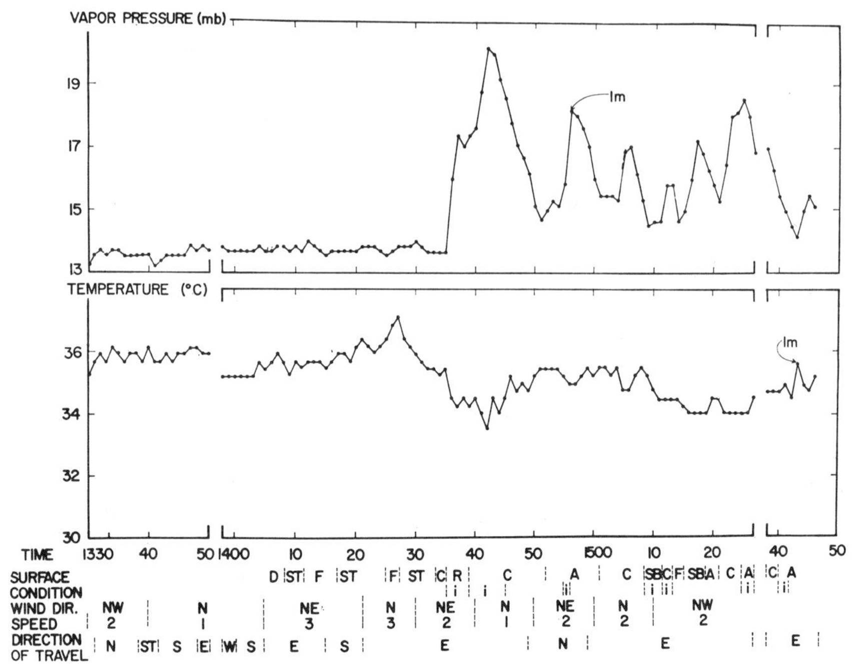

Fig. 4. Vapor pressure and temperature measured during the transect of the lower San Joaquin Valley. Surface condition: C is cotton upwind; A, alfalfa; SB, sugar beets; R, rice; D, desert; F, fallow; ST, stubble; and i, being irrigated. Direction of travel: ST is stop.

14 mb and was similar to the vapor pressure at the Bakersfield Airport. The peaks represent cross sections of vapor-pressure clouds, generated over rapidly evaporating surfaces. The peak between 12:44 to 12:53 P.M. is a good example of a cloud from an isolated irrigated area less than 1.6 km², west of the first southerly course. Adjusting for the sensor distance constant, the cloud, about 2.4 km across, was detected about 0.5 km after the start of the irrigated area and extended 1.3 km south of the area, a situation that would be expected with a northwesterly wind.

The peaks at 12:13 and 12:31 P.M. appear to be associated with irrigated cotton, and the peak at 2:42 P.M. was definitely associated with an irrigated rice field. The other peaks represent clouds from smaller acreages; their origin is difficult to determine.

The upwind irrigated area of the last 11 km of easterly traverse (3:00 to 3:55 P.M.) was at least 8 km, yet the overall vapor-pressure level did not increase greatly but tended to be represented by many clouds. The size and shape of the peaks indicate that the fields represented must have been small and near the road. This is to be expected in irrigated agriculture with the variety of crops cultivated, different growing seasons, and the physical limitation of irrigating a large area. A typical irrigated area is then heterogeneous with respect to surface wetness or evaporation potential.

These data support the data previously cited concerning the areal extent of the modification of the climate due to irrigation. The degree of modification is dependent upon the size of the area under irrigation. Greater modification was noticed in vapor pressure than in air temperature, because the energy extraction lowers the temperature of the air mass slightly, whereas the addition of vapor greatly increases the vapor pressure of the cloud generated by an irrigated area, making detection of changes in vapor pressure easier. The modification appears to be restricted to the cloud generated over the irrigated area and would be detected only over the area and immediately downwind. The detectable distance downwind is dependent upon the amount of transfer by convection versus advection. Strong surface heating and light winds, usually found in the arid southwestern United States, favor convection, thereby limiting the downwind influence of irrigation.

Application of Data

How does the construction of an irrigation project in an arid environment alter the requirement for irrigation water? The combination formula for potential evapotranspiration,

$$LE_0 = -\left(\frac{\Delta}{\Delta + \gamma}\right)\left(Rn + S\right) - \left(\frac{\gamma}{\Delta + \gamma}\right)\frac{L\rho\epsilon k^2}{P}\,\frac{d_a U_a}{[\ln(Z_a - D)/Z_0]^2},$$

may be used to answer the question. LE is the evaporative flux; Δ, the slope of the saturated vapor pressure versus temperature relation; γ, the psychrometric constant; Rn, net radiation; S, soil heat flow; L, latent heat of vaporization; ρ, density of air; ϵ, ratio of mole weight of dry air to water vapor; k, Von Karman's constant; P, atmospheric pressure; d, vapor-pressure deficit of the air; U, wind speed; Z, height; D, zero-plane displacement; a, height of measurement; Z_0, roughness.

As previously stated, cultivation and irrigation of a desert area would increase (Rn + S), decrease air temperature, and increase vapor pressure. These changes are somewhat compensating. Solving the combination formula by using the extremes of data recorded on the San Joaquin transect (i.e., data obtained in the desert before encountering the irrigated rice field and the data at the irrigated rice field) and an assumed value for (Rn + S) of 0.89 ly/min and $(Z_a - D)/Z_0$ of 100 cm yields the results in Table 9. The differences are small and amount to less than 10 percent for average wind speeds. Thus the use of local climatic data (air temperature, vapor pressure, and wind speed), plus net radiation calculated from solar radiation, could be used to predict the potential water requirement for an anticipated irrigation project with a slight overestimation.

Summary and Conclusions

The influence of irrigation on the microclimate has been examined with respect to the energy balance, temperature, and vapor pressure. The processes are interrelated, each influencing the other, and the combination determines the microclimate. The energy incident upon a bare soil will be disposed of by reflection, thermal radiation, heating the soil, heating the air, and evaporation. Wetting a bare soil will increase the energy used in evaporation, change the color, and, consequently, decrease the energy reflected. Evaporation, being the largest heat sink, lowers the surface temperature, thereby reducing thermal radiation, soil heat flow, and the energy available to heat the air.

The expected result, a cool-humid microclimate, may be obtained if vast areas are irrigated or wet by rainfall. However, in the arid

Table 9. Potential evaporation (ly/min) and difference computed for desert and irrigated rice field environment.

Wind speed (m/sec)	Potential evaporation		
	Desert	Irrigated rice	Difference %
1	0.89	0.84	5
3	1.18	1.06	10
5	1.48	1.27	13

southwestern United States relatively small areas can be or are irrigated. These irrigated areas, in addition to using radiant energy, also extract energy from the air mass to support the evaporation process, thus increasing the water requirement.

Data from the arid portions of the United States and Russia indicate that the microclimate in irrigated areas is modified. The air is cooler and more humid, and the degree of modification depends upon the height of measurement above the surface in relation to the upwind fetch. At 1.5 m the modification was less than 5°C and 10 mb.

Strong surface heating and light winds—usually found in arid regions—favor convection over advection, thus limiting the areal extent of microclimate modification. Cooler and more humid air has been detected downwind from an irrigated area. The detectable distance ranged from a few meters to 500 meters, and appeared to be a function of the wind speed and the size of the wetted area. Certainly, the bulk of the modification was noted within 30 m downwind from the field. In general, the effects of irrigation are of limited areal extent and duration, and in the main do little to the microclimate of an area.

A traverse of the lower San Joaquin Valley revealed that the air temperature was 1° to 2°C cooler in the irrigated areas. Vapor pressures appeared more variable than air temperatures, ranging from 13 mb in the desert to over 20 mb in irrigated areas. The variation in vapor pressure appeared to represent cross sections of vapor-pressure clouds, generated over recently irrigated fields adjacent to the traverse.

The potential irrigation requirements of an anticipated project can be calculated with existing temperature, humidity, and wind-speed data, and an estimation of net radiation based on solar radiation. The potential thus calculated would be from 5 to 15 percent high, depending upon the average wind speed, but certainly good enough for broad planning purposes.

Authors' Note: Presented at the Section on Applications of Ground Level Climatology, Annual Meeting of the American Association for Advancement of Science, Berkeley, California, December 27–30, 1965. Contribution from the Soil and Water Conservation Research Division, Agricultural Research Service, U.S. Department of Agriculture.

Supported in part by the Atmospheric Science Research Division, U. S. Army Electronic Research and Development Activity, Fort Huachuca, Arizona.

The microclimate transect of the San Joaquin Valley, California, mentioned in this paper was made in cooperation with the Department of Water Resources, State of California.

REFERENCES

Alissow, B. P., O. A. Drosdow, and E. S. Rubinstein, 1956. *Lehrbuch Der Klimatologie (Handbook of Climatology)* (German translation of a book published in the Soviet Union). Veb Deutscher Verlag der Wissenschaften, Berlin.

American Meteorological Society (A.M.S.), 1959. *Glossary of Meteorology.* Am. Meteorol. Soc., Boston, Massachusetts.

Arkhipova, E. P., and M. Y. Glebova, 1952. Nekotorye dannye o klimate oroshaemogo polyo (Some data on the climate of an irrigated field). *Meteorol. i. Gidrol., 6:* 8–11.

Bennett, I., and R. A. Nelson, 1960. *The Nighttime Influence of Irrigation upon Desert Humidities, Technical Report EP-136.* Environmental Protection Research Division, Natick Laboratories, U.S. Army Materiel Command, Natick, Massachusetts.

De Vries, D. A., 1959. The influence of irrigation on the energy and the climate near the ground. *J. Meteorol., 16:* 256–270.

De Vries, D. A., and J. W. Birch, 1961. The modification of climate near the ground by irrigation for pastures on the Riverine Plain. *Australian J. Agr. Res., 12:* 260–272.

Fritschen, L. J., 1966. Evapotranspiration rates of field crops determined by the Bowen ratio method. *Agron. J., 58:* 339–342.

Fritschen, L. J., 1967. Net and solar radiation relations over irrigated field crops. *Agr. Meteorol., 4:* 55–62.

Fritschen, L. J., and C. H. M. Van Bavel, 1962. Energy balance components of evaporating surfaces in arid lands. *J. Geophys. Res., 67:* 5179–5185.

Lemon, E. R., A. H. Glaser, and L. E. Satterwhite, 1957. Some aspects of the relationship of soil, plant, and meteorological factors to evapotranspiration. *Soil Sci. Soc. Am. Proc., 21:* 464–468.

Liakhov, M. E. 1953. *Mikroklimaticheskie Nabliudeniia V Raione Chernoso IAra Astrakhanskoi Oblasti (Microclimatic Observations in the District of Chernyi IAr, Astrakhan Region)*; pp. 86–93. Akademiia Nauk SSSR, Institut Geografii (and) Institut Lesa, Moscow.

McDonald, J. E., 1962. The evaporation precipitation fallacy. *Weather, 17:* 1–9.

Ohman, H. L., and R. L. Pratt, 1956. *The Daytime Influence of Irrigation upon Desert Humidities, Technical Report EP-35.* Environmental Protection Research Division, Natick Laboratories, U.S. Army Materiel Command, Natick, Massachusetts.

Thornthwaite, C. W., 1958. Introduction to arid zone climatology. In *Arid Zone Research XI, Climatology and Microclimatology. Proc. Canberra Symposium,* UNESCO, Paris.

Ecological Implications of Weather Modification

R. H. WHITTAKER, *Department of Population and Environmental Biology, University of California, Irvine, California*

WHEN, AS AN ECOLOGIST, I consider the implications of weather modification, I have two regrets—first that, along with other ecologists, I find myself in dissent from the technologically oriented majority in evaluating these implications; second that I cannot offer the kind of effective evidence from controlled experiment that a scientist desires as a basis for this evaluation. The logic of an ecologist's reservations regarding weather modification must be considered in relation to phenomena on two levels, that of particular natural communities which may be affected by weather modification and that of man's own ecology, or relation to his environment.

Effects on Natural Communities

Community and Ecosystem

A natural community is an assemblage of different species of plants, animals, and saprobes which live together, compete, and otherwise influence one another in a particular environment. One might, for example, stand in a woodland of scattered oaks and a grassy ground cover on a southwest-facing hillside. The woodland as a living system of tree, grass, and other populations interacting and balanced against one another is a community; the place where it grows, the hillside with the kinds of climatic and soil factors affecting plants there, is its environment. The community and its environment together form an ecosystem. If, now, we should change the environment by increasing mean annual precipitation by ten percent, what change in the community will result?

It would be convenient if we could assume that a ten percent increase in precipitation implies a ten percent increase in various measurable moisture characteristics of environment and a ten percent transformation of the plant community. It does not, for the change in environment acts in various indirect ways through the function of the community and the dynamics of populations. Community and environment bear an intimate, coupled, interdeterminant relation to one another, as one may conveniently illustrate with water relations. The kind of plant community present contributes, along with more direct effects of climate on soil processes, to the development of soil characteristics which affect water penetration into the soil, subsurface flow, and availability to plants. The plant community aboveground affects the water available to the community and the evaporative stress on plant foliage in the community by transpiration, reevaporation of rain from plant surfaces, and microclimatic effects on wind and humidity. Moisture conditions, as we measure them in the ecosystem, and as they affect the life of plants, are determined not merely by precipitation but by functions of ecosystems which develop in relation to precipitation and other characteristics of environments.

Temperature acts on the plant in various ways, among them the internal temperature of leaves and other tissues affecting rates of photosynthesis and respiration, and effects on the rate of water loss by transpiration. Effects on heat balance and temperature of plants have been worked out with detail and precision by Gates (1962, 1965). Increase of internal temperature beyond a certain point can subject the plant to a thermal avalanche of mutually aggravating effects which overwhelms its physiology. Respiration increases, photosynthesis decreases, carbon dioxide in guard cells drops, turgor pressure drops, stomata close, transpiration diminishes; these effects are increased by temperature and tend to increase temperature. As a result the leaf warms at an accelerating rate; the plant wilts and is on its way toward death. An amount of temperature increase which seems modest in number of degrees, but which causes the physiology of a plant to cross its limit of thermal tolerance, can thus have relatively abrupt lethal effects. It should also be observed that through effects on transpiration and other processes, increased temperature affects water movement and availability in the ecosystem. Increased temperature means, in effect, that for a given amount of precipitation a smaller amount of water is available to plants at a given time; it reduces the usefulness to plants of a given amount of rainfall.

These indirect and nonlinear effects of weather in the ecosystem make it difficult to predict effects of weather modification from measurements taken on a single community. If we want to know the effect of increasing precipitation by ten percent, we need other kinds of data. One approach to an answer regarding probable long-range consequences is to look at an existing community that receives ten percent more precipitation, but with an otherwise similar environment. We must concern ourselves, however, with three kinds of effects of changed environment on communities—effects relating to overall community function, species composition of particular communities, and species migration along environmental gradients.

Community Production

The most interesting single expression of community function is primary productivity, the amount of organic matter produced, or energy bound, by green plants per unit of the earth's surface for a unit of time. An appropriate expression for our purposes is net primary production, the amount of productivity which is not respired by the plants but remains as measurable weight increase per unit of surface area for a unit of time. The amount of production is a resultant of temperature, moisture conditions, and other factors (Odum, 1959). In communities of arid climates productivity is a nearly linear function of precipitation, as illustrated in African communities studied by Walter (1962, 1964). At the other extreme of the moisture gradient, in the humid forests of the Great Smoky Mountains, there is no apparent difference in the production of humid and subhumid communities, but forests of markedly drier environments have lower production (Whittaker, 1966). There is thus an apparent plateau beyond which increased moisture available to stable or climax forests does not increase their production. In between these extremes the response of production to increased moisture is curvilinear, and may be approximated by the relation (computed by N. G. Hairston), $\log Y = 0.15\,X - 2.62$, where Y is the net primary production in grams per square meter per day of the growing season and X is the average annual rainfall in centimeters.

The effects of temperature on production are less clearly known, though production increases from the arctic to the tropics. Data from the Great Smoky Mountains show no decrease of production with elevation in the moist forests of lower and middle elevations, but lower production in the forests of highest elevations (Whittaker, 1966). The relation appears curvilinear, and the increase of production with temperature appears to be smaller than the Van't Hoff relation (of two- to threefold increase in rate of physiological reactions with a 10°C increase in temperature) would suggest. As has been indicated, an increase in temperature also implies reduced usefulness of the water available to a community. It may be that increased temperature could reduce the production of an arid community. It seems unlikely that reasonable increases in mean temperatures could produce economically useful increases in production of temperate-zone communities.

Population Response to Weather Modification

There is some direct evidence of effects of changed environment on plant populations in communities. Weaver (1954) and Weaver and Albertson (1956) followed the changes in Midwestern grasslands for many years through cycles of drought and higher rainfall. The changes were dramatic, with striking population alterations and reduction of grass coverage during drought, and recovery toward the previous condition following the drought. A New Jersey pine forest has received heavy artificial rainfall as a means of waste disposal; the long-lived pine trees at first survived while the undergrowth was altered; later the pines, too, were killed and the community completely changed (Little *et al.*, 1959). Ellenberg (1953) and Knapp (1954) have shown differences in species proportions in experimental grass communities exposed to different moisture conditions. There is no doubt that a change in a plant community's environment changes the balance among plant populations in the community. To find the meaning both of this and of our third level of consideration, species movements, we may turn with advantage to concepts that have developed recently on the relations of communities to environmental gradients.

Community Gradients

The environments of plant communities are mostly related to one another along gradients of environmental factors. Moisture gradients, for example, appear in climatic and geographic expression, such as the gradient of increasing aridity westward across the Middle West from forest through tall grasslands to desert plains. They also appear in topographic expression, like the moisture gradient from the wet valley bottom through moist lower slopes to dry, south-facing upper slopes in mountains.

Research in the Great Smoky Mountains (Whittaker, 1951, 1956), Wisconsin (Curtis, 1959; Curtis and McIntosh, 1951), and elsewhere has shown that plant and animal populations are generally distributed along environmental gradients in the manner illustrated in the upper part of Figure 1. This may represent any gradient, running from left to right on the horizontal axis, with the vertical scale representing the densities of plant or animal populations along that gradient. Each curve represents a species, with a population distribution of binomial form. Each has a central peak where the environment (the total environment in the ecosystem, including effects of other organisms) is optimum for the population, and tapering curves of decreasing densities on each side of this peak. Altogether, the populations form a complex, flowing continuum along the environmental gradient.

Such distributions have been worked out primarily for undisturbed plant communities which have had time to develop to stable, self-maintaining conditions, climax communities in a current sense (Whittaker, 1953). In such communities the ecosystem functions and the populations are in steady state. Mean mortality and reproduction are in balance with one another, and populations are relatively constant in time, but with some fluctuation, at levels determined by competitive interplay of species populations in relation to the environment of a given community. The particular combination of populations in a given environment develops in relation to the conditions of the environment; a different environment has

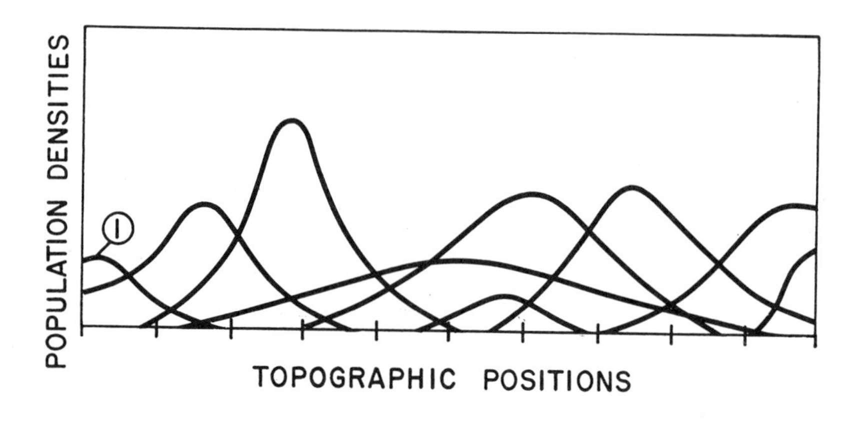

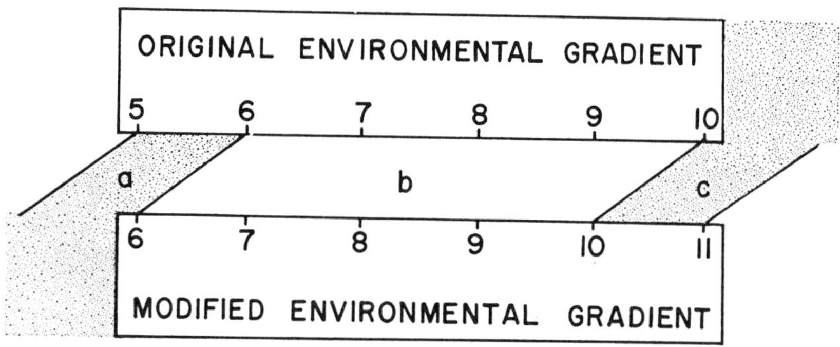

Fig. 1. Species populations along a topographic moisture gradient in mountains and effect of altering the gradient by weather modification.

Above—population curves for species distributions along the gradient.

Below—relative positions along the gradient as represented by arbitrary numbers from 5 (a dry slope) to 10 (a moist ravine) before weather modification and after modification to increase precipitation.

a different combination of species populations. The community response to an environmental gradient consequently includes a gradient of species populations.

Each point along the gradient represents an ecosystem, with a system of interacting plant populations developed in relation to that environment. The gradient as a whole is a gradient of ecosystems. In this ecosystem gradient we may recognize as parallel and interdependent a community gradient and an environmental gradient. The latter includes various aspects of moisture relations and many other environmental factors which vary more or less in parallel.

The gradient of actual environments affecting plants, comprising all these gradients of factors, may be termed a complex gradient. Climax vegetation of a given environment may be conceived as a steady state system of interacting populations adapted to that environment. Climax vegetation of a landscape forms a pattern mostly of intergrading communities, corresponding to the pattern of environmental complex gradients of that landscape (Whittaker, 1953, 1956).

Population Shifts in Response to Weather Modification

Effects of weather modification may be considered in relation to a particular complex gradient, such as a topographic moisture gradient. In the lower part of Figure 1, positions along a gradient are represented by arbitrary numbers. We may interpret the gradient as extending from point 10, a wet valley bottom, to point 5, a dry south slope. An increase in mean precipitation has a dual effect. First, it modifies the moisture conditions at each point along the topographic gradient; point 7, for example, which might be an open east slope, after increase in precipitation has the more favorable moisture conditions formerly present at point 8, a north slope. Second, increased precipitation has the effect of shifting the range of environmental conditions available. The plant populations illustrated in the upper part of the figure must respond to these environmental changes. Consequences of these changes may differ in the three parts of the gradient indicated as "a", "b", and "c".

Part "a". Environments of one extreme, those between points 5 and 6 on the scale, disappear. As they do so, species requiring such environments (species 1 in the upper part of the figure and others similarly distributed) must also disappear for lack of tolerable environments. If, for example, weather modification increases rainfall in such a manner that open oak woodlands on dry southwest slopes in the area are replaced by closed forests and by species formerly occurring on east and west slopes, then the species limited to southwest slopes may become extinct in the area. If weather modification increases mean temperatures so that the summits of a range of low mountains, which have had alpine meadows, are occupied by forests which move upward in response to increased temperatures, some species of the alpine meadows may be expected to disappear from that range of mountains. It is a common observation that many of the rarer species in a given area occur in just such special environments as southwest slopes and summits where they would be most vulnerable to extinction by weather modification.

Part "b". The range of environments between points 6 and 10 on the scale is displaced in relation to the land surface. A species whose optimum environment was, perhaps, at point 7 (an east slope, say) would now need to migrate to a new position (such as a southeast slope) to find an environment corresponding to its optimum. Extensive migrations, affecting all species populations, may be expected in the range between points 6 and 10. Species of a community differ widely in length of life cycle and in means of dispersal which affect rates of migration. The shifts along the gradient would, in consequence, not be harmonious ones of whole communities in movement, but a disordered movement of different species at different rates. The effects on communities would upset existing population balances and the communities would be partially disturbed. It is likely that, if the environmental changes are both substantial and abrupt, some more vulnerable and less mobile species in the range of 6 to 10 would become extinct in the area. Also, disturbance of communities in the range of 6 to 10 might permit some spread into these communities of highly mobile, rapidly reproducing species not normally part of them, and these intruders might contribute to the pressures toward extinction affecting some vulnerable species.

Part "c". The range of 10 to 11 is an environment new to this area, and a high degree of instability and disturbance could be produced in the communities occupying the former range of 9 to 10. If the change in environment is large, few native species adapted to the new environment would be available, and the new environment is likely to be invaded by species of high mobility and broad environmental tolerance.

Magnitude of Effects

It is possible to estimate magnitudes of changes in environment which would effect such disturbance and displacement of communities. In mountain ranges mean annual temperatures decrease with elevation at a rate of around 3° to 4°F per 1,000 feet; in the eastern United States a similar change in mean temperature results from traveling northward about 100 miles without change of elevation. The extent of change in plant and animal populations observed in an ascent of 1,000 feet or a distance of 100 miles differs in different areas and kinds of vegetation. It may be generalized, however, that the change brings a noticeable difference in population levels of plants and animals and in presence and absence of some species, although in many cases there is the same broad kind of vegetation. A change of twice this magnitude brings replacement of many species by others, wide change in population levels of species present at both extremes, and in many cases replacement of one major kind of community by another. In a southwestern mountain range (Shreve, 1915; Whittaker and Niering, 1965) in which moisture, rather than temperature, seems most effective in limiting vertical distribution of vegetation, mean annual rainfall increases upward at a rate of almost four inches per 1,000 feet. In some parts of the eastern United States a similar increase results from travel eastward of 50 to 100 miles. Again, a change of 1,000 feet or 100 miles results in a noticeable change in the composition of vegetation, and twice that change implies fundamental change in community composition and sometimes the replacement of one major kind of community by another.

Changes in rainfall or temperature of sufficient magnitude to have substantial usefulness to man seem likely also to be of sufficient magnitude to produce disturbance in natural communities. This judgment should be qualified by the variability of the response to be expected. A given increment, for example five inches of rainfall, should produce an early and striking alteration, at least in populations of short-lived plants, in a desert adapted to a mean annual total rainfall of five inches. The same increment of five inches might produce slighter changes, imperceptible for some years, applied as a ten percent increase in a forest adapted to an annual rainfall of fifty inches. When weather modification pushes major plants which characterize a community across a threshold of survival, dramatic changes in the community as a whole may result. When it is mainly minor plant species that are affected, there may be a marked change in species composition of the community without any conspicuous change in community structure. Life cycles of plants affect both the rate of change in response to, and the rate of recovery after, a period of weather modification. Populations of plants with shorter life cycles, like those of the prairies studied by Weaver (1954), may both change and recover within a few years. In communities dominated by long-lived plants, such as forest trees, the changes may be somewhat slower, but not necessarily so; recovery, on the other hand, which may depend on new individuals of the dominant plants growing to maturity, may be much slower. Effects of weather modification, affecting differently the various species of the community, cannot be stated in a strong and consistent manner. Significant alteration of communities, however, should be expected, generally, to result from a continued significant modification of climate, even if some of those alterations would not noticeably change dominant plant populations within a few years.

Species Extinction

Changes in climate of greater magnitudes than those discussed have occurred in evolutionary time. During and following the glacial period major changes in climate caused many species to migrate hundreds of miles. One may well ask whether we should concern ourselves with smaller changes in climate and smaller displacements of species which might result from weather modification. There are reasons to think so:

1. Glacial and postglacial changes occurred through centuries and millenia, during which most of the species moved slowly in response to slowly changing climates, and communities were restabilized. Man's changes would occur through years, not centuries. Species would be confronted with abrupt environmental changes requiring substantial migration for which there was less time than the normal life cycles of many dominant plants, and the communities would be unstabilized. Such disturbances favor the spread of weeds, particularly certain species which migrate rapidly, and occupy disturbed environments, and which are mostly unwelcome to man.
2. With the growth of human population and the spread of land occupation in the United States, native species are increasingly confined to small sanctuaries, such as parks, wildlife refuges, and moun-

tain ranges. Like American Indian cultures, native species exist in reservations by the sufferance of the dominant technological civilization. These reservations are islands surrounded by oceans of land intensively occupied by man, and it is not generally possible for wild species to migrate across the rural and suburban oceans from one island to another, to survive climatic change. If we so change climate that a species is no longer able to survive in a given natural area, that species cannot migrate but must become extinct there. The species may or may not survive in another reservation; but if it does it cannot migrate back to the first area after the period of weather modification.

Glacial and postglacial history offer instructive examples of the effect of barriers to migration. In glacial time in the eastern United States, many species were able to migrate far southward without obstruction as climates cooled, and later to migrate back to the north as climates warmed. In Europe, glaciers and glacial climates forced species to migrate southward until they encountered an east-west mountain range, the Alps, as a barrier to migration. Unable to migrate far enough to escape unfavorable environments, a large portion of the species became extinct. Figure 2 illustrates a case in which survival of a major species (and many minor species associated with it) in half of a mountain range is believed to have been made possible only by migration to higher elevations during warmer postglacial climates. In the other half of the mountain range, where such migration was impossible, these species became extinct.

3. Extinction of species reduces diversity of species, that is, the richness of natural communities in numbers of species. Stability of natural communities depends in part on the diversity of species—on the numbers of species interacting and tending to limit or control one another's populations. Although the correlation of diversity and stability is probably not a strict one, a reduced diversity of species should be accompanied by reduced stability of communities and expressed in spread of short-lived and weedy species. The instability may also imply increased vulnerability of some species to outbreaks of parasites, pathogens, or pests, reduced attractiveness to man of some of the communities preserved in natural areas, and reduced value of these communities as "normal" natural communities for scientific research.

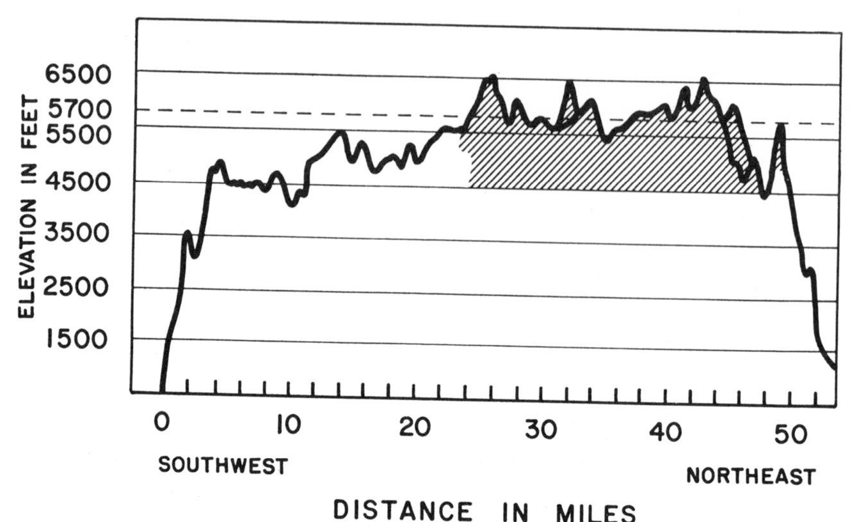

Fig. 2. A profile of the Great Smoky Mountains, Tennessee and North Carolina, to illustrate a hypothesis on the southern limit of Appalachian spruce-fir forests (Whittaker, 1956.) The present distribution of spruce-fir forests on higher peaks in the northeast half of the range is indicated by diagonal shading. The lower limits of the spruce-fir forests are believed to have been displaced upward to approximately 5,700 feet during warmer climates of the past. The spruce-fir forests were thus displaced off the tops of the mountains and became extinct in the lower, southwest part of the range. In the northeast half of the range spruce-fir forests survived on the higher peaks and migrated back downward as climates became cooler again, to their present 4,500 foot lower limit.

Recommendations in Relation to Natural Communities

One can imagine special cases of weather modification, for example reducing the effect of drought on a grassland on a temporary basis, which would not be unstabilizing, irreversible, nor unfavorable. More generally, however, effects of weather modification will be predominantly detrimental to natural communities, decreasing community stability, pressing rarer and more vulnerable species toward extinction, favoring the spread of weeds and undesirable species, and reducing the attraction and value of the communities to man. If weather modification is both significant in degree of change and sustained in time, these unfavorable changes in natural communities may be substantial and, in some respects, irreversible.

Ecologists are unlikely to regard the effects of weather modification on natural communities with enthusiasm, but research on these effects is needed. Three types of research may be suggested. The first of these is the deliberate subjection of selected natural communities to controlled, strictly localized weather modification. Since increased rainfall is more likely to be in question than temperature change (at least as an intentional modification of weather), first experiments might best concern the effects of artificial rainfall. Such experiments could yield not only better knowledge of the implications of weather modification, but fundamental findings on plant population dynamics. A second approach is computer simulation of effects of weather modification on particular communities as ecosystems, and on landscape patterns of vegetation. Problems and possibilities of such research have been discussed by Watt (Livingstone, 1966).

The third approach is one of monitoring effects of weather modification in the field. In an area in which weather is to be modified, natural communities would be selected for study and permanent plots established in them. Communities would be chosen to represent the full range of environments and major types of communities in the area, including such extreme environments as ravines, dry slopes, and exposed rock outcrops. Before weather modification, sample plots of these communities would be mapped and photographed, and measurements taken of wood rings and other indications of plant growth rates. The plots would be restudied during and after a period of weather modification to determine changes. Control plots in similar conditions outside the area of weather modification should be sought, and for maximum value both these and the sample plots should be in areas subject to long-term protection and should be available for continued observation. Creation and observation of protected, long-term study plots in national parks and monuments, independently of any proposed weather modification, should also have value. Such plots could serve as well-studied controls for possible future experiments, as documentation of normal community stability versus fluctuation, and as bases for studying effects on natural communities of possible unintended, widespread weather modification or pollution effects.

In relation to effects of weather modification on natural communities I thus recommend:

1. Research into ecological implications of weather modification should be pressed and actual experiments on weather modification

should be accompanied by monitoring research, including establishment and observation of the study communities before modification.

2. Protection of our most important preserves of natural communities should be considered a permanent constraint on the area and extent of weather modification. The magnificent system of national parks and monuments and wilderness areas should be a source of lasting pride and pleasure to the people of this country. Weather modification is potentially a means by which the quality and value of these preserves might be reduced, not merely locally as is the case with heavy visitor use, but over wide areas.

3. Any weather modification beyond exploratory experiments should be governed by a strategy of minimum application for only the most clearly defined and most clearly needed benefits, rather than by a strategy of maximum application for (hopefully) maximum benefits or for possible but uncertain benefits.

Weather Modification and Human Ecology

Restraint in experimentation goes against the grain of a technological society. The American nation has grown prosperous and powerful by unrestricted application of technology to the use of environments and to other problems. Advocacy of a change of orientation toward a strategy of restraint in the use of environment is based, however, not on quixotism or sentiment for nature but on reasoning in regard to man's own long-range interests.

Man's effects on environment were local and limited in a sparsely settled world of modest technology. The "conquest of nature" for man's benefit could be pursued as an objective without serious concern about unforeseen consequences. Space for the disposal of wastes was abundant, and toxic materials released into environment were diluted by natural processes to virtual disappearance.

The world is now occupied with human beings in a density which, combined with powerful technology, implies fundamental change in the terms of man's relation to environment. Past environmental modifications were local, but some present ones are cumulative, general, and pervasive. In the last two decades we have been subject to unwelcome instruction in the limitations of the world's capacity and the interrelatedness of natural processes. Among these experiences three may be mentioned:

1. Radioactive materials from the testing of atomic weapons have been observed to spread through the atmosphere, thence into soil and water, and by varied routes of concentration into organisms. The principles of the processes of transfer and concentration are understood by ecologists. The details of the complex processes, differently affecting different radioactive materials, and the different kinds and degrees of their potential hazard to man, could not be predicted.

2. The group of poisons termed "pesticides" have become increasingly widespread in environment, including bodies of water remote from the places where they were used, and have become concentrated in organisms with extensive mortality of vulnerable species, among them birds and fish as well as insects. The early use of pesticides was accompanied by reassurances that mortality to wildlife and return to man in food would not be significant problems.

3. An increasingly conspicuous consequence of technology is the release of products of combustion into the atmosphere, chemical transformation of some of these in the atmosphere, and concentration in organisms of some products detrimental to them. The particular, intricate, atmospheric chemistry of smog and the physiological implications for different agricultural crops, native species, and man could not have been foreseen. Atmospheric pollution is now in transition from localized to more widespread occurrence.

Certain characteristics of these experiences may be observed. Effects are cumulative, partly unpredictable, and ultimately detrimental to man's own interests. The individual acts of releasing materials into environment may be unobjectionable in their foreseeable consequences, but the combined effect of many instances may be both unforeseen and conspicuously disadvantageous. The effects may be difficult to control or reverse. Effects are not recognized until a practice is widespread and it may by then be difficult, or enormously expensive, to alter reliance on such practices as wide use of pesticides and the automobile. Rates of increase of environmental pollution and modification are affected by geometric increase in both population and technological power. The result of these in combination is an exponentially accelerating rate of environmental modification, with steepening curves of detriment of which we see now only the beginnings. The implication of this ecological backlash for the dream of ever-expanding population and technology is not yet widely recognized. A philosophy of "conquest of nature" and unlimited modification of environment is already outmoded. Continued tenancy of this world by technological man should be based on control of population and technological exploitation to avoid progressive, irreversible detriment to a limited world which must provide man's food and water, space, and air.

These three ecological experiences may well prove relevant to widespread weather modification by release of silver iodide and other substances. Effects of weather modification involve exceedingly complex, interlinked atmospheric and ecological processes. Computer simulations of very complex systems, both atmospheric and ecological, are at best imperfect representations from incomplete understanding for predictions of limited longer-range reliability. Indirect and cumulative effects of weather modification, in particular, cannot be adequately foreseen. It is likely that some of these unforeseen consequences will be unwelcome ones. If weather modification should change climatic patterns of precipitation to which present agriculture, flood control, and urban settlement are adapted, the unwelcome effects will not necessarily be small ones. Effects of modification once established and recognized, and by then based on widespread practice, may be difficult to control or reverse.

No one can foresee with assurance the balance of advantage and disadvantage from weather modification. It is my opinion, however, that in discussions of the problem to date technological enthusiasm has prevailed over thoughtful consideration of possible disadvantages of weather modification and alternative solutions to water problems. Desirability of weather modification has been discussed as primarily a question of atmospheric science and economics. It is of course a question of these, but it is primarily a question of human ecology—of the broader and longer-range best interests of man in relation to a limited environment which is vulnerable to man's disturbance of it, while man is vulnerable to the consequences of that disturbance. I suggest that deliberate, widespread weather modification may be an unwise endeavor, based on a view of man's relation to his environment which is not now appropriate, motivated by no pressing hardship, and likely to produce limited foreseeable benefits in exchange for uncertain and possibly substantial disadvantages.

I must, again, regret that ecological evaluation of weather modification cannot be phrased in terms of effective quantitative prediction. Additional research on weather modification is clearly needed, if only to seek possible ways of responding to modification which might result inadvertently from atmospheric pollution. But a final ecological recommendation regarding weather modification is, most simply, a counsel of caution.

Conclusion

Effects of weather modification on natural communities would act through community processes and population dynamics in complex and nonlinear ways. Productivity of communities may be increased by increased precipitation, but probably not usefully increased by increased temperature. Weather modification continued for more than a short period will both shift population balances among species in particular communities and cause migration of species populations along environmental gradients. The communities will thus be made less stable; the extinction of some vulnerable species and the spread of other, aggressive species or weeds may be expected. Effects of weather modification on natural communities will, in consequence, be predominantly detrimental. Because of the relation of weather modification to complex atmospheric and ecological processes, the longer-range effects on man's own environment are to some extent unpredictable and may be disadvantageous. Research on effects of weather modification is needed, but ecological considerations suggest a policy of caution and restraint.

Author's Note: This article is a publication from work in the ecology program, Biology Department, Brookhaven National Laboratory, Upton, New York, under the auspices of the U. S. Atomic Energy Commission. I am indebted for some of the ideas discussed to members of a panel on weather modification of the Ecological Society of America, from which the report of Livingstone (1966) resulted.

REFERENCES

Curtis, J. T., 1959. *The Vegetation of Wisconsin; an Ordination of Plant Communities.* Univ. Wisconsin Press, Madison, Wisconsin.

Curtis, J. T., and R. P. McIntosh, 1951. An upland forest continuum in the prairie-forest border region of Wisconsin. *Ecology, 32:* 476–496.

Ellenberg, H., 1953. Physiologisches and ökologisches Verhalten derselben Pflanzenarten. *Ber. Deut. Bot. Ges., 65:* 350–361.

Gates, D. M., 1962. *Energy Exchange in the Biosphere.* Harper and Row, New York.

Gates, D. M., 1965. Energy, plants, and environment. *Ecology, 46:* 1–13.

Knapp, R., 1954. *Experimentelle Soziologie der hoheren Pflanzen. Vol. 1.* Eugen Ulmer, Stuttgart, Germany.

Little, S., H. W. Lull, and I. Remson, 1959. Changes in woodland vegetation and soils after spraying large amounts of waste water. *Forest Sci., 5:* 18–27.

Livingstone, D. A., 1966. Biological aspects of weather modification. A report from the Ecological Society of America's *ad hoc* weather working group of the Ecology Study Committee to the Special Commission for Weather Modification of the National Science Foundation. *Bull. Ecol. Soc. Am., 47:* 39–78.

Odum, E. P., 1959. *Fundamentals of Ecology.* Saunders, Philadelphia and London.

Shreve, F., 1915. The vegetation of a desert mountain range as conditioned by climatic factors. *Carnegie Inst. Wash. Publ., 217.*

Walter, H., 1962. *Die Vegetation der Erde in okologischer Betrachtung. I. Die tropischen und subtropischen Zonen.* Fischer, Jena, Germany.

Walter, H., 1964. Productivity of vegetation in arid countries, the savannah problem and bush encroachment after overgrazing. *Proc. and Pap. IUCN 9th Tech. Meeting (Nairobi, 1963)—IUCN Publ., N.S. No. 4 (Part III, The Impact of Man on the Tropical Environment):* 221–229.

Weaver, J. E., 1954. *The North American Prairie.* Johnson Publ. Co., Lincoln, Nebraska.

Weaver, J. E., and F. W. Albertson, 1956. *Grasslands of the Great Plains.* Johnson Publ. Co., Lincoln, Nebraska.

Whittaker, R. H., 1951. A criticism of the plant association and climatic climax concepts. *Northwest Sci. 25:* 17–31.

Whittaker, R. H., 1953. A consideration of climax theory: the climax as a population and pattern. *Ecol. Monographs, 23:* 41–78.

Whittaker, R. H., 1956. Vegetation of the Great Smoky Mountains. *Ecol. Monographs, 26:* 1–80.

Whittaker, R. H., 1966. Forest dimensions and production in the Great Smoky Mountains. *Ecology, 47:* 103–121.

Whittaker, R. H., and W. A. Niering, 1965. Vegetation of the Santa Catalina Mountains, Arizona: A gradient analysis of the south slope. *Ecology, 46:* 429–452.

Index

Index

Acclimation (acclimatization) of animals, 199, 222, 249, 261–262, 280–283
Ad libitum, 194, 196–199, 200–202
Adrenal cortex and appetite, 261
Adreno-medullary activity, 241–245
Advection, 353, 357, 359, 363, 365
Aerodynamic parameters
  drag coefficient, 343–346
  eddy transfer coefficient, 343–346
  exchange coefficient, 343–346
  friction velocity, 343–346
  Richardson number, 343–346
  shear stress, 343–346
  wind shear, 343–346
  zero plane, 343–346
Aerodynamic roughness, 353
Air conditioning and animals, 209
Air pollution, 305
Albedo of surfaces, 303, 352
Animal performance, factors reducing adverse effects, 277–290
Animal response, characterizing, 279–283
Animal shape factor, 217
Appetite and temperature, 192
Apple scab, 151–152
Aridity and tree growth, 45, 47, 52, 60–63
Atmometer, 176–178, 337, 339–340

Barley
  aphid vectors, 160
  yellow dwarf virus, 159–160
Bedding and animal growth, 225–227
Beta vulgaris (see Sugar beet)
Biological rhythm, 247–248
Biological variation, 265
Biometeorological data system, requirements for, 5–6
Biometeorology, definition, 3
Blister blight of tea, 152
Blood flow, 222, 225, 233–234, 238–239
Blood gas, 241–243
Blood pressure, 235–238, 244
Blood volume, 235–240

Caloric content of ration, effect on feed consumed, 247–248, 250–251
Caloric intake, 250–251
Calorigenesis, 198–199
Cambium cells, 46–47, 62
Carbon dioxide, 55–59, 97–98, 342, 347
Cardiac output, 235–238, 244
Caribou, hair coat, 226–227
Catecholamines, 197–198, 244–245
Cattalo, hair coat, 226
Cattle
  Aberdeen Angus, 227
  beef cattle, 216–217, 226–227, 289
  Braford, 210
  Brahman, 203–204
  Brown Swiss, 280
  Charolais, 227
  dairy, 210, 228, 250, 258–259, 261, 267 (see Cattle, milk production)
  effect of cold climate on, 226–228
  effect of fogging, 219
  effect of hot climate on, 207–219
  embryonic death, 267
  energy input, 282–289
  feed intake and temperature, 217, 228, 253, 260–261
  heat loss, 233–234, 245
  Hereford, 210, 212–218
  Holstein, 193–196, 202–204, 208, 228, 280, 283–289
  Indian, 228
  Jersey, 217, 228, 261, 280, 283
  milk production, lactation, and envi-

ronment, 189, 200–204, 210, 217, 228, 258–261, 280, 283–289
milk yield–energy input efficiency, 283–287
physiological consequences of heat loss, 234–245
pulse rate, 215
respiratory rate, 215
Shorthorn, 261, 280–281
water intake, 217
water loss and temperature, 289
Zebu, 260, 280, 283–287
Cercospora beticola (see Sugar beet leaf spot)
Cereal rust, 151
Chicken
caloric intake and temperature, 250–251, 259, 260
effect of ration on food consumed, 247
feeding efficiency, 255–256
growth and temperature, 251–252, 255
heat production and temperature, 256–257
photoperiod and feed intake, 256
photoperiod and mortality, 258
temperature and production, 208
water use and temperature, 259–260
Chilling
crops, 75, 76, 77, 146
lilac bloom, 31
Circulation
pulmonary, 237–239
systemic, 234
Citrus
producing areas in U. S., 130
production and weather, 128–129
Citrus sinensis L. (see Orange, Valencia)
Climate
continental, 101, 103
local, 110
maritime, 78, 100–102
regional, 110
Climate of
Auburn, California, 115–116
Bend, Oregon, 118, 121–122
Central Valley of California, 101–103, 116
coastal region, 100–101, 114
Crescent City, California, 100, 113–114
Dana Plateau, California, 105, 119–120
Davis, California, 115–116
Dickinson, North Dakota, 167–168
Ellery Lake, California, 105, 117, 119
Fallon, Nevada, 120–121
Giant Forest, 104, 117
Joshua tree forest, 109
Las Vegas, Nevada, 123, 126
Los Gatos, California, 116–117
northern desert shrub, 107–108, 124
northern Great Basin, 106–108, 121
Palmdale, California, 123, 126
Pt. Reyes, California, 100, 113–114
Redmond, Oregon, 121–122
Reno, Nevada, 121–122
Rocklin, California, 115–116
Scotia, California, 114–115
Sierran vegetation, 103–105, 118–119
Soda Springs, California, 117, 119
southern hot desert, 109, 126
White Mountains, California, 119–120
xeric vegetation, 125
Climatic data, 114, 116, 118–119, 121, 124–126
Climatic index, 297–298
Climatic maps, 67–91
Climatic variation and tree-ring patterns, 48–54
Climatographs, use of, 81–84, 86, 190
Eureka, California, 86
Imperial Valley, California, 83
Mojave Desert, 86
North American regions, 190
Salinas, Watsonville, California, 83
San Luis Valley, Colorado, 83
Willcox, Arizona, 83
Clouds
cone crop, relationship to, 10, 12
effect on radiation 305–307
radiant heat load of animals, relationship to, 218
weather modification, relationship to, 305–306
CO_2, exchange and supply (see Photosynthesis)

Comfort zone of animals, 203, 228
Competition in trees, 47
Conception rate and temperature, 267
Condensation trails, 305–306
Cone crop, Douglas fir
  abundance of, 4–6, 10–12
  meteorological requirements, 10–12
Continentality, 98, 100, 106, 109
  windbreak effect, 333
Convection, 363, 365
Cooling of animals
  evaporative (see Evaporative cooling)
  water spray, 219
Crop prospecting, 85–87

Degree-hour accumulations, 127–128, 132–135, 138–139, 142–146
  base temperature, 138–139
  ceiling temperature, 138–139
Dendrochronology, 45
Dew and plant diseases, 152–158
Douglas fir (*Pseudotsuga menziesii*), 4–6, 10–13
  cone crop, 4–6, 10–12
  flowering, precocious, 12
  photosynthesis, 58
  tree rings, 48
Doves, feeding habits, 247–248
Downdrafts and forest fires, 310–311
Downy mildew
  cucurbits, 153
  grapes, 156–157
  lima bean, 157
Drought, 51, 61
Dry bean (*Phaseolis vulgaris*), 335, 340–341

Early Ridge of isophanes, 19, 26, 31
Earlywood, 46
Ecoclimate, definition, 296
Ecosystem, 367–369, 371–372
Electric field of lightning breakdown, 324
Elevation and effect on blooming date of lilacs, 17–29, 33–42
Embryonic death, 267, 270–275
Energy
  balance, 331, 334, 352–356, 364 (see Radiant heat load, Heat balance)
  convection exchange, 137
  radiant, 132, 136–142, 146
Energy requirement, minimum, 286, 287
Energy utilization by animals (see Heat production of animals)
Environment, characterizing animal response to, 279–283
Environmental gradient and plant populations, 371–374
Evaporation
  atmometer, 176–178, 337, 339–340
  effect of surface on, 353–357, 364
  energy balance, 352, 364
  factors affecting, 336–337
  mulch, 171
  net radiation ratio, 354, 355, 356
  open-pan, 168
  potential of air for, 181
  wind speed, 335–336
Evaporative cooling of animals
  evaporative coolers, 210
  respiratory, 193–194, 233–234, 239, 289
  skin, 193–194, 203, 233–234, 239, 289
Evapotranspiration
  actual, 97, 99, 101, 103–109, 113–125
  air temperature, 96, 334
  definition, 95
  effect of irrigation on, 356, 359
  methods of estimating, 96
  plant cover, 305
  potential, 93–110, 300, 363–365
  tree-ring index, 50–51
  windbreaks, 334–342, 346–347
Exobasidium vexans (see Blister blight of tea)

False tree ring, 47
Feathering, 253–254
Feed
  quality and lactation, 286–288
  supply and lactation, 288–290
Feeding efficiency, 251–255
Feed intake
  animal factors affecting, 249–250, 261
  environmental factors affecting, 248, 250–255, 258, 260–261
Feed-regulating mechanism, 260–262
Fertility (mammalian)

high temperature, 266–267, 270–275
interaction with environment, 266–269
Fetch to height ratio, 354, 360, 365
Flax rust, 150
Fleece length and critical temperature, 251
Foehn and lilac bloom, 24, 27, 31, 36, 41
Forest fires
conditions, 309–311
downdrafts, 310–311
lightning, 311–313, 325
wind, 310, 311
Forest Service lightning research, 312–325
Frost, 70, 75–77, 88
Frost protection requirement, 76
Fruit development of orange, chilling requirement, 139–142, 146

Germination, windbreak effect on, 337–338, 347
Goats, temperature and behavior, 262
Grassland microenvironment, modification of, 182–183
Grazing
effect on microclimate, 170
mulch removal, 170
time, 262, 288–289
Growing season of trees, 47
Growth and windbreaks, 331
Growth chamber, field unit, 56
Growth rate
animals, 252, 254
cattle and acclimation (acclimatization), 280–283, 289

Hair coat, 222, 226–227, 249–250, 281–282
Heart rate, 235–236, 238
Heart stroke volume, 235–236
Heat accumulations, net, 134–136, 142–145
Heat balance of animals (see Energy balance, Radiant heat load), 193–194, 197
heat loss of animals, 222, 233–234, 245
hormonal effect, 197–199
Heat index, 133
Heat, latent, 351, 354, 356
Heat loss of animals (see Heat balance of animals)
Heat production of animals, 191–204, 222–223, 226, 251, 253, 256–257, 259–261 (see Heat balance of animals)
effect of hormones on, 199
endocrine functions, 198
minimum, 201–202
Heat, sensible, 351, 354, 356, 364
Heat stress in animals and acclimation (acclimatization), 280–283, 290
Heat units (see Degree-hour accumulations)
Homoiothermy (see Temperature, animal)
Hopkins Bioclimatic Law, 24, 26–28
Hormones and heat balance in animals, 189, 191–192, 197–199
Housing of animals
confinement, 227
winter, 221
Humidity
absolute, 10, 335–346
effect on animals, 227–228, 235–237, 242, 244
embryo death, 267
fertility, 266–270
gradient, 165
Humidity, relative
animal response, 218–219, 280–285
crop diseases, 150–158
dew duration, 155–156, 158
forest fires, 311
oasis effect, 358–359
over grass prairie, 166, 179–182
shelter effect on, 335, 346
temperature, 190
Hyperthermia, 196, 234, 236–243, 245, 280, 283
Hypothalamus, 191–193, 233–234, 238–239, 241, 243–245, 259, 261
Hypoxia, 239–241

Inference, biometeorological, 3–13
Insulation of animals, 222–223, 225, 227–228, 250
Irrigation

effect on microclimate, 351–365
effect on soil temperature, 334
oasis effect, 342
Isohyet, 67
Isophanes, 19–22, 29–34
orientation, 29
Isotherms, 67
lilac isophanes, 33–34

Lactation (see Cattle, milk production, lactation, and environment)
Lactuca sativa (see Lettuce, head)
Lapse rate, 105
Latewood, 46–47
Latitude, effect on blooming date of lilacs, 21, 23–26
Leaf
energy exchange, 136–138
reradiation, 136
supercooling, 137–138
temperature, 136–138, 155, 368
wetness, 151–156
Lettuce, head (*Lactuca sativa*), temperameter, 82–83
Light and cone production, 10
Light and reproduction, 267–269
Lightning
discharges, identification of, 320–323
discharges, occurrence of, 312, 315–317
forest fires, 311–313, 325
hail, 315–317
hybrid, 322–323
modification, 316, 318–320, 323–325
radar echo, 315–316
research (see Forest Service)
return stroke, 321, 323
sparking potential, 325
storm duration, 315
theoretical basis for suppression, 323–325
Lilac, purple
as phenological indicator, 17–42
blooming date, 17–42
departure of observed from predicted, 31–32
freeze date, 37
Longitude, effect on blooming date of lilacs, 23–27

Macroclimate, definition, 296
Macroenvironment, factors, 267–269, 277–279
Mammalian reproduction, environmental effects on, 265–275
Mesoclimate, definition, 296
modification, 297–307
Metabolic rate and temperature, 251, 253–254
Mice, temperature and tail length, 249
Microclimate
data, 57–59
definition, 207, 296, 351
factors in, 207
modification, 297, 303, 306, 308
of prairie grass, 165–183
station, 131–132, 165–166, 328–329
mobile, 360
Microenvironment, factors, 267–269
Milk energy, 202
Milk yield (see Cattle, milk production)
Model, as hypothesis, 3, 54
Modification (see Weather modification)

Native plants as climate indicators, 69, 376–377
Newborn animal, effect of cold temperatures on, 223–224

Oasis effect, 95–96, 342, 347
large, 358–363
small, 353–358, 360–363
Orange, Valencia (*Citrus sinensis* L.), 127–146
Ovum, effect of environment on, 270–275
Oxygen consumption, 192, 201, 222–223
Oxygen tension, 239, 241–243

Panting, 234–237, 239
Peanut leaf spot, 151
Peripheral resistance, 235–236, 239
Pesticides, pollution, 381
Phaseolis vulgaris (see Dry bean)
Phenological
climatology, 39
data, 129–130, 141–145, 165

climatic parameters, 39–40, 42
geographic anomolies, 39
limits of application, 40–41
requirement, 82
uses, 37–41
Phenology of lilac, 17–43
Phosphorylation, 192
Photoperiod, 41, 80
effect of feed intake, 256, 258
Photosynthesis, 55–60, 97, 342, 344, 347
Physical adaptability factors, 280, 283
Phytopthora infestans (see Potato blight)
Pinus aristata
needle length, 60–62
tree rings, 50
Pinus edulis
needle length, 60–61
tree rings, 48
Pinus ponderosa
photosynthesis, 55, 57, 59–60
tree rings, 48–49
Piricularia oryzae (see Rice blast)
Plant associations, 87–88
Plant community
definition, 367
gradients, 371–374
production, 369–370, 383
Plant disease
epiphytotics and ground level climate, 149–156
forecasting, 156–159
Plant species
diversity, 377
extinction, 376–378, 383
Plantclimate, 74–80
coastal, 78
definition, 69
indexes, 127–128
interior, 78, 83, 88
mapping, 67–91
maps and uses of maps, 72, 73, 75, 80, 81–91
maritime, 78
micro-, 79, 90
mini-, 79
regional, temperature-determined and wind-modified, 74–79, 88
subzones, 67–68, 74–80
transitional, 78
Plants as temperature indicators, 69
Plasma hydrocortisone, 197–198
Poikilothermy (see Temperature, animal, body)
Pollution, air and pesticides, 381
Potato blight, 153–155, 157–159
Powdery mildew of lettuce, 150
Precipitation
changes in character by modification, 302
data, 93–94, 113–125, 167–169
deficiency, 299–301
New Brunswick, N. J., 299, 301
Lincoln, Neb., 300–301
distribution in mountain thunderstorms, 314–315
effect of increase (see Weather modification)
interception, 170
modification, 358
modification and effect on plant community, 368–375, 380
plant community production, 370, 380
plant disease, 151–153, 157
relation to cone production, 9–11
surplus, 299–301
New Brunswick, N. J., 299, 301
Lincoln, Neb., 300–301
tree rings, 49, 52–54, 58, 62
Production of grass prairie, 169
Productive adaptability factors, 280, 283
Pseudotsuga menziesii (see Douglas fir)

Quercus alba tree rings, 52

Rabbits, fertility and environment, 272–275
Radiant heat load, 211, 215–218 (see Energy balance)
clouds, 218
flux rate, 217
Radiation
balance (see Energy balance)
effect on animals, 210–218, 283–285
effect on plants, 36–38
greenhouse effect, 305
lilac bloom, 36–38
longwave (see Thermal)

net, 352–356, 360, 364
plant cover, 304
reflectance of swine, 217–218
solar, 217, 352, 356, 360
thermal, 215, 217, 352–353, 364
Rainfall (see Precipitation)
Rats
body temperature, 259
effect of ration on food consumed, 247
response to low temperature, 222
temperature and metabolism, 260–262
Relative turgidity, 340–341
Reproductive efficiency, 286, 289
Reproductive rate (see Fertility)
Respiration of plants, 60
Respiration rates of animals, 193–194, 222, 235–236, 238–243, 270, 280–282
Rice blast, 153
Rumen cannula, 194, 195, 200–201
Rumen fistula, 195–196, 258

Satellites and temperature measurements, 305–307
Shades, sun, 208–210, 212–218, 287, 290
Sheep
effect of cold temperature on, 223–224, 227–228
heat production and temperature, 251, 253, 260
reproduction and environment, 267, 270, 272
reproduction and photoperiod, 266
Shelter belts (see Windbreaks)
Shivering, 191, 196, 222–223
Silver iodide generator, 318–319
Snow, 104, 107
fencing (see Windbreaks)
windbreak effect on, 336
Soil heat, 354–356, 364
Soil moisture
characteristics, 96–97
data, 168–169
effect of windbreak on, 335–340, 347
tree growth, 51, 53–55, 58–63
Sperm and high temperature, 266, 272–275
Statistics
conditional probability, 9
correlation of environment with ring width, 53
null hypothesis, 8
polynomial fit, 50–51
regression and lilac bloom, 21, 23, 25
standard error and radiant temperature, 140–142
Stomatal regulation by windbreaks, 339–342, 347
Sugar beet (*Beta vulgaris*), 335, 337–338, 344–345
Sugar beet leaf spot, 150–151, 160
Sunshine and plant disease, 152
Swine
effect of cold temperature on, 223–226
effect of environment on, 208–211, 216–217
effect of wind on, 210–211
feed consumption and temperature, 253–254
nutmeg liver of, 224
reflectance, 217–218
stress temperature, 209
use of air-conditioned house, 208–210
use of shade, 208–210
use of wallow, 208–210
Sympatho-adrenal system, 236–237
Syringa vulgaris L. (see Lilac, purple)

Temperameter, 82–86
Temperature
blackglobe, 132
dew point, 340–341
hair coat, 228
spore germination, 157, 160
leaf, 136–138, 155, 368
leaf and air, 136–137, 155
meristematic tissue, 12
radiant, 132, 134–136, 138–142
soil, 146, 171–175
irrigation effect on, 334–335
windbreak effect on, 334–335
Temperature, air
animal response, 189–291
critical for animals, 251
data, 93–94, 113–125, 167–168, 190
day, 80–86

degree-hour accumulations, 132–133
effect on cardiovascular changes, 234–239
adreno-medullary activity, 241–245
thermal polypnea, 239–241
effect of cold on animals, 221–229
effect of irrigation on, 353–365
effect on newborn animal, 223–224
effect on plant community, 368–370, 374–375, 377, 383
effective, 284–285
evaporation, 352–365
feed-regulating mechanisms, 247–262
fertility of animals, 88, 266–275, 289
gradient above grass prairie, 165, 171–175
ideal, 190
lilac bloom, 33–38, 41–42
milk yield (see Cattle, milk production)
night, 12, 59, 80–86, 88, 153
plant disease, 150–158
plantclimate zone, 70, 74–81
radiant energy, 132
relation to cone production, 9–12
relation to soil temperature, 171–174
requirement, 81–87
screen effect on, 328
threshold, 127
tree rings, 53–55, 57–59, 62
water loss in cattle, 289
wind, 190
windbreak effect on, 333–335, 340–341, 347
Temperature, animal
body, 222–227, 234–235, 239, 259–260, 262
critical, 223–225, 227
homoiothermy, 222, 224–225
newborn, 223–224
poikilothermy, 223
shivering (see Shivering)
skin, 225
core, 222, 225
rectal, 193–194, 196, 198, 203, 215, 218, 227, 235–237, 242–244, 270, 280–282
rumen, 226–227
skin, 193–194
surface, 215–218
Temperature regulation in animals, 259–262
Thermal
neutrality zone, 251
polypnea, 239–241
stress and mammalian reproduction, 266, 270–275
wave and lilac bloom, 35–36
zones, 70, 74, 77
Thermoneutral zone, 203
Thermoperiod, 41
Thermoregulatory mechanisms, 223, 233, 239
Thunderstorms
characteristics of mountain, 313–316
forest fires, 310–311, 316, 325
Total digestible nutrients, 200, 202, 281
Transpiration, 54, 57–58 (see Evapotranspiration)
Tree crown growth, 46–47
Tree-ring index, 50
Tree rings and climate, 45–63
Turkeys, effect of ration on food consumed, 248

Validity, biological, 10
Vapor flux, 358
Vapor pressure, 335–336, 341–342
animal response, 218–219, 280–281
deficit, 166, 181
effect of irrigation on, 353–365
Vegetation (see Climate of)
far western, 99–110, 114, 116, 118–119, 121, 124–126
Venturia inaequalis (see Apple scab)

Water balance, 96–125, 300
New Brunswick, N. J., 300
Lincoln, Neb., 300
Water consumption of animals, 250, 258, 260, 289
Water deficit (see Water storage in soil)
Water intake of animals, 193–194, 203
Water requirement, 169, 364–365
Water sprays for cooling, 219
Water storage in soil, 96–101, 113–123
Water surplus (see Water storage in soil)
Water use (see Water balance)

Water use by animals (see Water consumption of animals)
Water use efficiency, 338–339, 347
Weather modification, 295–383
 by irrigation, 351–365
 convective clouds, 297
 detrimental effects on communities, 378, 383
 ecological evaluation, 379–380, 383
 energy balance, 303
 human ecology, 380–383
 hurricanes, 302–303
 indirect effects, 303, 305–306
 lightning, 316, 318–320, 323–325
 microclimate, 296
 monitoring effects on plants, 379–380
 precipitation and effects of change, 297–302
 plant population response, 370–378, 383
 recommendations for plant research, 378–380
 seeding methods and forest fires, 319–320
Weight
 body, 196
 gain in animals, 281–282, 289
 gain in temperature, 210–219
Wind
 air temperature, 190
 CO_2, 342
 data, 168, 174–176
 effect of windbreaks on, 330–347
 effect on animals, 210–214, 227
  cattle, 210–214
  swine, 210–211
 effect on photosynthesis, 58
 forest fires, 310–311
 plantclimates, 74
Wind profile
 parameters, 343–346
 windbreaks, 343–347
Windbreaks, 331–348
 air temperature, 333–335, 340–341, 347
 effect on evaporation, 337–342, 346–347
 humidity, 335–336, 341–342, 346
 moisture conservation, 335–339, 347
 permeability of, 331–332
 radiation, 331, 333
 soil temperature, 334–335
 stomatal regulation, 339–342, 347
 types
  corn, 329, 331, 335, 344–345
  snow fence, 329–332, 335–345
White pine blister rust, 151

Xylem, 46

Yield and windbreaks, 338–339, 347–348